GCSE

Combined Science
Biology

There's a lot of Biology to learn in GCSE Combined Science, that's for sure. Luckily, this CGP book explains all the facts, theory and practical skills you'll need!

On top of all that, we've added exam-style practice for every topic — plus a set of mock Biology exam papers to *really* test you on what you've learned.

We've also included fully-worked answers, so it's easy to mark your work and learn from any mistakes. Everything you need for a top grade!

How to access your free Online Edition

This book includes a free Online Edition to read on your PC, Mac or tablet.
You'll just need to go to **cgpbooks.co.uk/extras** and enter this code:

0151 9775 8078 2119

By the way, this code only works for one person. If somebody else has used this book before you, they might have already claimed the Online Edition.

Complete
Revision & Practice
<u>Everything</u> you need to pass the exams!

Contents

Throughout this book you'll see grade stamps like these:

These grade stamps help to show how difficult the questions are.
Remember — to get a top grade you need to be able to answer **all** the questions, not just the hardest ones.

In the real exams, some questions test how well you can write (as well as your scientific knowledge).
In this book, we've marked these questions with an asterisk (*).

Topic 3 — Infection and Response

Topic 4 — Bioenergetics

Topic 5 — Homeostasis and Response

Topic 6 — Inheritance, Variation and Evolution

Published by CGP

Editors: Katherine Faudemer, Ciara McGlade, Rachael Rogers and Camilla Simson.

Contributor: Paddy Gannon.

From original material by Richard Parsons.

With thanks to Charlotte Burrows for the proofreading.

With thanks to Jan Greenway for the copyright research.

With thanks to SCIENCE PHOTO LIBRARY for permission to reproduce the image of a contraceptive implant on page 213.

With thanks to iStock.com/AbelBrata for permission to reproduce the image of a condom on page 213.

Printed by Elanders Ltd, Newcastle upon Tyne.
Clipart from Corel®

The Scientific Method

This section isn't about how to 'do' science — but it does show you the way most scientists work.

Scientists Come Up With **Hypotheses** — Then **Test** Them

1) Scientists try to explain things. They start by observing something they don't understand.

2) They then come up with a hypothesis — a possible explanation for what they've observed.

3) The next step is to test whether the hypothesis might be right or not. This involves making a prediction based on the hypothesis and testing it by gathering evidence (i.e. data) from investigations. If evidence from experiments backs up a prediction, you're a step closer to figuring out if the hypothesis is true.

Hundreds of years ago, we thought demons caused illness.

Several Scientists Will **Test** a Hypothesis

1) Normally, scientists share their findings in peer-reviewed journals, or at conferences.

2) Peer-review is where other scientists check results and scientific explanations to make sure they're 'scientific' (e.g. that experiments have been done in a sensible way) before they're published. It helps to detect false claims, but it doesn't mean that findings are correct — just that they're not wrong in any obvious way.

3) Once other scientists have found out about a hypothesis, they'll start basing their own predictions on it and carry out their own experiments. They'll also try to reproduce the original experiments to check the results — and if all the experiments in the world back up the hypothesis, then scientists start to think the hypothesis is true.

4) However, if a scientist does an experiment that doesn't fit with the hypothesis (and other scientists can reproduce the results) then the hypothesis may need to be modified or scrapped altogether.

Then we thought it was caused by 'bad blood' (and treated it with leeches).

If **All** the **Evidence** Supports a Hypothesis, It's **Accepted** — For Now

1) Accepted hypotheses are often referred to as theories. Our currently accepted theories are the ones that have survived this 'trial by evidence' — they've been tested many times over the years and survived.

2) However, theories never become totally indisputable fact. If new evidence comes along that can't be explained using the existing theory, then the hypothesising and testing is likely to start all over again.

Now we've collected more evidence, we know that illnesses that can be spread between people are due to microorganisms.

Scientific models are constantly being refined...

The scientific method has been developed over time. Aristotle (a Greek philosopher) was the first person to realise that theories need to be based on observations. Muslim scholars then introduced the ideas of creating a hypothesis, testing it, and repeating work to check results.

Models and Communication

Once scientists have made a <u>new discovery</u>, they <u>don't</u> just keep it to themselves. Oh no. Time to learn about how scientific discoveries are <u>communicated</u>, and the <u>models</u> that are used to represent theories.

Theories Can Involve Different Types of Models

1) A <u>representational model</u> is a <u>simplified description</u> or <u>picture</u> of what's going on in real life. Like all models, it can be used to <u>explain</u> <u>observations</u> and <u>make predictions</u>. E.g. the <u>lock and key model</u> of enzyme action is a simplified way of showing how <u>enzymes</u> work (see p.42). It can be used to explain why enzymes only catalyse particular reactions.

Scientists test models by carrying out experiments to check that the predictions made by the model happen as expected.

2) <u>Computational models</u> use computers to make <u>simulations</u> of complex real-life processes, such as climate change. They're used when there are a <u>lot</u> of different <u>variables</u> (factors that change) to consider, and because you can easily <u>change their design</u> to take into account <u>new data</u>.

3) All models have <u>limitations</u> on what they can <u>explain</u> or <u>predict</u>. <u>Climate change models</u> have several limitations — for example, it's hard to take into account <u>all</u> the biological and chemical processes that influence climate. It can also be difficult to include <u>regional variations</u> in climate.

Scientific Discoveries are Communicated to the General Public

Some scientific discoveries show that people should <u>change their habits</u>, or they might provide ideas that could be <u>developed</u> into new <u>technology</u>. So scientists need to <u>tell the world</u> about their discoveries.

<u>Gene technologies</u> are used in <u>genetic engineering</u> to produce <u>genetically modified crops</u>. Information about these crops needs to be communicated to <u>farmers</u> who might <u>benefit</u> from growing them and to the <u>general public</u>, so they can make <u>informed decisions</u> about the food they buy and eat.

Scientific Evidence can be Presented in a Biased Way

1) Scientific discoveries that are reported in the <u>media</u> (e.g. newspapers or television) <u>aren't</u> peer-reviewed.

2) This means that, even though news stories are often <u>based</u> on data that has been peer-reviewed, the data might be <u>presented</u> in a way that is <u>over-simplified</u> or <u>inaccurate</u>, making it open to <u>misinterpretation</u>.

3) People who want to make a point can sometimes <u>present data</u> in a <u>biased way</u> (sometimes <u>without knowing</u> they're doing it). For example, a scientist might overemphasise a relationship in the data, or a newspaper article might describe details of data <u>supporting</u> an idea without giving any evidence <u>against</u> it.

Companies can present biased data to help sell products...

Sometimes a company may only want you to see half of the story so they present the data in a <u>biased way</u>. For example, a pharmaceutical company may want to encourage you to buy their drugs by telling you about all the <u>positives</u>, but not report the results of any <u>unfavourable studies</u>.

Issues Created by Science

Science has helped us make progress in loads of areas, from medicine to space travel. But science still has its issues. And it can't answer everything, as you're about to find out.

Scientific Developments are Great, but they can Raise Issues

Scientific knowledge is increased by doing experiments. And this knowledge leads to scientific developments, e.g. new technologies or new advice. These developments can create issues though. For example:

Economic issues: Society can't always afford to do things scientists recommend (e.g. investing in alternative energy sources) without cutting back elsewhere.

Social issues: Decisions based on scientific evidence affect people — e.g. should alcohol be banned (to prevent health problems)? Would the effect on people's lifestyles be acceptable?

Personal issues: Some decisions will affect individuals. For example, someone might support alternative energy, but object if a wind farm is built next to their house.

Environmental issues: Human activity often affects the natural environment. For example, genetically modified crops may help us to produce more food — but some people think they could cause environmental problems (see p.147).

Science Can't Answer Every Question — Especially Ethical Ones

1) We don't understand everything. We're always finding out more, but we'll never know all the answers.
2) In order to answer scientific questions, scientists need data to provide evidence for their hypotheses.
3) Some questions can't be answered yet because the data can't currently be collected, or because there's not enough data to support a theory.
4) Eventually, as we get more evidence, we'll answer some of the questions that currently can't be answered, e.g. what the impact of global warming on sea levels will be. But there will always be the "Should we be doing this at all?"-type questions that experiments can't help us to answer...

Think about new drugs which can be taken to boost your 'brain power'.
- Some people think they're good as they could improve concentration or memory. New drugs could let people think in ways beyond the powers of normal brains.
- Other people say they're bad — they could give some people an unfair advantage in exams. And people might be pressured into taking them so that they could work more effectively, and for longer hours.

There are often issues with new scientific developments...

The trouble is, there's often no clear right answer where these issues are concerned. Different people have different views, depending on their priorities. These issues are full of grey areas.

Risk

Scientific discoveries are often great, but they can prove risky. With dangers all around, you've got to be aware of hazards — this includes how likely they are to cause harm and how serious the effects may be.

Nothing is Completely Risk-Free

1) A hazard is something that could potentially cause harm.

2) All hazards have a risk attached to them — this is the chance that the hazard will cause harm.

3) The risks of some things seem pretty obvious, or we've known about them for a while, like the risk of causing acid rain by polluting the atmosphere, or of having a car accident when you're travelling in a car.

4) New technology arising from scientific advances can bring new risks, e.g. scientists are unsure whether nanoparticles that are being used in cosmetics and suncream might be harming the cells in our bodies. These risks need to be considered alongside the benefits of the technology, e.g. improved sun protection.

5) You can estimate the size of a risk based on how many times something happens in a big sample (e.g. 100 000 people) over a given period (e.g. a year). For example, you could assess the risk of a driver crashing by recording how many people in a group of 100 000 drivers crashed their cars over a year.

6) To make decisions about activities that involve hazards, we need to take into account the chance of the hazard causing harm, and how serious the consequences would be if it did. If an activity involves a hazard that's very likely to cause harm, with serious consequences if it does, that activity is considered high risk.

People Make Their Own Decisions About Risk

1) Not all risks have the same consequences, e.g. if you chop veg with a sharp knife you risk cutting your finger, but if you go scuba-diving you risk death. You're much more likely to cut your finger during half an hour of chopping than to die during half an hour of scuba-diving. But most people are happier to accept a higher probability of an accident if the consequences are short-lived and fairly minor.

2) People tend to be more willing to accept a risk if they choose to do something (e.g. go scuba diving), compared to having the risk imposed on them (e.g. having a nuclear power station built next door).

3) People's perception of risk (how risky they think something is) isn't always accurate. They tend to view familiar activities as low-risk and unfamiliar activities as high-risk — even if that's not the case. For example, cycling on roads is often high-risk, but many people are happy to do it because it's a familiar activity. Air travel is actually pretty safe, but a lot of people perceive it as high-risk.

4) People may over-estimate the risk of things with long-term or invisible effects, e.g. ionising radiation.

The pros and cons of new technology must be weighed up...

The world's a dangerous place and it's impossible to rule out the chance of an accident altogether. But if you can recognise hazards and take steps to reduce the risks, you're more likely to stay safe.

Designing Investigations

Dig out your lab coat and dust off your badly-scratched safety goggles... it's <u>investigation time</u>.

Evidence Can Support or Disprove a Hypothesis

1) Scientists <u>observe</u> things and come up with <u>hypotheses</u> to test them (see p.1).
You need to be able to do the same. For example:

> <u>Observation</u>: People with big feet have spots. <u>Hypothesis</u>: Having big feet causes spots.

2) To <u>determine</u> whether or not a hypothesis is <u>right</u>, you need to do an <u>investigation</u> to gather evidence. To do this, you need to use your hypothesis to make a <u>prediction</u> — something you think <u>will happen</u> that you can test. E.g. people who have bigger feet will have more spots.

Investigations include experiments and studies.

3) Investigations are used to see if there are <u>patterns</u> or <u>relationships</u> between <u>two variables</u>, e.g. to see if there's a pattern or relationship between the variables 'number of spots' and 'size of feet'.

Evidence Needs to be Repeatable, Reproducible and Valid

1) <u>Repeatable</u> means that if the <u>same person</u> does an experiment again using the <u>same methods</u> and equipment, they'll get <u>similar results</u>.

2) <u>Reproducible</u> means that if <u>someone else</u> does the experiment, or a <u>different</u> method or piece of equipment is used, the results will still be <u>similar</u>.

3) If data is <u>repeatable</u> and <u>reproducible</u>, it's <u>reliable</u> and scientists are more likely to <u>have confidence</u> in it.

4) <u>Valid results</u> are both repeatable and reproducible AND they <u>answer the original question</u>. They come from experiments that were designed to be a <u>fair test</u>...

Make an Investigation a Fair Test By Controlling the Variables

1) In a lab experiment you usually <u>change one variable</u> and <u>measure</u> how it affects <u>another variable</u>.

2) To make it a fair test, <u>everything else</u> that could affect the results should <u>stay the same</u> — otherwise you can't tell if the thing you're changing is causing the results or not.

3) The variable you <u>CHANGE</u> is called the <u>INDEPENDENT</u> variable.

4) The variable you <u>MEASURE</u> when you change the independent variable is the <u>DEPENDENT</u> variable.

5) The variables that you <u>KEEP THE SAME</u> are called <u>CONTROL</u> variables.

> You could find how <u>temperature</u> affects the rate of an <u>enzyme-controlled reaction</u>. The <u>independent variable</u> is the <u>temperature</u>. The <u>dependent variable</u> is the <u>rate of reaction</u>. <u>Control variables</u> include the <u>concentration</u> and <u>amounts</u> of reactants, <u>pH</u>, the <u>time period</u> you measure, etc.

6) Because you can't always control all the variables, you often need to use a <u>control experiment</u>. This is an experiment that's kept under the <u>same conditions</u> as the rest of the investigation, but <u>doesn't</u> have anything <u>done</u> to it. This is so that you can see what happens when you don't change anything at all.

Designing Investigations

The Bigger the Sample Size the Better

1) Data based on small samples isn't as good as data based on large samples. A sample should represent the whole population (i.e. it should share as many of the characteristics in the population as possible) — a small sample can't do that as well. It's also harder to spot anomalies if your sample size is too small.

2) The bigger the sample size the better, but scientists have to be realistic when choosing how big. For example, if you were studying how lifestyle affects people's weight it'd be great to study everyone in the UK (a huge sample), but it'd take ages and cost a lot. It's more realistic to study a thousand people, with a mixture of ages, gender and race.

Your Equipment has to be Right for the Job

1) The measuring equipment you use has to be sensitive enough to measure the changes you're looking for. For example, if you need to measure changes of 1 cm^3 you need to use a measuring cylinder that can measure in 1 cm^3 steps — it'd be no good trying with one that only measures 10 cm^3 steps.

2) The smallest change a measuring instrument can detect is called its resolution. E.g. some mass balances have a resolution of 1 g, some have a resolution of 0.1 g, and some are even more sensitive.

3) Also, equipment needs to be calibrated by measuring a known value. If there's a difference between the measured and known value, you can use this to correct the inaccuracy of the equipment.

Data Should be Repeatable, Reproducible, Accurate and Precise

1) To check repeatability you need to repeat the readings and check that the results are similar. You need to repeat each reading at least three times.

2) To make sure your results are reproducible you can cross check them by taking a second set of readings with another instrument (or a different observer).

3) Your data also needs to be accurate. Really accurate results are those that are really close to the true answer. The accuracy of your results usually depends on your method — you need to make sure you're measuring the right thing and that you don't miss anything that should be included in the measurements. E.g. estimating the amount of gas released from a reaction by counting the bubbles isn't very accurate because you might miss some of the bubbles and they might have different volumes. It's more accurate to measure the volume of gas released using a gas syringe.

Repeat	Data set 1	Data set 2
1	12	11
2	14	17
3	13	14
Mean	13	14

Data set 1 is more precise than data set 2.

4) Your data also needs to be precise. Precise results are ones where the data is all really close to the mean (average) of your repeated results (i.e. not spread out).

Designing Investigations

You Need to Look out for Errors and Anomalous Results

1) The results of your experiment will always <u>vary a bit</u> because of <u>random errors</u> — unpredictable differences caused by things like <u>human errors</u> in <u>measuring</u>. E.g. the errors you make when reading from a measuring cylinder are <u>random</u>. You have to <u>estimate</u> or <u>round</u> the distance when it's between two marks — so sometimes your figure will be a bit above the real one, and sometimes it will be a bit below.

2) You can <u>reduce</u> the effect of random errors by taking <u>repeat readings</u> and finding the <u>mean</u>. This will make your results <u>more precise</u>.

If there's no systematic error, then doing repeats and calculating a mean could make your results more accurate.

3) If a measurement is wrong by the <u>same amount every time</u>, it's called a <u>systematic error</u>. For example, if you measured from the very end of your ruler instead of from the 0 cm mark every time, all your measurements would be a bit small. Repeating the experiment in the exact same way and calculating a mean <u>won't</u> correct a systematic error.

4) Just to make things more complicated, if a systematic error is caused by using <u>equipment</u> that <u>isn't zeroed properly</u>, it's called a <u>zero error</u>. For example, if a mass balance always reads 1 gram before you put anything on it, all your measurements will be 1 gram too heavy.

5) You can <u>compensate</u> for some systematic errors if you know about them, e.g. if a mass balance always reads 1 gram before you put anything on it, you can subtract 1 gram from all your results.

6) Sometimes you get a result that <u>doesn't fit in</u> with the rest at all. This is called an <u>anomalous result</u>. You should investigate it and try to <u>work out what happened</u>. If you can work out what happened (e.g. you measured something wrong) you can <u>ignore</u> it when processing your results.

Investigations Can be Hazardous

1) <u>Hazards</u> from science experiments might include:

- <u>Microorganisms</u>, e.g. some bacteria can make you ill.
- <u>Chemicals</u>, e.g. sulfuric acid can burn your skin and alcohols catch fire easily.
- <u>Fire</u>, e.g. an unattended Bunsen burner is a fire hazard.
- <u>Electricity</u>, e.g. faulty electrical equipment could give you a shock.

You can find out about potential hazards by looking in textbooks, doing some internet research, or asking your teacher.

2) Part of planning an investigation is making sure that it's <u>safe</u>.

3) You should always make sure that you <u>identify</u> all the hazards that you might encounter. Then you should think of ways of <u>reducing the risks</u> from the hazards you've identified. For example:

- If you're working with <u>sulfuric acid</u>, always wear gloves and safety goggles. This will reduce the risk of the acid coming into contact with your skin and eyes.
- If you're using a <u>Bunsen burner</u>, stand it on a heat proof mat. This will reduce the risk of starting a fire.

Designing an investigation is an involved process...
Collecting <u>data</u> is what investigations are all about. Designing a good investigation is really important to make sure that any data collected is <u>accurate</u>, <u>precise</u>, <u>repeatable</u> and <u>reproducible</u>.

Processing Data

Processing your data means doing some <u>calculations</u> with it to make it <u>more useful</u>.

Data Needs to be Organised

1) <u>Tables</u> are dead useful for <u>organising data</u>.

2) When you draw a table <u>use a ruler</u> and make sure <u>each column</u> has a <u>heading</u> (including the <u>units</u>).

There are Different Ways of Processing Your Data

1) When you've done repeats of an experiment you should always calculate the <u>mean</u> (average). To do this <u>add together</u> all the data values and <u>divide</u> by the total number of values in the sample.

2) You might also need to calculate the <u>range</u> (how spread out the data is). To do this find the <u>largest</u> number and <u>subtract</u> the <u>smallest</u> number from it.

Ignore anomalous results when calculating the mean and the range.

 EXAMPLE: **The results of an experiment to find the volume of gas produced in an enzyme-controlled reaction are shown below. Calculate the mean volume and the range.**

Repeat 1 (cm³)	Repeat 2 (cm³)	Repeat 3 (cm³)	Mean (cm³)	Range (cm³)
28	37	32	(28 + 37 + 32) ÷ 3 = 32	(37 − 28) = 9

3) You might also need to calculate the <u>median</u> or <u>mode</u> (two more types of average). To calculate the <u>median</u>, put all your data in <u>numerical order</u> — the median is the <u>middle value</u>. The number that appears <u>most often</u> in a data set is the <u>mode</u>.

If you have an even number of values, the median is halfway between the middle two values.

> E.g. If you have the data set: 1 2 1 1 3 4 2
> The <u>median</u> is: 1 1 1 <u>2</u> 2 3 4.   The <u>mode</u> is <u>1</u> because 1 appears most often.

Round to the Lowest Number of Significant Figures

The <u>first significant figure</u> of a number is the first digit that's <u>not zero</u>. The second and third significant figures come <u>straight after</u> (even if they're zeros). You should be aware of significant figures in calculations.

1) In <u>any</u> calculation where you need to round, you should round the answer to the <u>lowest number of significant figures</u> (s.f.) given.

2) Remember to write down <u>how many</u> significant figures you've rounded to after your answer.

3) If your calculation has multiple steps, <u>only</u> round the <u>final</u> answer, or it won't be as accurate.

 EXAMPLE: **A plant produces 10.2 cm³ of oxygen in 6.5 minutes whilst photosynthesising. Calculate the rate of photosynthesis.**

rate = 10.2 cm³ ÷ 6.5 min = 1.5692... = 1.6 cm³/min (2 s.f.)

3 s.f.   2 s.f.   Final answer should be rounded to 2 s.f.

 EXAM TIP

Don't forget your calculator...

In the exam you could be given some <u>data</u> and be expected to <u>process it</u> in some way. Make sure you keep an eye on <u>significant figures</u> in your answers and <u>always write down your working</u>.

Presenting Data

Once you've processed your data, e.g. by calculating the mean, you can present your results in a nice <u>chart</u> or <u>graph</u>. This will help you to <u>spot any patterns</u> in your data.

If Your Data Comes in **Categories**, Present It in a **Bar Chart**

1) If the independent variable is <u>categoric</u> (comes in distinct categories, e.g. flower colour, blood group) you should use a <u>bar chart</u> to display the data.

2) You also use them if the independent variable is <u>discrete</u> (the data can be counted in chunks, where there's no in-between value, e.g. number of bacteria is discrete because you can't have half a bacterium).

3) There are some <u>golden rules</u> you need to follow for <u>drawing</u> bar charts:

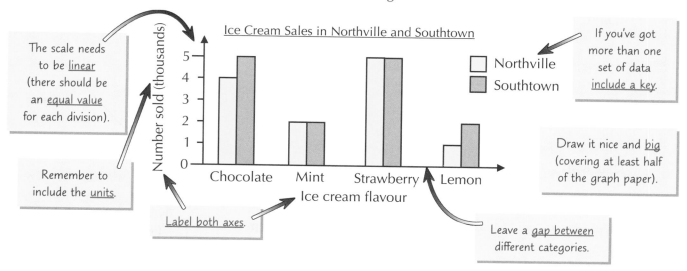

The scale needs to be <u>linear</u> (there should be an <u>equal value</u> for each division).

Remember to include the <u>units</u>.

Label both axes.

If you've got more than one set of data <u>include a key</u>.

Draw it nice and <u>big</u> (covering at least half of the graph paper).

Leave a <u>gap between</u> different categories.

If Your Data is **Continuous**, Plot a **Graph**

1) If both variables are <u>continuous</u> (numerical data that can have any value within a range, e.g. length, volume, temperature) you should use a <u>graph</u> to display the data.

2) Here are the <u>rules</u> for plotting points on a graph:

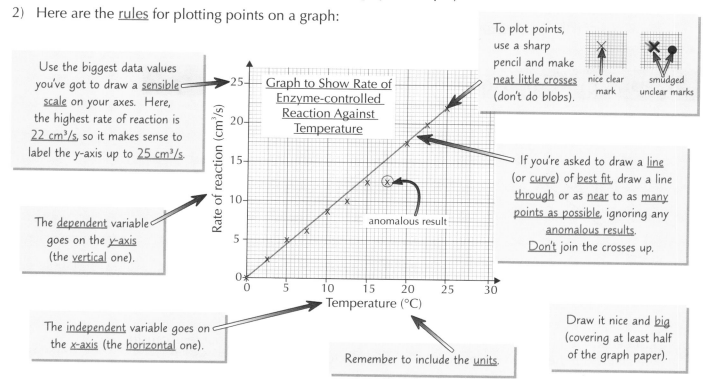

Use the biggest data values you've got to draw a <u>sensible</u> <u>scale</u> on your axes. Here, the highest rate of reaction is <u>22 cm³/s</u>, so it makes sense to label the y-axis up to <u>25 cm³/s</u>.

The <u>dependent</u> variable goes on the <u>y-axis</u> (the <u>vertical</u> one).

To plot points, use a sharp pencil and make <u>neat little crosses</u> (don't do blobs). nice clear mark smudged unclear marks

If you're asked to draw a <u>line</u> (or <u>curve</u>) of <u>best fit</u>, draw a line <u>through</u> or as <u>near</u> to as <u>many points as possible</u>, ignoring any <u>anomalous results</u>. <u>Don't</u> join the crosses up.

anomalous result

The <u>independent</u> variable goes on the <u>x-axis</u> (the <u>horizontal</u> one).

Remember to include the <u>units</u>.

Draw it nice and <u>big</u> (covering at least half of the graph paper).

More on Graphs

Graph's aren't just fun to plot, they're also really useful for showing <u>trends</u> in your data.

Graphs Can Give You a Lot of Information About Your Data

1) The <u>gradient</u> (slope) of a graph tells you how quickly the <u>dependent variable</u> changes if you change the <u>independent variable</u>.

You can use this method to calculate any rates from a graph, not just the rate of a reaction. Just remember that a rate is how much something changes over time, so x needs to be the time.

$$\text{gradient} = \frac{\text{change in } y}{\text{change in } x}$$

The <u>graph</u> below shows the <u>volume of gas</u> produced in a reaction against <u>time</u>. The graph is <u>linear</u> (it's a straight line graph), so you can simply calculate the <u>gradient</u> of the line to find out the <u>rate of reaction</u>.

1) To calculate the gradient, pick <u>two points</u> on the line that are easy to read and a <u>good distance</u> apart.

2) <u>Draw a line down</u> from one of the points and a <u>line across</u> from the other to make a <u>triangle</u>. The line drawn down the side of the triangle is the <u>change in y</u> and the line across the bottom is the <u>change in x</u>.

Change in y = 6.8 − 2.0 = 4.8 cm   Change in x = 5.2 − 1.6 = 3.6 s

$$\text{Rate} = \text{gradient} = \frac{\text{change in } y}{\text{change in } x} = \frac{4.8 \text{ cm}^3}{3.6 \text{ s}} = \underline{1.3 \text{ cm}^3/\text{s}} \text{ or } \underline{1.3 \text{ cm}^3\text{s}^{-1}}$$

The units of the gradient are (units of y)/(units of x). cm³/s can also be written as cm³s⁻¹.

2) If you've got a <u>curved graph</u>, you can find the rate at any point by drawing a <u>tangent</u> — a straight line that touches a <u>single point</u> on a curve. You can then find the gradient of the tangent in the usual way, to give you the rate at that <u>point</u>.

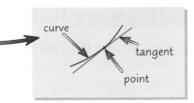

3) The <u>intercept</u> of a graph is where the line of best fit crosses one of the <u>axes</u>. The <u>x-intercept</u> is where the line of best fit crosses the x-axis and the <u>y-intercept</u> is where it crosses the y-axis.

Graphs Show the Relationship Between Two Variables

1) You can get <u>three</u> types of <u>correlation</u> (relationship) between variables:

<u>POSITIVE</u> correlation: as one variable <u>increases</u> the other <u>increases</u>.

<u>INVERSE</u> (negative) correlation: as one variable <u>increases</u> the other <u>decreases</u>.

<u>NO</u> correlation: <u>no relationship</u> between the two variables.

2) Just because there's correlation, it doesn't mean the change in one variable is <u>causing</u> the change in the other — there might be <u>other factors</u> involved (see page 13).

Units

Graphs and maths skills are all very well, but the numbers don't mean much if you don't get the <u>units</u> right.

S.I. Units Are Used All Round the World

1) It wouldn't be all that useful if I defined volume in terms of <u>bath tubs</u>, you defined it in terms of <u>egg-cups</u> and my pal Fred defined it in terms of <u>balloons</u> — we'd never be able to compare our data.

2) To stop this happening, scientists have come up with a set of <u>standard units</u>, called S.I. units, that all scientists use to measure their data. Here are some S.I. units you'll see in biology:

Quantity	S.I. Base Unit
mass	kilogram, kg
length	metre, m
time	second, s

Always Check The Values Used in Equations Have the Right Units

1) Equations (sometimes called formulas) show <u>relationships</u> between <u>variables</u>.

2) To <u>rearrange</u> an equation, make sure that whatever you do to <u>one side</u> of the equation you also do to the <u>other side</u>.

For example, you can find the <u>magnification</u> of something using the equation: <u>magnification = image size ÷ real size</u>. You can <u>rearrange</u> this equation to find the <u>image size</u> by <u>multiplying each side</u> by the real size: <u>image size = magnification × real size</u>

See p.18 for more on magnification calculations.

3) To use an equation, you need to know the values of <u>all but one</u> of the variables. <u>Substitute</u> the values you do know into the formula, and do the calculation to work out the final variable.

4) Always make sure the values you put into an equation have the <u>right units</u>. For example, if you're calculating the magnification of something, but your image size is in <u>mm</u> and the real size is in <u>μm</u>, you'll have to convert both measurements into the <u>same unit</u> (either mm or μm) before you start.

5) To make sure your units are <u>correct</u>, it can help to write down the <u>units</u> on each line of your <u>calculation</u>.

S.I. units help scientists to compare data...

You can only really <u>compare</u> things if they're in the <u>same units</u>. E.g. if the rate of blood flow was measured in ml/min in one vein and in l/day in another vein, it'd be hard to know which was faster.

Converting Units

You can convert units using scaling prefixes. This can save you from having to write a lot of 0's...

Scaling Prefixes Can Be Used for Large and Small Quantities

1) Quantities come in a huge range of sizes. For example, the volume of a swimming pool might be around 2 000 000 000 cm³, while the volume of a cup is around 250 cm³.

2) To make the size of numbers more manageable, larger or smaller units are used. These are the S.I. base units (e.g. metres) with a prefix in front:

Prefix	tera (T)	giga (G)	mega (M)	kilo (k)	deci (d)	centi (c)	milli (m)	micro (µ)	nano (n)
Multiple of Unit	10^{12}	10^9	1 000 000 (10^6)	1000	0.1	0.01	0.001	0.000001 (10^{-6})	10^{-9}

3) These prefixes tell you how much bigger or smaller a unit is than the base unit. So one kilometre is one thousand metres.

The conversion factor is the number of times the smaller unit goes into the larger unit.

4) To swap from one unit to another, all you need to know is what number you have to divide or multiply by to get from the original unit to the new unit — this is called the conversion factor.

- To go from a bigger unit (like m) to a smaller unit (like cm), you multiply by the conversion factor.
- To go from a smaller unit (like g) to a bigger unit (like kg), you divide by the conversion factor.

5) Here are some conversions that'll be useful for biology:

To convert from bigger units to smaller units...

...multiply by the conversion factor, and to convert from smaller units to bigger units, divide by the conversion factor. Don't go getting this the wrong way round or you'll get some odd answers.

Drawing Conclusions

Once you've carried out an experiment and processed your data, it's time to work out <u>what your data shows</u>.

You Can **Only Conclude** What the Data Shows and **No More**

1) Drawing conclusions might seem pretty straightforward — you just <u>look at your data</u> and <u>say what pattern or relationship you see</u> between the dependent and independent variables.

The table on the right shows heights of pea plant seedlings grown for three weeks with <u>different fertilisers</u>.

Fertiliser	Mean growth / mm
A	13.5
B	19.5
No fertiliser	5.5

<u>CONCLUSION</u>: Fertiliser <u>B</u> makes <u>pea plant</u> seedlings grow taller over a <u>three week</u> period than fertiliser A.

2) But you've got to be really careful that your conclusion <u>matches the data</u> you've got and <u>doesn't go any further</u>.

You <u>can't</u> conclude that fertiliser B makes <u>any other type of plant</u> grow taller than fertiliser A — the results could be totally different.

3) You also need to be able to <u>use your results</u> to <u>justify your conclusion</u> (i.e. back up your conclusion with some specific data).

Over the three week period, fertiliser B made the pea plants grow <u>6 mm more</u> on average than fertiliser A.

4) When writing a conclusion you need to <u>refer back</u> to the original hypothesis and say whether the data <u>supports it</u> or not:

The hypothesis for this experiment might have been that adding fertiliser would increase the growth of plants and that different types of fertiliser would affect growth by different amounts. If so, the data <u>supports</u> the hypothesis.

Correlation **DOES NOT** Mean **Cause**

If two things are correlated (i.e. there's a relationship between them) it <u>doesn't</u> necessarily mean a change in one variable is <u>causing</u> the change in the other — this is <u>REALLY IMPORTANT</u> — <u>DON'T FORGET IT</u>. There are <u>three possible reasons</u> for a correlation:

1) <u>CHANCE</u>: It might seem strange, but two things can show a correlation purely due to <u>chance</u>.

For example, one study might find a correlation between people's hair colour and how good they are at frisbee. But other scientists <u>don't</u> get a correlation when they investigate it — the results of the first study are just a <u>fluke</u>.

2) <u>LINKED BY A 3RD VARIABLE</u>: A lot of the time it may <u>look</u> as if a change in one variable is causing a change in the other, but it <u>isn't</u> — a <u>third variable links</u> the two things.

For example, there's a correlation between <u>water temperature</u> and <u>shark attacks</u>. This isn't because warmer water makes sharks crazy. Instead, they're linked by a third variable — the <u>number of people swimming</u> (more people swim when the water's hotter, and with more people in the water you get more shark attacks).

3) <u>CAUSE</u>: Sometimes a change in one variable does <u>cause</u> a change in the other. You can only conclude that a correlation is due to cause when you've <u>controlled all the variables</u> that could affect the result.

For example, there's a correlation between <u>smoking</u> and <u>lung cancer</u>. This is because chemicals in tobacco smoke cause lung cancer. This conclusion was only made once <u>other variables</u> (such as age and exposure to other things that cause cancer) had been <u>controlled</u>.

Uncertainty

Uncertainty is how sure you can really be about your data. There's a little bit of maths to do, and also a formula to learn. But don't worry too much — it's no more than a simple bit of subtraction and division.

Uncertainty is the Amount of Error Your Measurements Might Have

1) When you repeat a measurement, you often get a slightly different figure each time you do it due to random error (see page 7). This means that each result has some uncertainty to it.

2) The measurements you make will also have some uncertainty in them due to limits in the resolution of the equipment you use (see page 6).

3) This all means that the mean of a set of results will also have some uncertainty to it. You can calculate the uncertainty of a mean result using the equation:

$$\text{uncertainty} = \frac{\text{range}}{2}$$

The range is the largest value minus the smallest value (see p.8).

4) The larger the range, the less precise your results are and the more uncertainty there will be in your results. Uncertainties are shown using the '±' symbol.

EXAMPLE:

The table below shows the results of a respiration experiment to determine the volume of carbon dioxide produced. Calculate the uncertainty of the mean.

Repeat	1	2	3	mean
Volume of CO_2 produced (cm^3)	20.1	19.8	20.0	20.0

1) First work out the range:

   Range = 20.1 − 19.8 = 0.300 cm^3

2) Use the range to find the uncertainty:

   Uncertainty = range ÷ 2 = 0.300 ÷ 2 = 0.150 cm^3

   So the uncertainty of the mean = 20.0 ± 0.150 cm^3

5) Measuring a greater amount of something helps to reduce uncertainty.

For example, in a rate of reaction experiment, measuring the amount of product formed over a longer period compared to a shorter period will reduce the uncertainty in your results.

The smaller the uncertainty, the more precise your results...

Remember that equation for uncertainty. You never know when you might need it — you could be expected to use it in the exams. You need to make sure all the data is in the same units though. For example, if you had some measurements in metres, and some in centimetres, you'd need to convert them all into either metres or centimetres before you set about calculating uncertainty.

Evaluations

Hurrah! The end of another investigation. Well, now you have to work out all the things you did _wrong_. That's what _evaluations_ are all about I'm afraid. Best get cracking with this page...

Evaluations — Describe How Investigations Could be Improved

An evaluation is a _critical analysis_ of the whole investigation.

1) You should comment on the _method_ — was it _valid_?
   Did you control all the other variables to make it a _fair test_?

2) Comment on the _quality_ of the _results_ — was there _enough evidence_ to reach a valid _conclusion_? Were the results _repeatable_, _reproducible_, _accurate_ and _precise_?

3) Were there any _anomalous_ results? If there were _none_ then _say so_.
   If there were any, try to _explain_ them — were they caused by _errors_ in measurement?
   Were there any other _variables_ that could have _affected_ the results?
   You should comment on the level of _uncertainty_ in your results too.

4) All this analysis will allow you to say how _confident_ you are that your conclusion is _right_.

5) Then you can suggest any _changes_ to the _method_ that would _improve_ the quality of the results, so that you could have _more confidence_ in your conclusion. For example, you might suggest _changing_ the way you controlled a variable, or _increasing_ the number of _measurements_ you took. Taking more measurements at _narrower intervals_ could give you a _more accurate result_. For example:

> _Enzymes_ have an _optimum temperature_ (a temperature at which they _work best_).
> Say you do an experiment to find an enzyme's optimum temperature and take measurements at 10 °C, 20 °C, 30 °C, 40 °C and 50 °C. The results of this experiment tell you the optimum is _40 °C_. You could then _repeat_ the experiment, _taking more measurements around 40 °C_ to a get a _more accurate_ value for the optimum.

6) You could also make more _predictions_ based on your conclusion, then _further experiments_ could be carried out to test them.

When suggesting improvements to the investigation, always make sure that you say why you think this would make the results better.

Always look for ways to improve your investigations

So there you have it — _Working Scientifically_. Make sure you know this stuff like the back of your hand. It's not just in the lab or the field, when you're carrying out your groundbreaking _investigations_, that you'll need to know how to work scientifically. You can be asked about it in the _exams_ as well. So swot up...

Cells

When someone first peered down a microscope at a slice of cork and drew the <u>boxes</u> they saw, little did they know that they'd seen the <u>building blocks</u> of <u>every organism on the planet</u>...

Organisms can be **Prokaryotes** or **Eukaryotes**

1) <u>All living things</u> are made of <u>cells</u>.

2) Cells can be either <u>prokaryotic</u> or <u>eukaryotic</u>. Eukaryotic cells are <u>complex</u> and include all <u>animal</u> and <u>plant</u> cells. Prokaryotic cells are <u>smaller</u> and <u>simpler</u>, e.g. bacteria (see next page).

You might see the sizes of cells written in standard form — see p.18 for more on this.

3) <u>Eukaryotes</u> are organisms that are made up of <u>eukaryotic cells</u>.

4) A <u>prokaryote</u> is a <u>prokaryotic cell</u> (it's a single-celled organism).

Plant and Animal Cells have Similarities and Differences

Animal Cells

The different parts of a cell are called <u>subcellular structures</u>.
Most <u>animal</u> cells have the following subcellular structures — make sure you know them all:

1) <u>Nucleus</u> — contains <u>genetic material</u> that controls the activities of the cell.

2) <u>Mitochondria</u> — these are where most of the reactions for <u>aerobic respiration</u> take place (see page 102). Respiration transfers <u>energy</u> that the cell needs to work.

3) <u>Cytoplasm</u> — gel-like substance where most of the <u>chemical reactions</u> happen. It contains <u>enzymes</u> (see page 42) that control these chemical reactions.

4) <u>Cell membrane</u> — holds the cell together and controls what goes <u>in</u> and <u>out</u>.

5) <u>Ribosomes</u> — these are where <u>proteins</u> are made in the cell.

Subcellular structures are all the different parts of a cell

Make sure you get to grips with the different <u>subcellular structures</u> that animal cells contain before you move on to the next page. There are more subcellular structures coming up that you <u>need to know</u>...

Cells

Plant Cells

Plant cells usually have <u>all the bits</u> that <u>animal</u> cells have, plus a few <u>extra</u> things that animal cells <u>don't</u> have:

The cells of algae (e.g. seaweed) also have a rigid cell wall and chloroplasts.

1) Rigid <u>cell wall</u> — made of <u>cellulose</u>. It <u>supports</u> the cell and strengthens it.

2) <u>Chloroplasts</u> — these are where <u>photosynthesis</u> occurs, which makes food for the plant (see page 91). They contain a <u>green</u> substance called <u>chlorophyll</u>, which absorbs the <u>light</u> needed for photosynthesis.

3) <u>Permanent vacuole</u> — contains <u>cell sap</u>, a weak solution of sugar and salts.

You could get asked to estimate the area of a subcellular structure. If you do, treat it as a regular shape. For example, if it's close to a rectangle, use the area formula 'area = length × width'.

Bacterial Cells Are Much Smaller

1) Bacteria are <u>prokaryotes</u>.

2) Bacterial cells <u>don't</u> have a 'true' <u>nucleus</u> — instead they have a <u>single circular strand</u> of <u>DNA</u> that floats <u>freely</u> in the cytoplasm.

3) They may also contain one or more small rings of DNA called <u>plasmids</u>.

4) Bacteria <u>don't</u> have <u>chloroplasts</u> or <u>mitochondria</u>.

Here's what a bacterial cell might look like:

 ## There's quite a bit to learn in biology — but that's life, I guess...

On these pages are a <u>typical animal cell</u>, <u>plant cell</u> and <u>bacterial cell</u>. Make sure you're familiar with all their <u>structures</u>. A good way to check that you know what all the bits and pieces are is to copy out the diagrams and see if you can remember all the labels. No cheating.

Microscopy

Microscopes are pretty important for biology. There's a lot you need to know about them...

Cells are **Studied** Using **Microscopes**

1) Microscopes let us see things that we can't see with the naked eye. The microscopy techniques we can use have developed over the years as technology and knowledge have improved.
2) Light microscopes use light and lenses to form an image of a specimen and magnify it (make it look bigger). They let us see individual cells and large subcellular structures, like nuclei.
3) Electron microscopes use electrons instead of light to form an image. They have a much higher magnification than light microscopes.

See pages 19-20 for how to use a light microscope.

4) They also have a higher resolution. (Resolution is the ability to distinguish between two points, so a higher resolution gives a sharper image.)
5) Electron microscopes let us see much smaller things in more detail, like the internal structure of mitochondria and chloroplasts. They even let us see tinier things like ribosomes and plasmids.

You Need to be Able to Use the **Formula** for **Magnification**

You can calculate the magnification of an image using this formula:

$$\text{magnification} = \frac{\text{image size}}{\text{real size}}$$

Both image size and real size should have the same units. If they don't, you'll need to convert them first (see page 12).

EXAMPLE:

A specimen is 50 μm wide. Calculate the width of the image of the specimen under a magnification of × 100. Give your answer in mm.

1) Rearrange the formula.   image size = magnification × real size
2) Fill in the values you know.   image size = 100 × 50
3) Remember the units in your answer.   = 5000 μm
4) Convert the units.   = 5 mm

Remember, to convert from micrometres (μm) to millimetres (mm), you need to divide by 1000 (see p.12). E.g. 5000 μm ÷ 1000 = 5 mm

You Need to Know How to Work With Numbers in **Standard Form**

1) As microscopes can see such tiny objects, sometimes it's useful to write numbers in standard form.
2) This is where you change very big or small numbers with lots of zeros into something more manageable, e.g. 0.017 can be written 1.7×10^{-2}.
3) To do this you just need to move the decimal point left or right.
4) The number of places the decimal point moves is then represented by a power of 10 — this is positive if the decimal point's moved to the left, and negative if it's moved to the right.

EXAMPLE:

A mitochondrion is approximately 0.0025 mm long. Write this figure in standard form.

1) The first number needs to be between 1 and 10 so the decimal point needs to move after the '2'.

0.0025

2) Count how many places the decimal point has moved — this is the power of 10. Don't forget the minus sign because the decimal point has moved right.

2.5×10^{-3}

Microscopy

It's all very well knowing what microscopes <u>do</u> — you also have to know how to actually <u>use</u> one.

You Need to **Prepare** Your **Slide**

If you want to look at a specimen (e.g. plant or animal cells) under a light microscope, you need to put it on a <u>microscope slide</u> first. A slide is a strip of clear <u>glass</u> or <u>plastic</u> onto which the specimen is <u>mounted</u>. For example, here's how to prepare a slide to view onion cells:

1) Add a <u>drop of water</u> to the middle of a clean slide.

2) Cut up an onion and separate it out into <u>layers</u>. Use <u>tweezers</u> to peel off some <u>epidermal tissue</u> from the bottom of one of the layers.

3) Using the tweezers, place the epidermal tissue into the <u>water</u> on the slide.

4) Add a drop of <u>iodine solution</u>. Iodine solution is a <u>stain</u>. Stains are used to highlight objects in a cell by adding <u>colour</u> to them.

5) Place a <u>cover slip</u> (a square of thin, transparent plastic or glass) on top. To do this, stand the cover slip <u>upright</u> on the slide, <u>next to</u> the water droplet. Then carefully <u>tilt</u> and <u>lower</u> it so it covers the specimen. Try <u>not</u> to get any <u>air bubbles</u> under there — they'll <u>obstruct</u> your view of the specimen.

Know the Parts of a **Light Microscope**

To look at your prepared slides, you need to know how to use a light microscope. Here are the main parts you'll use:

Stains can make subcellular structures easier to see

Carry on to the next page for <u>how to use</u> the microscope above to view your specimen.

PRACTICAL

Microscopy

Use a **Light Microscope** to Look at Your **Slide**

1) Clip the <u>slide</u> you've prepared onto the <u>stage</u>.

Have a look back at the previous page if you need a reminder of where these parts are on the microscope.

2) Select the <u>lowest-powered objective lens</u> (i.e. the one that produces the lowest magnification).

3) Use the <u>coarse adjustment knob</u> to move the stage up to just below the objective lens.

4) Look down the <u>eyepiece</u>. Use the coarse adjustment knob to move the stage downwards until the image is <u>roughly in focus</u>.

5) Adjust the <u>focus</u> with the <u>fine adjustment knob</u>, until you get a <u>clear image</u> of what's on the slide.

6) If you need to see the slide with <u>greater magnification</u>, swap to a <u>higher-powered objective lens</u> and refocus.

Draw Your Observations **Neatly** with a **Pencil**

1) Draw what you see under the microscope using a <u>pencil</u> with a <u>sharp point</u>.
2) Make sure your drawing takes up <u>at least half</u> of the space available and that it is drawn with <u>clear, unbroken lines</u>.
3) Your drawing should not include any <u>colouring</u> or <u>shading</u>.
4) If you are drawing <u>cells</u>, the <u>subcellular structures</u> should be drawn in <u>proportion</u>.
5) Remember to include a <u>title</u> of what you were observing and write down the <u>magnification</u> that it was observed under.
6) <u>Label</u> the <u>important features</u> of your drawing (e.g. nucleus, chloroplasts), using <u>straight, uncrossed lines</u>.

You can measure the real size of the cells using a stage micrometer and an eyepiece graticule (see p.182). You can work out the magnification of your drawing using this formula:
magnification = length of drawing of cell ÷ real length of cell.
So here, magnification = 33 mm ÷ 0.3 mm = × 110.

 PRACTICAL TIP

Your microscope might look a bit different

The appearance of light microscopes can <u>vary</u> (e.g. they might have two eyepieces rather than one) but they should have the <u>same basic features</u> shown on the previous page.

Warm-Up & Exam Questions

So, hopefully you've read the last five pages. But could you cope if a question on cells or microscopes came up in the exam? With amazing new technology we can simulate that very situation...

Warm-Up Questions

1) Name the subcellular structures where aerobic respiration takes place.
2) Give three ways in which animal cells are different from plant cells.
3) Give two differences in structure between prokaryotic and eukaryotic cells.
4) What type of microscope should be used to look at the internal structure of chloroplasts?
5) Write the number 0.00045 μm in standard form.

Exam Questions

1 Which of the following subcellular structures would you not expect to find in a prokaryotic cell? Tick **one** box. *(Grade 4-6)*

☐ plasmid   ☐ nucleus   ☐ cell wall   ☐ cell membrane

[1 mark]

2 **Figure 1** shows a typical plant cell. *(Grade 4-6)*

Figure 1

2.1 Which label points to a chloroplast? Tick **one** box.

☐ A   ☐ B   ☐ C   ☐ D

[1 mark]

2.2 What is the function of a chloroplast?

[1 mark]

2.3 **Figure 1** also shows ribosomes.
What is the function of a ribosome?

[1 mark]

PRACTICAL

3 A light microscope can be used to observe a layer of onion cells on a slide. *(Grade 6-7)*

3.1* Describe how you would use a light microscope to view onion cells.
Include how you would prepare the slide.

[6 marks]

3.2 When the onion cell is viewed with × 100 magnification, the image of the cell is 7.5 mm wide.
Calculate the real width of the onion cell using the formula:

$$\text{magnification} = \frac{\text{image size}}{\text{real size}}$$

Give your answer in μm.

[3 marks]

Cell Differentiation and Specialisation

Cells <u>don't</u> all look the <u>same</u>. They have <u>different structures</u> to suit their <u>different functions</u>.

Cells **Differentiate** to Become **Specialised**

<u>Differentiation</u> is the process by which a cell <u>changes</u> to become <u>specialised</u> for its job.

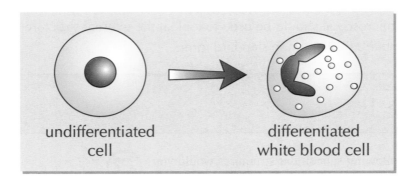

undifferentiated cell → differentiated white blood cell

1) As cells change, they develop <u>different subcellular structures</u> and turn into <u>different types of cells</u>. This allows them to carry out <u>specific functions</u>.

2) Most differentiation occurs as an organism <u>develops</u>. In most <u>animal</u> cells, the ability to differentiate is then <u>lost</u> at an early stage, after they become specialised. However, lots of <u>plant</u> cells <u>don't</u> ever lose this ability.

3) The cells that differentiate in <u>mature animals</u> are mainly used for <u>repairing</u> and <u>replacing cells</u>, such as skin or blood cells.

4) Some cells are undifferentiated cells — they're called <u>stem cells</u>. There's more about them on page 24.

You Need To Know These **Examples** of **Specialised Cells**

Sperm Cells are Specialised for **Reproduction**

1) The function of a <u>sperm</u> is basically to get the <u>male DNA</u> to the <u>female DNA</u>.
2) It has a <u>long tail</u> and a <u>streamlined head</u> to help it <u>swim</u> to the egg.
3) There are a lot of <u>mitochondria</u> in the cell to provide the <u>energy</u> needed.
4) It also carries <u>enzymes</u> in its head to digest through the egg cell membrane.

Nerve Cells are Specialised for **Rapid Signalling**

1) The function of <u>nerve cells</u> is to <u>carry electrical signals</u> from one part of the body to another.
2) These cells are <u>long</u> (to cover more distance) and have <u>branched connections</u> at their ends to <u>connect</u> to other nerve cells and form a <u>network</u> throughout the body.

Cell Specialisation

Muscle Cells are Specialised for Contraction

1) The function of a <u>muscle cell</u> is to contract quickly.
2) These cells are <u>long</u> (so that they have space to <u>contract</u>) and contain <u>lots of mitochondria</u> to generate the <u>energy</u> needed for contraction.

Root Hair Cells are Specialised for Absorbing Water and Minerals

1) Root hair cells are cells on the surface of plant roots, which grow into long "<u>hairs</u>" that stick out into the soil.
2) This gives the plant a <u>big</u> <u>surface area</u> for absorbing <u>water</u> and <u>mineral ions</u> from the soil.

Phloem and Xylem Cells are Specialised for Transporting Substances

1) <u>Phloem</u> and <u>xylem cells</u> form phloem and xylem <u>tubes</u>, which <u>transport</u> substances such as <u>food</u> and <u>water</u> around plants.
2) To form the tubes, the cells are long and joined <u>end to end</u>.
3) Xylem cells are <u>hollow</u> in the centre and phloem cells have <u>very few subcellular structures</u>, so that stuff can <u>flow through</u> them.

phloem   xylem

There's more about phloem and xylem on page 69.

Cells have the same basic bits but are specialised for their function

Not all cells contain <u>all</u> of the bits shown on pages 16-17. This is because some specialised cells don't have a use for certain subcellular structures — it depends on their <u>function</u>. For example, root hair cells grow <u>underground</u> in the soil, so they <u>don't need chloroplasts</u> because they don't photosynthesise.

Stem Cells

Stem cell research has exciting <u>possibilities</u>, but it's also pretty <u>controversial</u>.

Embryonic Stem Cells Can Turn into ANY Type of Cell

stem cell

replication

stem cell

differentiation

differentiated
white blood cell

1) <u>Differentiation</u> is the process by which a cell <u>changes</u> to become <u>specialised</u> for its job — see p.22.

2) <u>Undifferentiated</u> cells, called <u>stem cells</u>, can divide to produce lots <u>more</u> undifferentiated cells. They can differentiate into <u>different types of cell</u>, depending on what <u>instructions</u> they're given.

3) Stem cells are found in early <u>human embryos</u>. They're <u>exciting</u> to doctors and medical researchers because they have the potential to turn into <u>any</u> kind of cell at all. This makes sense if you think about it — <u>all</u> the <u>different types</u> of cell found in a human being have to come from those <u>few cells</u> in the early embryo.

4) Adults also have stem cells, but they're only found in certain places, like <u>bone marrow</u>.

5) Unlike embryonic stem cells, adult stem cells <u>can't</u> turn into <u>any</u> cell type at all — only certain ones, such as blood cells.

6) Stem cells from embryos and bone marrow can be grown in a lab to produce <u>clones</u> (<u>genetically identical cells</u>) and made to <u>differentiate</u> into specialised cells to use in <u>medicine</u> or <u>research</u>.

Stem Cells May Be Able to Cure Many Diseases

1) Medicine already uses <u>adult stem cells</u> to cure <u>disease</u>. For example, <u>stem cells</u> transferred from the bone marrow of a <u>healthy person</u> can <u>replace faulty blood cells</u> in the patient who receives them.

2) <u>Embryonic stem cells</u> could also be used to <u>replace faulty cells</u> in sick people — you could make <u>insulin-producing cells</u> for people with <u>diabetes</u>, <u>nerve cells</u> for people <u>paralysed by spinal injuries</u>, and so on.

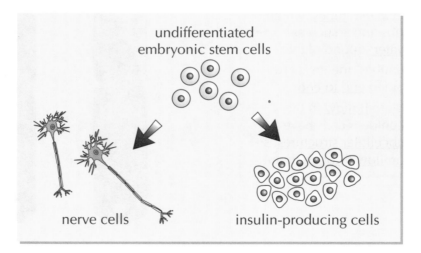

undifferentiated
embryonic stem cells

nerve cells

insulin-producing cells

3) In a type of cloning, called <u>therapeutic cloning</u>, an embryo could be made to have the <u>same genetic information</u> as the patient. This means that the <u>stem cells</u> produced from it would also contain the <u>same genes</u> and so <u>wouldn't</u> be <u>rejected</u> by the patient's body if used to replace faulty cells.

4) However, there are <u>risks</u> involved in using stem cells in medicine. For example, stem cells grown in the lab may become <u>contaminated</u> with a <u>virus</u> which could be <u>passed on</u> to the patient and so make them <u>sicker</u>.

Stem Cells

Some People Are **Against Stem Cell Research**

1) Some people are <u>against</u> stem cell research because they feel that human embryos <u>shouldn't</u> be used for experiments since each one is a <u>potential human life</u>.

2) Others think that curing patients who <u>already exist</u> and who are <u>suffering</u> is more important than the rights of <u>embryos</u>.

3) One fairly convincing argument in favour of this point of view is that the embryos used in the research are usually <u>unwanted ones</u> from <u>fertility clinics</u> which, if they weren't used for research, would probably just be <u>destroyed</u>. But of course, campaigners for the rights of embryos usually want this banned too.

4) These campaigners feel that scientists should concentrate more on finding and developing <u>other sources</u> of stem cells, so people could be helped <u>without</u> having to use embryos.

5) In some countries stem cell research is <u>banned</u>, but it's allowed in the UK as long as it follows <u>strict guidelines</u>.

Stem Cells Can Produce **Identical Plants**

1) In plants, stem cells are found in the <u>meristems</u> (parts of the plant where <u>growth</u> occurs — see p.68).

2) Throughout the plant's <u>entire life</u>, cells in the meristem tissues can differentiate into <u>any type</u> of plant cell.

3) These stem cells can be used to produce <u>clones</u> (identical copies) of whole plants <u>quickly</u> and <u>cheaply</u>.

4) They can be used to grow more plants of <u>rare species</u> (to prevent them being wiped out).

5) Stem cells can also be used to grow crops of <u>identical</u> plants that have desired <u>features</u> for farmers, for example, <u>disease resistance</u>.

Some species of orchid are endangered in the UK. Many can be successfully reproduced by cloning using stem cells.

Alternative sources of stem cells would avoid the controversy

Research has been done into getting human stem cells from <u>other sources</u> — e.g. it may be possible to 'reprogramme' differentiated adult cells back to an undifferentiated stage. But whatever your opinion of stem cell research is, it's good to know what their <u>uses</u> are and the arguments <u>for</u> and <u>against</u> using them.

Chromosomes and Mitosis

In order to survive and grow, our cells have got to be able to <u>divide</u>. And that means our DNA as well...

Chromosomes Contain Genetic Information

1) Most cells in your body have a <u>nucleus</u>. The nucleus contains your <u>genetic material</u> in the form of <u>chromosomes</u>.
2) Chromosomes are <u>coiled up</u> lengths of <u>DNA molecules</u>.
3) Each chromosome carries a <u>large number</u> of genes. Different genes <u>control</u> the development of different <u>characteristics</u>, e.g. hair colour.
4) <u>Body cells</u> normally have <u>two copies</u> of each <u>chromosome</u> — one from the organism's 'mother', and one from its '<u>father</u>'. So, humans have two copies of chromosome 1, two copies of chromosome 2, etc.
5) The diagram shows the <u>23 pairs of</u> <u>chromosomes</u> from a human cell.

The Cell Cycle Makes Cells for Growth, Development and Repair

1) <u>Body cells</u> in <u>multicellular</u> organisms <u>divide</u> to produce new cells as part of a series of stages called the <u>cell cycle</u>.
2) The stage of the cell cycle when the cell divides is called <u>mitosis</u>.

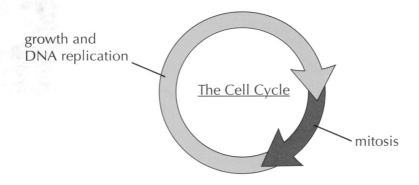

growth and DNA replication

The Cell Cycle

mitosis

There's more about mitosis on the next page.

3) Multicellular organisms use <u>mitosis</u> to <u>grow</u> and <u>develop</u> or <u>replace cells</u> that have been <u>damaged</u>.
4) The end of the cell cycle results in two new cells <u>identical</u> to the <u>original</u> cell, with the <u>same number</u> of chromosomes.

The cell cycle is important for growth and repair

Not all cells are going through the cell cycle at the same time, but when a cell does go through these stages, you end up with <u>two cells</u> where you originally had just one. The body <u>closely controls</u> which cells divide and when — if this control <u>fails</u>, it can result in <u>cancer</u> (see page 66).

Chromosomes and Mitosis

There are two main stages of the <u>cell cycle</u>...

Growth and DNA Replication

In a cell that's not dividing, the DNA is all spread out in <u>long strings</u>.

Before it divides, the cell has to <u>grow</u> and <u>increase</u> the amount of <u>subcellular structures</u> such as <u>mitochondria</u> and <u>ribosomes</u>.

It then <u>duplicates</u> its DNA — so there's one copy for each new cell. The DNA is copied and forms <u>X-shaped</u> chromosomes. Each 'arm' of the chromosome is an <u>exact duplicate</u> of the other.

The left arm of the chromosome has the same DNA as the right arm.

Mitosis

Once its contents and DNA have been copied, the cell is ready for <u>mitosis</u>...

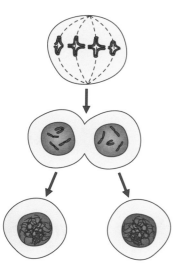

The chromosomes <u>line up</u> at the centre of the cell and <u>cell fibres</u> pull them apart. The <u>two arms</u> of each chromosome go to <u>opposite ends</u> of the cell.

<u>Membranes</u> form around each of the sets of chromosomes. These become the <u>nuclei</u> of the two new cells — the <u>nucleus</u> has <u>divided</u>.

Lastly, the <u>cytoplasm</u> and <u>cell membrane</u> divide.

The cell has now produced <u>two new daughter cells</u>.
The daughter cells contain exactly the <u>same DNA</u> — they're <u>identical</u>. Their DNA is also <u>identical</u> to the <u>parent cell</u>.

Mitosis produces two identical daughter cells

Mitosis can seem tricky at first. But don't worry — just go through it slowly, one step at a time.
This type of division produces <u>identical cells</u>, but there's another type which doesn't... (see page 128).

Warm-Up & Exam Questions

There's only one way to do well in the exam — learn the facts and then practise lots of exam questions to see what it'll be like on the big day. We couldn't have made it easier for you — so do it.

Warm-Up Questions

1) What does cell 'differentiation' mean?
2) Describe how a root hair cell is specialised for its function.
3) How can stem cells be used to preserve rare plant species?
4) Where in the cell are chromosomes found?
5) True or false? The cells produced in mitosis are genetically identical.

Exam Questions

1   **Figure 1** shows how the amount of DNA per cell changes as a cell undergoes two cell divisions by mitosis. Point **C** is the time when the chromosomes first become visible in the cells.

Figure 1

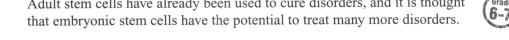

1.1   Describe what is happening to the DNA during stage **A**.
Suggest why this needs to happen.

[2 marks]

1.2   Suggest what happens at time **B**.

[1 mark]

1.3   How many cells are there after the first cell division?

[1 mark]

2   Adult stem cells have already been used to cure disorders, and it is thought that embryonic stem cells have the potential to treat many more disorders. `Grade 6-7`

2.1   Describe how stem cells could be used to treat disorders.

[1 mark]

2.2   Explain why embryonic stem cells have the potential to treat more disorders than adult stem cells.

[1 mark]

2.3   Give **one** place where adult stem cells are found in the body.

[1 mark]

Diffusion

Diffusion is <u>really important</u> in living organisms — it's how a lot of <u>substances</u> get <u>in</u> and <u>out</u> of cells.

Don't be Put Off by the **Fancy Word**

1) <u>Diffusion</u> is simple. It's just the <u>gradual movement</u> of particles from places where there are <u>lots</u> of them to places where there are <u>fewer</u> of them.

2) That's all it is — just the <u>natural tendency</u> for stuff to <u>spread out</u>.

3) Unfortunately you also have to learn the fancy way of saying the same thing, which is this:

> Diffusion is the <u>spreading out</u> of particles from an area of <u>higher concentration</u> to an area of <u>lower concentration</u>.

4) Diffusion happens in both <u>solutions</u> and <u>gases</u> — that's because the particles in these substances are free to <u>move about</u> randomly.

5) The <u>simplest type</u> is when different <u>gases</u> diffuse through each other. This is what's happening when the smell of perfume diffuses through a room:

air

perfume particles

perfume particles diffused in the air

> The <u>bigger</u> the <u>concentration gradient</u> (the <u>difference</u> in concentration), the <u>faster</u> the diffusion rate. A <u>higher temperature</u> will also give a <u>faster</u> diffusion rate because the particles have <u>more energy</u>, so move around faster.

Cell Membranes Are Kind of Clever...

1) They're clever because they <u>hold</u> the cell together <u>but</u> they let stuff <u>in and out</u> as well.

2) Dissolved substances can move in and out of cells by <u>diffusion</u>.

3) Only very <u>small</u> molecules can <u>diffuse</u> through cell membranes though — things like <u>oxygen</u> (needed for respiration — see page 102), <u>glucose</u>, <u>amino acids</u> and <u>water</u>.

4) <u>Big</u> molecules like <u>starch</u> and <u>proteins</u> can't fit through the membrane:

protein

starch

glucose

amino acid

5) Just like with diffusion in air, particles flow through the cell membrane from where there's a <u>higher concentration</u> (a lot of them) to where there's a <u>lower concentration</u> (not such a lot of them).

6) They're only moving about <u>randomly</u> of course, so they go <u>both</u> ways — but if there are a lot <u>more</u> particles on one side of the membrane, there's a <u>net</u> (overall) movement <u>from</u> that side.

> The <u>larger</u> the <u>surface area</u> of the membrane, the <u>faster</u> the diffusion rate because more particles can pass through at once — see page 34.

Osmosis

If you've got your head round <u>diffusion</u>, osmosis will be a <u>breeze</u>.
If not, have another look at the previous page...

Osmosis is a **Special Case** of **Diffusion**, That's All

Learn this definition of osmosis:

> Osmosis is the <u>movement of water molecules</u> across a <u>partially permeable membrane</u> from a region of <u>higher water concentration</u> to a region of <u>lower water concentration</u>.

1) A <u>partially permeable</u> membrane is just one with very small holes in it.
   So small, in fact, only tiny <u>molecules</u> (like water) can pass through them,
   and bigger molecules (e.g. <u>sucrose</u>) can't.

2) The water molecules actually pass <u>both ways</u> through the membrane during osmosis.
   This happens because water molecules <u>move about randomly</u> all the time.

3) But because there are <u>more</u> water molecules on one side than on the other,
   there's a steady <u>net flow</u> of water into the region with <u>fewer</u> water molecules,
   i.e. into the <u>stronger</u> sugar solution.

4) This means the <u>strong sugar</u> solution gets more <u>dilute</u>. The water acts like
   it's trying to "<u>even up</u>" the concentration either side of the membrane.

5) Osmosis is a type of <u>diffusion</u> — passive movement of <u>water particles</u> from
   an area of <u>higher water concentration</u> to an area of <u>lower water concentration</u>.

Diffusion is movement from where there's lots to where there's few...

...so osmosis is really just a fancy word for the <u>diffusion of water molecules</u>. It's simple really.

Osmosis

There's an <u>experiment</u> you can do to show osmosis at work.

You can **Observe** the Effect of **Sugar Solutions** on **Plant Tissue**

1) Cut up a <u>potato</u> into identical cylinders, and get some beakers with <u>different sugar solutions</u> in them. One should be <u>pure water</u> and another should be a <u>very concentrated sugar solution</u> (e.g. 1 mol/dm³). Then you can have a few others with concentrations <u>in between</u> (e.g. 0.2 mol/dm³, 0.4 mol/dm³, 0.6 mol/dm³, etc.)

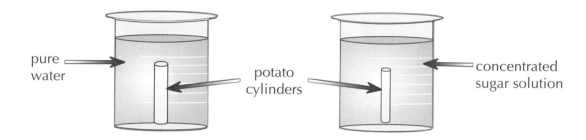

pure water — potato cylinders — concentrated sugar solution

2) You measure the <u>mass</u> of the cylinders, then leave one cylinder in each beaker for twenty four hours or so.

3) Then you take them out, <u>dry</u> them with a paper towel and measure their masses <u>again</u>.

4) If the cylinders have drawn in water by osmosis, they'll have <u>increased in mass</u>. If water has been drawn out, they'll have <u>decreased in mass</u>. You can calculate the <u>percentage change in mass</u>, then plot a few <u>graphs</u> and things.

By calculating the percentage change (see p.183), you can compare the effect of sugar concentration on cylinders that didn't have the same initial mass. An increase in mass will give a positive percentage change and a decrease will give a negative percentage change.

The <u>dependent variable</u> is the <u>chip mass</u> and the <u>independent variable</u> is the <u>concentration</u> of the sugar solution. All <u>other</u> variables (volume of solution, temperature, time, type of sugar used, etc.) must be kept the <u>same</u> in each case or the experiment won't be a <u>fair test</u>.

Like any experiment, you need to be aware of how <u>errors</u> (see p.7) may arise. Sometimes they may occur when <u>carrying out the method</u>, e.g. if some potato cylinders were not <u>fully dried</u>, the excess water would give a <u>higher mass</u>, or if water <u>evaporated</u> from the beakers, the <u>concentrations</u> of the sugar solutions would change. You can <u>reduce the effect</u> of these errors by <u>repeating</u> the experiment and calculating a <u>mean percentage change</u> at each concentration.

You could also carry out this experiment using different salt solutions and see what effect they have on potato chip mass.

You could do a similar experiment to work out the rate of osmosis by leaving the potato cylinders for 30 minutes, then dividing the change in mass (in grams) by the time taken (in minutes). So the units for the rate would be g/min.

Water always moves into the more concentrated solution

That's why it's bad to drink sea-water. The high <u>salt</u> content means you end up with a much <u>lower water concentration</u> in your blood and tissue fluid than in your cells. All the water is sucked out of your cells by osmosis and they <u>shrivel and die</u>. So next time you're stranded at sea, remember this...

Active Transport

Sometimes substances need to be absorbed against a concentration gradient, i.e. from a lower to a higher concentration. This process is referred to as <u>active transport</u>.

Root Hairs Take In Minerals and Water

Root Hair Cell

1) As you saw on page 23, the cells on plant roots grow into "<u>hairs</u>" which stick out into the soil.

2) Each branch of a root will be covered in <u>millions</u> of these microscopic hairs.

3) This gives the plant a <u>large surface area</u> for absorbing <u>water</u> and <u>mineral ions</u> from the soil.

4) Plants <u>need</u> these mineral ions for <u>healthy growth</u>.

5) The concentration of minerals is usually <u>higher</u> in the <u>root hair</u> cells than in the <u>soil</u> around them.

6) So the root hair cells <u>can't</u> use <u>diffusion</u> to take up minerals from the soil.

Root Hairs Take in Minerals Using Active Transport

1) Minerals should move <u>out</u> of the root hairs if they followed the rules of diffusion. The cells must use another method to draw them in.

2) That method is a process called "<u>active transport</u>".

3) Active transport allows the plant to absorb minerals from a very <u>dilute</u> solution, <u>against</u> a concentration gradient. This is essential for its growth. But active transport needs <u>energy</u> from <u>respiration</u> to make it work.

4) Active transport also happens in <u>humans</u>, for example in taking <u>glucose</u> from the <u>gut</u> (see below), and from the <u>kidney tubules</u>.

Water is taken into root hair cells by osmosis (see page 30).

We Need Active Transport to Stop Us Starving

<u>Active transport</u> is used in the gut when there is a <u>lower concentration</u> of nutrients in the <u>gut</u>, but a <u>higher concentration</u> of nutrients in the <u>blood</u>.

1) When there's <u>a higher concentration</u> of glucose and amino acids in the gut they <u>diffuse naturally</u> into the blood.

2) <u>BUT</u> — sometimes there's a <u>lower concentration</u> of nutrients in the gut than there is in the blood.

3) This means that the <u>concentration gradient</u> is the wrong way.

4) The same process used in plant roots is used here — <u>active transport</u>.

5) Active transport allows nutrients to be taken into the blood, despite the fact that the <u>concentration gradient</u> is the wrong way.

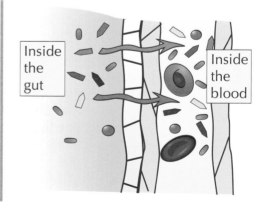

Inside the gut

Inside the blood

This means that <u>glucose</u> can be taken into the bloodstream when its concentration in the blood is already <u>higher</u> than in the gut. It can then be transported to cells, where it's used for <u>respiration</u> (see p.100).

Active transport uses energy

An important difference between <u>active transport</u> and <u>diffusion</u> is that active transport uses <u>energy</u>.

Exchanging Substances

How easily stuff <u>moves</u> between an <u>organism</u> and its <u>environment</u> depends on its <u>surface area to volume ratio</u>.

Organisms **Exchange Substances** with their **Environment**

1) Cells can use <u>diffusion</u> to <u>take in</u> substances they <u>need</u> and <u>get rid</u> of <u>waste products</u>.
   For example:

   - <u>Oxygen</u> and <u>carbon dioxide</u> are transferred between <u>cells</u> and the <u>environment</u> during <u>gas exchange</u>.
   - In humans, <u>urea</u> (a waste product produced from the breakdown of proteins) diffuses from <u>cells</u> into the <u>blood plasma</u> for removal from the body by the kidneys.

2) How <u>easy</u> it is for an organism to exchange substances with its environment depends on the organism's <u>surface area to volume ratio</u> (<u>SA : V</u>).

The importance of an organism's SA : V is explained on the next page.

You Can Compare **Surface Area to Volume Ratios**

A ratio shows <u>how big</u> one value is <u>compared</u> to another. The <u>larger</u> an organism is, the <u>smaller</u> its surface area is compared to its volume. You can show this by calculating <u>surface area to volume ratios</u>:

A hippo can be represented by a 2 cm × 4 cm × 4 cm block.

The area of a surface is found by the equation: LENGTH × WIDTH
So the hippo's total <u>surface area</u> is:

   (4 × 4) × 2 (top and bottom surfaces of block)
   + (4 × 2) × 4 (four sides of the block)
   = 64 cm².

The volume of a block is found by the equation: LENGTH × WIDTH × HEIGHT
So the hippo's <u>volume</u> is 4 × 4 × 2 = 32 cm³.

The surface area to volume ratio of the hippo can be written as <u>64 : 32</u>.
To <u>simplify</u> the ratio, <u>divide both sides</u> of the ratio by the <u>volume</u>.

So the surface area to volume ratio of the hippo is <u>2 : 1</u>.

A mouse can be represented by a 1 cm × 1 cm × 1 cm block.
Its <u>surface area</u> is (1 × 1) × 6 = 6 cm².
Its <u>volume</u> is 1 × 1 × 1 = 1 cm³.

So the surface area to volume ratio of the mouse is <u>6 : 1</u>.

The cube mouse's surface area is <u>six</u> times its volume, but the cube hippo's surface area is only <u>twice</u> its volume. So the <u>mouse</u> has a <u>larger</u> surface area compared to its volume.

Surface area to volume ratios crop up a lot in biology...

...so it's a good idea to try to understand them now. Remember that, generally speaking, a <u>smaller</u> object has a <u>larger</u> surface area to volume ratio than a bigger object. Now for why that's important...

Exchanging Substances

Multicellular Organisms Need Exchange Surfaces

1) In single-celled organisms, gases and dissolved substances can diffuse directly into (or out of) the cell across the cell membrane. It's because they have a large surface area compared to their volume, so enough substances can be exchanged across the membrane to supply the volume of the cell.

2) Multicellular organisms have a smaller surface area compared to their volume — not enough substances can diffuse from their outside surface to supply their entire volume. This means they need some sort of exchange surface for efficient diffusion (see below and pages 35-36 for some examples). The exchange surface structures have to allow enough of the necessary substances to pass through.

3) Exchange surfaces are adapted to maximise effectiveness:

   - They have a thin membrane, so substances only have a short distance to diffuse.
   - They have a large surface area so lots of a substance can diffuse at once.
   - Exchange surfaces in animals have lots of blood vessels, to get stuff into and out of the blood quickly.
   - Gas exchange surfaces in animals (e.g. alveoli) are often ventilated too — air moves in and out.

Gas Exchange Happens in the Lungs

1) The job of the lungs is to transfer oxygen to the blood and to remove waste carbon dioxide from it.

2) To do this the lungs contain millions of little air sacs called alveoli where gas exchange takes place.

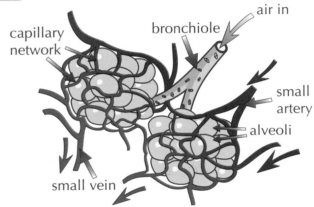

Blue = blood with carbon dioxide.
Red = blood with oxygen.

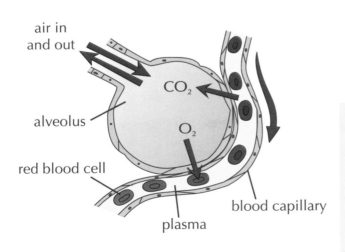

3) The alveoli are specialised to maximise the diffusion of oxygen and CO_2. They have:

   - An enormous surface area (about 75 m² in humans).
   - A moist lining for dissolving gases.
   - Very thin walls.
   - A good blood supply.

Humans need alveoli for gas exchange

You might well get asked to explain how the adaptations of the alveoli help gas exchange, so make sure you know what those adaptations are and why they affect the rate of diffusion. There are some more structures you need to know about coming up on the next couple of pages...

More on Exchanging Substances

The Villi Provide a Really Big Surface Area

1) The inside of the <u>small intestine</u> is covered in millions and millions of these tiny little projections called <u>villi</u>.

2) They increase the surface area in a big way so that digested food is <u>absorbed</u> much more quickly into the <u>blood</u>.

3) Notice they have:

- a <u>single</u> layer of surface cells
- a very good <u>blood supply</u> to assist <u>quick absorption</u>.

The digested food moves into the blood by diffusion and by active transport (see page 32).

The Structure of Leaves Lets Gases Diffuse In and Out of Cells

Carbon dioxide <u>diffuses into the air spaces</u> within the leaf, then it <u>diffuses into the cells</u> where photosynthesis happens. The leaf's structure is <u>adapted</u> so that this can happen easily:

1) The underneath of the leaf is an <u>exchange surface</u>. It's covered in biddy little holes called <u>stomata</u> which the carbon dioxide diffuses in through.

2) <u>Oxygen</u> (produced in photosynthesis) and <u>water vapour</u> also diffuse <u>out</u> through the stomata. (Water vapour is actually lost from all over the leaf surface, but most of it is lost through the stomata.)

3) The size of the stomata is controlled by <u>guard cells</u> — see page 72. These <u>close</u> the stomata if the plant is losing water faster than it is being replaced by the roots. Without these guard cells the plant would soon <u>wilt</u>.

4) The <u>flattened shape</u> of the leaf increases the <u>area</u> of this exchange surface so that it's more effective.

5) The <u>walls of the cells</u> inside the leaf form another exchange surface. The <u>air spaces</u> inside the leaf increase the <u>area</u> of this surface so there's more chance for carbon dioxide to get into the cells.

Oxygen and water vapour diffuse <u>out of</u> the leaf

CO_2 diffuses <u>into</u> leaf

The water vapour <u>evaporates</u> from the cells inside the leaf. Then it escapes by <u>diffusion</u> because there's a lot of it <u>inside</u> the leaf and less of it in the <u>air outside</u>.

More on Exchanging Substances

It's not just <u>humans</u> and <u>plants</u> that need specialised surfaces for gas exchange.
<u>Fish</u> need an exchange surface that allows them to <u>efficiently</u> exchange gases <u>underwater</u>.

Gills Have a Large Surface Area for Gas Exchange

1) The <u>gills</u> are the gas exchange surface in <u>fish</u>.

2) Water (containing <u>oxygen</u>) enters the fish through
its <u>mouth</u> and passes out through the <u>gills</u>.
As this happens, <u>oxygen</u> diffuses from the water
into the blood in the gills and <u>carbon dioxide</u>
diffuses from the blood into the water.

3) Each gill is made of lots of thin plates called <u>gill filaments</u>,
which give a <u>big surface area</u> for <u>exchange</u> of <u>gases</u>.

4) The gill filaments are covered in lots of tiny structures called
<u>lamellae</u>, which <u>increase</u> the <u>surface area</u> even more.

5) The lamellae have <u>lots of blood capillaries</u> to <u>speed up diffusion</u>.

6) They also have a <u>thin surface layer</u> of cells to <u>minimise</u> the <u>distance</u> that the gases have to diffuse.

7) <u>Blood</u> flows through the lamellae in one direction and <u>water</u> flows over in the opposite direction.
This maintains a <u>large concentration gradient</u> between the water and the blood.

8) The <u>concentration of oxygen</u> in the <u>water</u> is always <u>higher</u> than that in the <u>blood</u>,
so as much oxygen as possible diffuses from the water into the blood.

Exchange surfaces are specialised for efficient diffusion

Multicellular organisms are really <u>well adapted</u> for getting the substances they need to their cells. It makes
sense — if they couldn't do this well, they'd die out. A <u>large surface area</u> is a key way that organisms'
exchange surfaces are made more effective — molecules can only diffuse through a membrane when
they're right next to it, and a large surface area means that <u>a lot more molecules</u> are close to the membrane.

Warm-Up & Exam Questions

Question time again — Warm-Up first, then Exam (or the other way round if you want to be different).

Warm-Up Questions

1) Explain why temperature affects the rate of diffusion.
2) Explain what is meant by a partially permeable membrane.
3) Other than diffusion, by what two processes do substances move across exchange surfaces?
4) Give four ways in which exchange surfaces in animals are adapted to maximise their effectiveness.
5) Name two exchange surfaces in humans.
6) Give two ways in which the structure of a gill is adapted for effective gas exchange.

Exam Questions

1 A student adds a drop of ink to a glass of cold water.

1.1 What will the student observe to happen to the drop of ink.
Explain your answer.

[2 marks]

1.2 How might the observation differ if the ink was added to a glass of warm water?

[1 mark]

PRACTICAL

2 In an experiment, four 5 cm long cylinders were cut from a fresh potato.
The cylinders were then placed in different sugar solutions, as shown in **Figure 1**.
After 24 hours the potato cylinders were removed and measured.

Figure 1

Tube A   Tube B   Tube C   Tube D

distilled water | 1.0 mol/dm³ sugar solution | 2.0 mol/dm³ sugar solution | 3.0 mol/dm³ sugar solution

2.1 Which potato cylinder would you expect to be shortest after 24 hours?
Explain your answer.

[2 marks]

2.2 The potato cylinder in tube A increased in length during the 24 hours.
Explain why this happened.

[2 marks]

Exam Questions

3   **Figure 2** shows a villus from the small intestine.
Glucose and other products of digestion are absorbed into the blood through the villi.

Figure 2

network of capillaries

gland cells

circular muscle

longitudinal muscle

3.1   Suggest how the products of digestion move into the blood.

[2 marks]

3.2   Explain how the structure of villi is related to their function.

[3 marks]

4   A student made up some gelatine with cresol red solution and ammonium hydroxide. Cresol red solution is a pH indicator that is red in alkaline solutions and yellow in acidic solutions. The student cut the gelatine into cubes of different sizes, and placed the cubes in a beaker of dilute hydrochloric acid. He measured how long it took for the cubes to change from red to yellow as the acid moved into the gelatine and neutralised the ammonium hydroxide. His results are shown in **Table 1**.

Table 1

Size of cube (mm)	Time taken for cube to become yellow (s)			
	Trial 1	Trial 2	Trial 3	Trial 4
5 × 5 × 5	174	167	177	182
7 × 7 × 7	274	290	284	292
10 × 10 × 10	835	825	842	838

4.1   Name the process by which hydrochloric acid moves into the gelatine cubes in this experiment.

[1 mark]

4.2   Calculate the mean time for a 10 × 10 × 10 mm gelatine cube to become yellow in this experiment.

[2 marks]

4.3   Calculate the surface area to volume ratio of a 10 × 10 × 10 mm cube. Give the ratio in its simplest form.

[3 marks]

4.4   Describe and explain the relationship between the size of the gelatine cube and the time taken for the cube to become yellow.

[3 marks]

5   A bacterial cell can be represented by a 2 μm × 2 μm × 1 μm block. Calculate the cell's surface area to volume ratio.

[3 marks]

Revision Summary for Topic 1

Well, that's <u>Topic 1</u> done and dusted. Now there's only one way to find out whether you've learnt anything from it. And you know what that is, I'll bet. It's obvious... I mean, there's a whole load of questions staring you in the face — chances are, it's got to involve those in some way. And sure enough, it does.

- Try these questions and <u>tick off each one</u> when you <u>get it right</u>.
- When you've done <u>all the questions</u> under a heading and are <u>completely happy</u> with it, tick it off.

Cells and Microscopy (p.16-20) ☑

1) Name five subcellular structures that both plant and animal cells have. ☑

2) What three things do plant cells have that animal cells don't? ☑

3) Where is the genetic material found in:
    a) animal cells,
    b) bacterial cells? ☑

4) What type of organisms are bacteria — prokaryotes or eukaryotes? ☑

5) Which gives a higher resolution — a light microscope or an electron microscope? ☑

6) How have electron microscopes increased our understanding of subcellular structures? ☑

Differentiation and Stem Cells (p.22-25) ☑

7) Why do cells differentiate? ☑

8) Give three ways that a sperm cell is adapted for swimming to an egg cell. ☑

9) Draw a diagram of a nerve cell. Why is it this shape? ☑

10) Give two ways that embryonic stem cells could be used to cure diseases. ☑

11) Why might some people be opposed to the use of human embryos in stem cell research? ☑

Cell Division (p.26-27) ☑

12) What are chromosomes? ☑

13) What is the cell cycle? ☑

14) What is mitosis used for by multicellular organisms? ☑

Exchanging Substances (p.29-36) ☑

15) What is diffusion? ☑

16) Name three substances that can diffuse through cell membranes, and two that can't. ☑

17) What type of molecules move by osmosis? ☑

18) Give the two main differences between active transport and diffusion. ☑

19) Give one way in which alveoli are adapted for gas exchange. ☑

20) Give two ways that the villi in the small intestine are adapted for absorbing digested food. ☑

21) Explain how leaves are adapted to maximise the amount of carbon dioxide that gets to their cells. ☑

Cell Organisation

Some organisms contain loads of <u>cells</u>, but how, you might wonder, do all these cells mean you end up with a working human... the answer's <u>organisation</u>.

Large Multicellular Organisms are Made Up of Organ Systems

1) <u>Cells</u> are the <u>basic building blocks</u> that make up <u>all living organisms</u>.
2) As you know from page 22, <u>specialised cells</u> carry out a <u>particular function</u>.
3) The <u>process</u> by which cells become specialised for a particular job is called <u>differentiation</u>.

unspecialised cell   differentiation   specialised cell

4) Differentiation occurs during the <u>development</u> of a multicellular organism.
5) These specialised cells form <u>tissues</u>, which form <u>organs</u>, which form <u>organ systems</u> (see below and next page).
6) <u>Large multicellular organisms</u> (e.g. humans) have different <u>systems</u> inside them for <u>exchanging</u> and <u>transporting</u> materials.

Similar Cells are Organised into Tissues

1) A <u>tissue</u> is a <u>group</u> of <u>similar cells</u> that work together to carry out a particular <u>function</u>.
2) It can include <u>more than one type</u> of cell.
3) In <u>mammals</u> (like humans), examples of tissues include:

> • <u>Muscular tissue</u>, which <u>contracts</u> (shortens) to <u>move</u> whatever it's attached to.
> • <u>Glandular tissue</u>, which <u>makes</u> and <u>secretes</u> chemicals like <u>enzymes</u> and <u>hormones</u>.
> • <u>Epithelial tissue</u>, which <u>covers</u> some parts of the body, e.g. the <u>inside</u> of the <u>gut</u>.

less than 0.1 mm   <u>Epithelial cell</u>   <u>Epithelial tissue</u>

Cell Organisation

We left off at <u>tissues</u> on the previous page — now you need to know how they're organised...

Tissues are Organised into Organs

An <u>organ</u> is a group of <u>different tissues</u> that work together to perform a certain <u>function</u>.

For example, the <u>stomach</u> is an organ made of these tissues:
- <u>Muscular tissue</u>, which moves the stomach wall to <u>churn up the food</u>.
- <u>Glandular tissue</u>, which makes <u>digestive juices</u> to digest food.
- <u>Epithelial tissue</u>, which covers the <u>outside</u> and <u>inside</u> of the stomach.

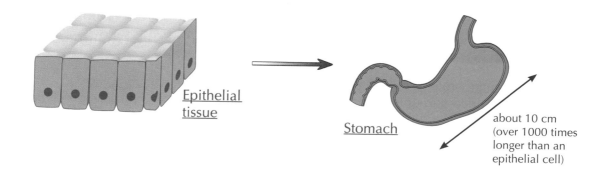

<u>Epithelial tissue</u>

<u>Stomach</u>

about 10 cm (over 1000 times longer than an epithelial cell)

Organs are Organised into Organ Systems

An <u>organ system</u> is a <u>group of organs</u> working together to perform a particular <u>function</u>.

For example, the <u>digestive system</u> (found in humans and other mammals) <u>breaks down</u> and <u>absorbs food</u>. It is made up of these organs:
1) <u>Glands</u> (e.g. the <u>pancreas</u> and <u>salivary glands</u>), which produce <u>digestive juices</u>.
2) The <u>stomach</u> and <u>small intestine</u>, which <u>digest</u> food.
3) The <u>liver</u>, which produces <u>bile</u>.
4) The <u>small intestine</u>, which <u>absorbs</u> soluble <u>food</u> molecules.
5) The <u>large intestine</u>, which <u>absorbs water</u> from undigested food, leaving <u>faeces</u>.

Organ systems work together to make entire <u>organisms</u>.

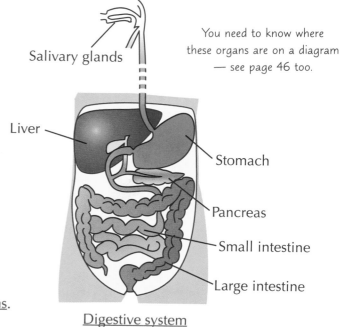

You need to know where these organs are on a diagram — see page 46 too.

Salivary glands

Liver

Stomach

Pancreas

Small intestine

Large intestine

<u>Digestive system</u>

Remember — cells, tissues, organs, organ systems

OK, so from the last couple of pages you know that <u>cells</u> are organised into <u>tissues</u>, the tissues into <u>organs</u>, the organs into <u>organ systems</u> and the organ systems into a whole <u>organism</u>.

Enzymes

Chemical reactions are what make you work. And enzymes are what make them work.

Enzymes Are Catalysts Produced by Living Things

1) Living things have thousands of different chemical reactions going on inside them all the time.
   These reactions need to be carefully controlled — to get the right amounts of substances.

2) You can usually make a reaction happen more quickly by raising the temperature. This would speed
   up the useful reactions but also the unwanted ones too... not good. There's also a limit to how far
   you can raise the temperature inside a living creature before its cells start getting damaged.

3) So... living things produce enzymes that act as biological catalysts. Enzymes reduce the need for
   high temperatures and we only have enzymes to speed up the useful chemical reactions in the body.

> A CATALYST is a substance which INCREASES the speed of a reaction,
> without being CHANGED or USED UP in the reaction.

4) Enzymes are all large proteins and all proteins are made up of chains of amino acids.
   These chains are folded into unique shapes, which enzymes need to do their jobs (see below).

Enzymes Have Special Shapes So They Can Catalyse Reactions

1) Chemical reactions usually involve things either being split apart or joined together.

2) Every enzyme has an active site with a unique shape that fits onto the substance involved in a reaction.

3) Enzymes are really picky — they usually only catalyse one specific reaction.

4) This is because, for the enzyme to work, the substrate has to fit into its
   active site. If the substrate doesn't match the enzyme's active site, then
   the reaction won't be catalysed.

   The substance that an enzyme acts on is called the substrate.

5) This diagram shows the 'lock and key' model of enzyme action.

6) This is simpler than how enzymes actually work. In reality, the active site changes shape a little as
   the substrate binds to it to get a tighter fit. This is called the 'induced fit' model of enzyme action.

Enzymes speed up chemical reactions

Just like you've got to have the correct key for a lock, you've got to have the right substance for an enzyme.
As you can see in the diagram above, if the substance doesn't fit, the enzyme won't catalyse the reaction...

Enzymes

Enzymes are clearly very clever, but they're <u>not</u> very versatile. They need just the right <u>conditions</u> if they're going to work properly.

Enzymes Need the **Right Temperature**...

1) Changing the <u>temperature</u> changes the <u>rate</u> of an enzyme-catalysed reaction.

2) Like with any reaction, a higher temperature <u>increases</u> the rate at first.

3) But if it gets <u>too hot</u>, some of the <u>bonds</u> holding the enzyme together <u>break</u>. This changes the shape of the enzyme's <u>active site</u>, so the substrate <u>won't fit</u> any more. The enzyme is said to be <u>denatured</u>.

4) All enzymes have an <u>optimum temperature</u> that they work best at.

... and the **Right pH**

1) The <u>pH</u> also affects enzymes. If it's too high or too low, the pH interferes with the <u>bonds</u> holding the enzyme together.

2) This changes the <u>shape</u> of the <u>active site</u> and <u>denatures</u> the enzyme.

3) All enzymes have an <u>optimum pH</u> that they work best at. It's often <u>neutral pH 7</u>, but <u>not always</u> — e.g. <u>pepsin</u> is an enzyme used to break down <u>proteins</u> in the <u>stomach</u>. It works best at <u>pH 2</u>, which means it's well-suited to the <u>acidic conditions</u> there.

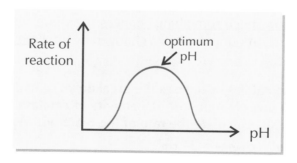

Most enzymes catalyse just one reaction

The <u>optimum temperature</u> for most human enzymes is around <u>normal body temperature</u>. And <u>stomach enzymes</u> work best at <u>low pH</u>, but the enzymes in your <u>small intestine</u> like a <u>higher pH</u>.

Investigating Enzymatic Reactions

You Can **Investigate** the Effect of **pH** on **Enzyme Activity** | PRACTICAL

The enzyme <u>amylase</u> catalyses the breakdown of <u>starch</u> to <u>maltose</u>. It's easy to <u>detect starch</u> using <u>iodine solution</u> — if starch is present, the iodine solution will change from <u>browny-orange</u> to <u>blue-black</u>. This is how you can <u>investigate</u> how pH affects <u>amylase activity</u>:

You could use an electric water bath, instead of a Bunsen and a beaker of water, to control the temperature.

1) Put a <u>drop</u> of iodine solution into every well of a <u>spotting tile</u>.

2) Place a <u>Bunsen burner</u> on a <u>heat-proof mat</u>, and a <u>tripod</u> and <u>gauze</u> over the Bunsen burner. Put a beaker of <u>water</u> on top of the tripod and <u>heat</u> the water until it is <u>35 °C</u> (use a <u>thermometer</u> to measure the temperature). Try to keep the temperature of the water <u>constant</u> throughout the experiment.

3) Use a <u>syringe</u> to add 1 cm³ of <u>amylase solution</u> and 1 cm³ of a <u>buffer solution</u> with a pH of 5 to a boiling tube. Using <u>test tube holders</u>, put the tube into the beaker of water and wait for five minutes.

4) Next, use a <u>different syringe</u> to add 5 cm³ of a <u>starch solution</u> to the boiling tube.

amylase, starch and buffer solution | **mixture sampled every 30 seconds** | **dropping pipette** | **drop of iodine solution** | **spotting tile**

5) Immediately <u>mix the contents</u> of the boiling tube and start a <u>stop clock</u>.

6) Use <u>continuous sampling</u> to record <u>how long</u> it takes for the amylase to break down all of the starch. To do this, use a dropping pipette to take a <u>fresh sample</u> from the boiling tube <u>every 30 seconds</u> and put a <u>drop</u> into a <u>well</u>. When the iodine solution <u>remains browny-orange</u>, starch is no longer present.

7) <u>Repeat</u> the whole experiment with buffer solutions of different <u>pH values</u> to see how pH <u>affects</u> the time taken for the starch to be broken down.

You could use a pH meter to accurately measure the pH of your solutions.

8) Remember to <u>control any variables</u> each time (e.g. concentration and volume of amylase solution) to make it a <u>fair test</u>.

Here's How to **Calculate** the **Rate of Reaction**

1) It's often useful to calculate the <u>rate of reaction</u> after an experiment. Rate is a measure of how much something changes over time.

$$\text{Rate} = \frac{1000}{\text{time}}$$

2) For the <u>experiment above</u>, you can calculate the rate of reaction using <u>this formula</u>: E.g.

> At <u>pH 6</u>, the <u>time taken</u> for amylase to break down all of the starch in a solution was <u>90 seconds</u>. So the <u>rate</u> of the reaction = <u>1000 ÷ 90 = 11 s⁻¹</u> (2 s.f.)

The units are in s⁻¹ since rate is given per unit time.

3) If an experiment measures <u>how much something changes</u> over time, you calculate the rate of reaction by <u>dividing</u> the <u>amount</u> that it has <u>changed</u> by the <u>time taken</u>.

> **EXAMPLE:** **The enzyme catalase catalyses the breakdown of hydrogen peroxide into water and oxygen. During an investigation into the activity of catalase, 24 cm³ of oxygen was released in 50 seconds (s). Calculate the rate of the reaction. Write your answer in cm³ s⁻¹.**
>
> **Amount of product formed = change = 24 cm³**
> **Rate of reaction = change ÷ time = 24 cm³ ÷ 50 s = 0.48 cm³ s⁻¹**
>
> *cm³ s⁻¹ is another way of writing cm³/s.*

You can investigate other factors too...

You could easily <u>adapt</u> this experiment to investigate how factors <u>other than pH</u> affect the rate of amylase activity. For example, you could use a <u>water bath</u> to investigate the effect of <u>temperature</u>.

Enzymes and Digestion

The <u>enzymes</u> used in <u>digestion</u> are produced by <u>cells</u> and then released into the <u>gut</u> to mix with food.

Digestive Enzymes Break Down Big Molecules

1) <u>Starch</u>, <u>proteins</u> and <u>fats</u> are <u>big</u> molecules. They're too big to pass through the walls of the digestive system, so <u>digestive enzymes</u> break these <u>big</u> molecules down into <u>smaller</u> ones like <u>sugars</u> (e.g. glucose and maltose), <u>amino acids</u>, <u>glycerol</u> and <u>fatty acids</u>. These <u>smaller</u>, <u>soluble</u> molecules can <u>pass easily</u> through the walls of the digestive system, allowing them to be <u>absorbed</u> into the <u>bloodstream</u>.

Carbohydrases Convert Carbohydrates into Simple Sugars

<u>Amylase</u> is an example of a <u>carbohydrase</u>. It breaks down <u>starch</u>.

Starch is a carbohydrate.

Amylase is made in <u>three</u> places:
1) The <u>salivary glands</u>   2) The <u>pancreas</u>   3) The <u>small intestine</u>

Proteases Convert Proteins into Amino Acids

Proteases are made in <u>three</u> places: 1) The <u>stomach</u> (it's called <u>pepsin</u> there)
2) The <u>pancreas</u>
3) The <u>small intestine</u>

Lipases Convert Lipids into Glycerol and Fatty Acids

Remember, lipids are fats and oils.

Lipases are made in <u>two</u> places: 1) The <u>pancreas</u>   2) The <u>small intestine</u>

2) The body makes good use of the <u>products</u> of digestion. They can be used to make <u>new carbohydrates</u>, <u>proteins</u> and <u>lipids</u>. Some of the <u>glucose</u> (a carbohydrate) that's made is used in <u>respiration</u> (see p.100).

Bile Neutralises the Stomach Acid and Emulsifies Fats

1) Bile is <u>produced</u> in the <u>liver</u>. It's <u>stored</u> in the <u>gall bladder</u> before it's released into the <u>small intestine</u>.

2) The <u>hydrochloric acid</u> in the stomach makes the pH <u>too acidic</u> for enzymes in the small intestine to work properly. Bile is <u>alkaline</u> — it <u>neutralises</u> the acid and makes conditions <u>alkaline</u>. The enzymes in the small intestine <u>work best</u> in these alkaline conditions.

3) It <u>emulsifies</u> fats. In other words it breaks the fat into <u>tiny droplets</u>. This gives a much <u>bigger surface area</u> of fat for the enzyme lipase to work on — which makes its digestion <u>faster</u>.

More on Enzymes and Digestion

So now you know what the enzymes do, here's a nice big picture of the whole of the digestive system.

The Breakdown of Food is Catalysed by Enzymes

1) Enzymes used in the digestive system are produced by specialised cells in glands and in the gut lining.

2) Different enzymes catalyse the breakdown of different food molecules.

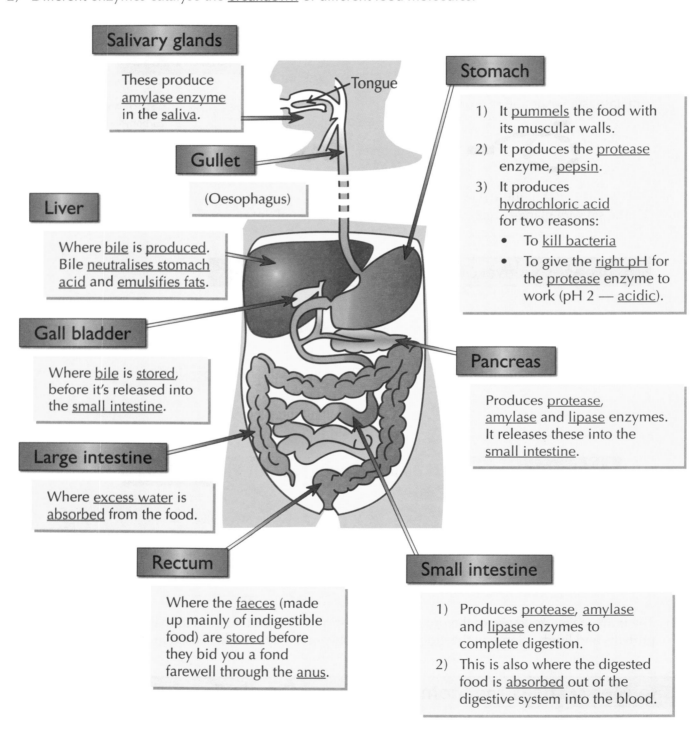

Salivary glands

These produce amylase enzyme in the saliva.

Tongue

Gullet

(Oesophagus)

Liver

Where bile is produced. Bile neutralises stomach acid and emulsifies fats.

Gall bladder

Where bile is stored, before it's released into the small intestine.

Large intestine

Where excess water is absorbed from the food.

Stomach

1) It pummels the food with its muscular walls.
2) It produces the protease enzyme, pepsin.
3) It produces hydrochloric acid for two reasons:
   • To kill bacteria
   • To give the right pH for the protease enzyme to work (pH 2 — acidic).

Pancreas

Produces protease, amylase and lipase enzymes. It releases these into the small intestine.

Rectum

Where the faeces (made up mainly of indigestible food) are stored before they bid you a fond farewell through the anus.

Small intestine

1) Produces protease, amylase and lipase enzymes to complete digestion.
2) This is also where the digested food is absorbed out of the digestive system into the blood.

That's nine different bits of the digestive system with different jobs

Did you know that the whole of your digestive system is actually a big hole that goes right through your body? It just gets loads of food, digestive juices and enzymes piled into it...

Food Tests

There are some clever ways to <u>identify</u> what type of <u>food molecule</u> a sample contains.
For each of the tests, you need to prepare a <u>food sample</u> first. It's the same each time though.

Prepare Your Food Sample First

<u>Before</u> you can carry out any of the food tests on these pages, you need to prepare a <u>food sample</u>.
Here's what you'd do:

1) Get a piece of food and <u>break it up</u> using a <u>pestle and mortar</u>.
2) Transfer the ground up food to a <u>beaker</u> and add some <u>distilled water</u>.
3) Give the mixture a good <u>stir</u> with a glass rod to <u>dissolve</u> some of the food.
4) <u>Filter</u> the solution using a funnel lined with filter paper to <u>get rid</u> of the <u>solid</u> bits of food.

Use the Benedict's Test to Test for Sugars

Sugars are found in all sorts of foods such as <u>biscuits</u>, <u>cereal</u> and <u>bread</u>. There are two types of sugars —
<u>non-reducing</u> and <u>reducing</u>. You can test for <u>reducing sugars</u> in foods using the <u>Benedict's test</u>:

1) Prepare a <u>food sample</u> and transfer <u>5 cm³</u> to a test tube.

2) Prepare a <u>water bath</u> so that it's set to <u>75 °C</u>.

3) Add some <u>Benedict's solution</u> to the test tube (about <u>10 drops</u>) using a pipette.

4) Place the test tube in the water bath using a test tube holder and leave it in there for <u>5 minutes</u>. Make sure the tube is <u>pointing away</u> from you.

5) If the food sample contains a reducing sugar, the solution in the test tube will change from the normal <u>blue</u> colour to <u>green</u>, <u>yellow</u> or <u>brick-red</u> — it depends on <u>how much</u> sugar is in the food.

Benedict's solution — water bath — food sample — colour change if reducing sugar present — higher sugar concentration

Use Iodine Solution to Test for Starch

You can also check food samples for the presence of <u>starch</u>. Foods like <u>pasta</u>, <u>rice</u> and <u>potatoes</u> contain a lot of starch. Here's how to do the test:

1) Make a <u>food sample</u> and transfer <u>5 cm³</u> of your sample to a test tube.

2) Then add a few drops of <u>iodine solution</u> and <u>gently shake</u> the tube to mix the contents. If the sample contains starch, the colour of the solution will change from <u>browny-orange</u> to <u>black</u> or <u>blue-black</u>.

iodine — colour remains browny-orange if starch isn't present — food sample — colour changes to blue-black if starch is present

PRACTICAL

Food Tests

There are a couple more <u>food tests</u> coming up on this page — for proteins and for lipids. As with the other tests, you need to use the method on the previous page to prepare a <u>sample</u> of your food first.

Use the **Biuret Test** to Test for **Proteins**

You can use the <u>biuret test</u> to see if a type of food contains <u>protein</u>.
<u>Meat</u> and <u>cheese</u> are protein rich and good foods to use in this test. Here's how it's done:

1) Prepare a <u>sample</u> of your food and transfer <u>2 cm³</u> of your sample to a test tube.

2) Add 2 cm³ of <u>biuret solution</u> to the sample and mix the contents of the tube by <u>gently shaking</u> it.

3) If the food sample contains protein, the solution will change from <u>blue</u> to <u>pink</u> or <u>purple</u>.
If no protein is present, the solution will stay blue.

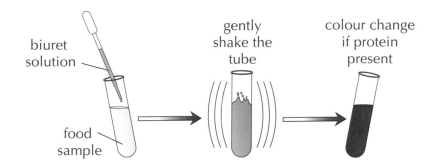

Use the **Sudan III Test** to Test for **Lipids**

<u>Lipids</u> are found in foods such as <u>butter</u>, <u>chocolate</u> and <u>cheese</u>.
You can test for the presence of lipids in a food using <u>Sudan III stain solution</u>.

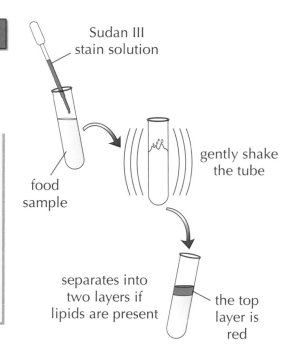

1) Prepare a <u>sample</u> of the food you're testing and transfer about <u>5 cm³</u> into a test tube.

2) Use a pipette to add <u>3 drops</u> of <u>Sudan III stain solution</u> to the test tube and <u>gently shake</u> the tube.

3) Sudan III stain solution <u>stains</u> lipids. If the sample contains lipids, the mixture will separate out into <u>two layers</u>. The top layer will be <u>bright red</u>. If no lipids are present, no separate red layer will form at the top of the liquid.

Make sure you think about all of the hazards...

<u>Iodine</u> is an <u>irritant</u> to the <u>eyes</u>, and the chemicals in the <u>biuret solution</u> are <u>dangerous</u>, so wear <u>safety goggles</u> for food tests. If you <u>spill</u> any of the chemicals on your <u>skin</u>, wash it off <u>straight away</u>. Be careful around the <u>water bath</u> in the <u>Benedict's test</u>, too. And if that's not enough to be cautious about, <u>Sudan III stain solution</u> is <u>flammable</u>, so keep it away from any <u>lit Bunsen burners</u>.

Warm-Up & Exam Questions

Doing well in exams isn't just about remembering all the facts, although that's important. You have to get used to the way the exams are phrased and make sure you always read the question carefully.

Warm-Up Questions

1) What is an organ system?
2) What is meant by the optimum pH of an enzyme?
3) Which enzyme digests: (a) starch   (b) protein   (c) lipids?
4) What are the products of the digestion of: (a) starch   (b) protein   (c) lipids?
5) Name the three parts of the digestive system that produce protease enzymes.
6) Describe how you would prepare a food sample before testing it for the presence of different food molecules.

Exam Questions

1   **Figure 1** shows the human digestive system.   Grade 4-6

Figure 1

1.1   Label the place where bile is produced.

[1 mark]

1.2   Describe why bile needs to have an alkaline pH.

[1 mark]

1.3   Outline how bile helps with the digestion of fats.

[2 marks]

2   **Figure 2** represents the action of an enzyme in catalysing a biological reaction.   Grade 4-6

Figure 2

2.1   In terms of the enzyme's shape, explain why an enzyme only catalyses one reaction.

[1 mark]

2.2   The optimum pH of the enzyme is pH 7.
       Explain what effect a very low pH would have on the activity of the enzyme.

[2 marks]

Exam Questions

3 **Figure 3** shows the effect of temperature on the action of two different enzymes.

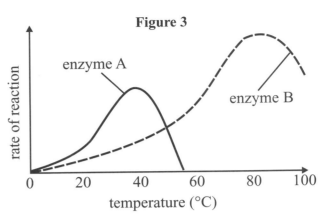

3.1 What is the optimum temperature for enzyme **A**?

[1 mark]

3.2 One of these enzymes was extracted from human liver cells. The other was extracted from bacteria living in hot underwater vents.

Suggest which enzyme came from the bacteria. Give a reason for your answer.

[1 mark]

PRACTICAL

4 A student wanted to know which substances were present in a food sample. She prepared a solution containing the food, and added some of the solution to each of three test tubes. She then added iodine solution to test tube **A**, biuret solution to test tube **B** and Sudan III stain solution to test tube **C**. Her results are shown in **Table 1**.

Table 1

Test tube	Description of solution in test tube
A	Blue-black
B	Blue
C	In two layers. Top layer red.

Describe what the student's results show about which substances are present in the food sample.

[3 marks]

PRACTICAL

5 A student was investigating the effect of pH on the rate of amylase activity. He used a syringe to put amylase solution and a buffer solution with a pH of 6 into a test tube. He then used a different syringe to add a starch solution to the boiling tube. He mixed the contents and then started a stop clock. Every 30 seconds he took a sample from the boiling tube and tested it for the presence of starch. When there was no starch present he stopped the stop clock. He repeated the experiment three times.

5.1 Suggest why he used two different syringes when adding substances to the boiling tube.

[1 mark]

5.2 His experiment showed that the average time taken for the starch in the boiling tube to be broken down was 60 seconds. Calculate the rate of the reaction. Give your answer in s⁻¹ to 2 significant figures. Use the formula: $\text{rate} = \frac{1000}{\text{time}}$

[1 mark]

5.3 Describe what the student needs to do next in his investigation to determine the effect of pH on the rate of amylase activity.

[1 mark]

The Lungs

When it comes to <u>breathing</u>, much more than just a pair of lungs is needed. There are some other vital parts that help to get the <u>oxygen</u> you need in, and the waste <u>carbon dioxide</u> out...

The **Lungs** Are in the **Thorax**

1) The <u>thorax</u> is the top part of your body.

2) It's separated from the lower part of the body by the <u>diaphragm</u>.

3) The <u>lungs</u> are like big pink <u>sponges</u> and are protected by the <u>ribcage</u>. They're surrounded by the <u>pleural membranes</u>.

4) The air that you breathe in goes through the <u>trachea</u>. This splits into two tubes called <u>bronchi</u> (each one is a bronchus), one going to each lung.

5) The bronchi split into progressively smaller tubes called <u>bronchioles</u>.

6) The bronchioles finally end at small bags called <u>alveoli</u> where the gas exchange takes place (see next page).

 ## Take a deep breath...

...and make sure you get to grips with the layout of the innards of your chest. Try sketching the diagram and adding the labels until you think you've got it sussed. If you know where the <u>trachea</u>, <u>bronchi</u>, <u>bronchioles</u> and <u>alveoli</u> are, then you're making a pretty good start.

The Lungs

Now that you know where the alveoli are, it's time to find out what they do.

Alveoli Carry Out Gas Exchange in the Body

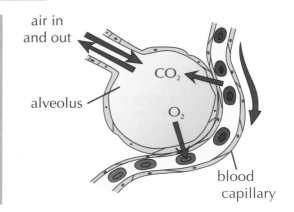

1) The lungs contain millions and millions of little air sacs called alveoli, surrounded by a network of blood capillaries. This is where gas exchange happens.

2) The blood passing next to the alveoli has just returned to the lungs from the rest of the body, so it contains lots of carbon dioxide and very little oxygen. Oxygen diffuses out of the alveolus (high concentration) into the blood (low concentration). Carbon dioxide diffuses out of the blood (high concentration) into the alveolus (low concentration) to be breathed out.

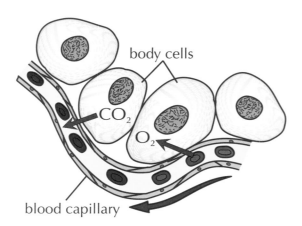

3) When the blood reaches body cells oxygen is released from the red blood cells (where there's a high concentration) and diffuses into the body cells (where the concentration is low).

4) At the same time, carbon dioxide diffuses out of the body cells (where there's a high concentration) into the blood (where there's a low concentration). It's then carried back to the lungs.

You Can Calculate the Breathing Rate in Breaths Per Minute

Rate calculations pop up all the time in biology, and you're expected to know how to do them — thankfully they're pretty easy. Breathing rate is the sort of thing that you could get asked to work out in your exam.

Bob takes 91 breaths in 7 minutes.
Calculate his average breathing rate in breaths per minute.

breaths per minute = number of breaths ÷ number of minutes

= 91 ÷ 7

= 13 breaths per minute

Alveoli are exchange surfaces

Back on page 34, you read about how exchange surfaces can be adapted to maximise their effectiveness. Alveoli have all of these adaptations to speed up the process of getting oxygen into the blood and getting the waste carbon dioxide out of the body — flick back to page 34 for a reminder.

Circulatory System — The Heart

The circulatory system carries <u>food</u> and <u>oxygen</u> to every cell in the body. As well as being a delivery service, it's also a waste collection service — it carries <u>waste products</u> to where they can be removed from the body.

It's a DOUBLE Circulatory System

The circulatory system is made up of the <u>heart</u>, <u>blood vessels</u> and <u>blood</u>. Humans have a <u>double circulatory system</u> — <u>two circuits</u> joined together:

Lungs

Rest of Body

1) In the first one, the <u>right ventricle</u> (see below) pumps <u>deoxygenated</u> blood (blood without oxygen) to the <u>lungs</u> to take in <u>oxygen</u>. The blood then <u>returns</u> to the heart.

2) In the second one, the <u>left ventricle</u> (see below) pumps <u>oxygenated</u> blood around all the <u>other organs</u> of the <u>body</u>. The blood <u>gives up</u> its oxygen at the body cells and the <u>deoxygenated</u> blood <u>returns</u> to the heart to be pumped out to the <u>lungs</u> again.

The Heart Contracts to Pump Blood Around The Body

1) The <u>heart</u> is a pumping <u>organ</u> that keeps the blood flowing around the body. The walls of the heart are mostly made of <u>muscle tissue</u>.

2) The heart has <u>valves</u> to make sure that blood flows in the right direction — they prevent it flowing <u>backwards</u>.

Atrium is when there is just one.
Atria is plural.

3) This is how the <u>heart</u> uses its <u>four chambers</u> (right atrium, right ventricle, left atrium and left ventricle) to pump blood around:

1) <u>Blood flows into</u> the two <u>atria</u> from the <u>vena cava</u> and the <u>pulmonary vein</u>.

2) The <u>atria contract</u>, pushing the blood into the <u>ventricles</u>.

3) The <u>ventricles contract</u>, forcing the blood into the <u>pulmonary artery</u> and the <u>aorta</u>, and <u>out</u> of the <u>heart</u>.

4) The blood then flows to the <u>organs</u> through <u>arteries</u>, and <u>returns</u> through <u>veins</u> (see next page).

5) The atria fill again and the whole cycle <u>starts over</u>.

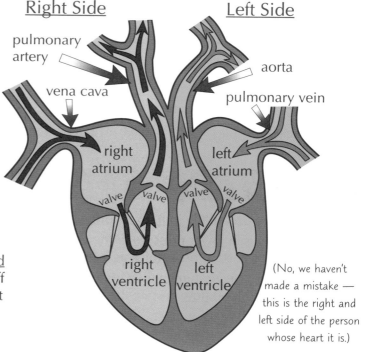

Right Side — Left Side

pulmonary artery

vena cava

aorta

pulmonary vein

right atrium

left atrium

valve valve valve valve

right ventricle

left ventricle

(No, we haven't made a mistake — this is the right and left side of the person whose heart it is.)

The heart also needs its <u>own</u> supply of <u>oxygenated</u> blood. Arteries called <u>coronary arteries</u> branch off the aorta and surround the heart, making sure that it gets all the <u>oxygenated</u> blood it needs.

The Heart Has a Pacemaker

1) Your resting heart rate is <u>controlled</u> by a group of cells in the right atrium wall that act as a <u>pacemaker</u>.

2) These cells produce a small <u>electric impulse</u> which spreads to the surrounding muscle cells, causing them to <u>contract</u>.

3) An <u>artificial pacemaker</u> is often used to control heartbeat if the natural pacemaker cells don't work properly (e.g. if the patient has an <u>irregular heartbeat</u>). It's a little device that's implanted under the skin and has a wire going to the heart. It produces an <u>electric current</u> to keep the heart <u>beating regularly</u>.

Circulatory System — Blood Vessels

Blood needs a good set of 'tubes' to carry it round the body. Here's a page on the different types:

Blood Vessels are Designed for Their Function

There are three different types of blood vessel:
1) ARTERIES — these carry the blood away from the heart.
2) CAPILLARIES — these are involved in the exchange of materials at the tissues.
3) VEINS — these carry the blood to the heart.

Arteries Carry Blood Under Pressure

elastic fibres and smooth muscle

lumen

1) The heart pumps the blood out at high pressure so the artery walls are strong and elastic.
2) The walls are thick compared to the size of the hole down the middle (the "lumen").
3) They contain thick layers of muscle to make them strong, and elastic fibres to allow them to stretch and spring back.

Capillaries are Really Small

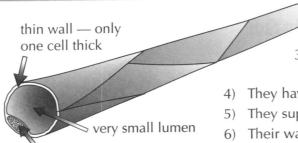

thin wall — only one cell thick

very small lumen

nucleus of cell

1) Arteries branch into capillaries.
2) Capillaries are really tiny — too small to see.
3) They carry the blood really close to every cell in the body to exchange substances with them.
4) They have permeable walls, so substances can diffuse in and out.
5) They supply food and oxygen, and take away wastes like CO_2.
6) Their walls are usually only one cell thick. This increases the rate of diffusion by decreasing the distance over which it occurs.

Veins Take Blood Back to the Heart

1) Capillaries eventually join up to form veins.
2) The blood is at lower pressure in the veins so the walls don't need to be as thick as artery walls.
3) They have a bigger lumen than arteries to help the blood flow despite the lower pressure.
4) They also have valves to help keep the blood flowing in the right direction.

elastic fibres and smooth muscle

large lumen

valve

You Can Calculate the Rate of Blood Flow

You might get asked to calculate the rate of blood flow in your exam. Thankfully, it's not too tricky. Take a look at this example:

EXAMPLE: 1464 ml of blood passed through an artery in 4.5 minutes. Calculate the rate of blood flow through the artery in ml/min.

rate of blood flow = volume of blood ÷ number of minutes
= 1464 ÷ 4.5 = 325 ml/min

Circulatory System — Blood

Blood is a <u>tissue</u>. It's part of a huge <u>transport system</u>. There are four main things in blood...

Red Blood Cells Carry Oxygen

1) The job of red blood cells is to carry <u>oxygen</u> from the lungs to all the cells in the body.

2) Their shape is a <u>biconcave disc</u> (like a doughnut) — this gives a <u>large surface area</u> for absorbing <u>oxygen</u>.

3) They <u>don't</u> have a nucleus — this allows more room to carry oxygen.

4) They contain a red pigment called <u>haemoglobin</u>.

5) In the <u>lungs</u>, haemoglobin binds to <u>oxygen</u> to become <u>oxyhaemoglobin</u>. In body tissues, the reverse happens — oxyhaemoglobin splits up into haemoglobin and oxygen, to <u>release oxygen</u> to the <u>cells</u>.

The more red blood cells you've got, the more oxygen can get to your cells. At high altitudes there's less oxygen in the air — so people who live there produce more red blood cells to compensate.

White Blood Cells Defend Against Infection

1) Some can change shape to engulf unwelcome <u>microorganisms</u>, in a process called <u>phagocytosis</u>.

2) Others produce <u>antibodies</u> to fight microorganisms, as well as <u>antitoxins</u> to neutralise any toxins produced by the microorganisms.

3) Unlike red blood cells, they <u>do</u> have a <u>nucleus</u>.

Platelets Help Blood Clot

1) These are <u>small fragments</u> of <u>cells</u>. They have <u>no nucleus</u>.

2) They help the blood to <u>clot</u> at a wound — to stop all your <u>blood pouring out</u> and to stop <u>microorganisms</u> getting in.

3) <u>Lack</u> of platelets can cause excessive bleeding and bruising.

Plasma is the Liquid That Carries Everything in Blood

This is a pale straw-coloured liquid which <u>carries just about everything</u>:

1) <u>Red</u> and <u>white blood cells</u> and <u>platelets</u>.

2) Nutrients like <u>glucose</u> and <u>amino acids</u>. These are the soluble products of digestion which are absorbed from the gut and taken to the cells of the body.

3) <u>Carbon dioxide</u> from the organs to the lungs.

4) <u>Urea</u> from the liver to the kidneys.

5) <u>Hormones</u>.

6) <u>Proteins</u>.

7) <u>Antibodies</u> and <u>antitoxins</u> produced by the white blood cells.

Blood — red blood cells, white blood cells, platelets and plasma

Sometimes, when you're ill, you might have a <u>sample of your blood</u> taken so that it can be <u>analysed</u>. Blood tests can be used to diagnose loads of things — <u>not</u> just disorders of the blood. This is because the blood transports <u>so many chemicals</u> produced by <u>so many organs</u>... and it's easy to take a sample of blood.

Warm-Up & Exam Questions

There are some nice diagrams to learn on the previous few pages. If you don't bother, you'll feel pretty silly if you turn over the exam paper and the first question asks you to label a diagram of the heart. Just saying... Anyway, let's see if these questions get your blood pumping...

Warm-Up Questions

1) What is the name of the tubes that the trachea splits into?
2) What is the function of the coronary arteries?
3) What is an artificial pacemaker?
4) What do veins do?
5) Describe the purpose of platelets in blood.

Exam Questions

1 A student ran for 12 minutes. Grade 4-6

1.1 During this 12 minute run, the student took 495 breaths.
Calculate his average breathing rate in breaths per minute.

[1 mark]

1.2 The student also measured his heart rate before and during his run.
Before his run, the student's heart rate was at its natural resting rate.
Outline how natural resting heart rate is controlled.

[1 mark]

2 The cell shown in **Figure 1** transports oxygen around the body. Grade 6-7

2.1 Explain how this cell's shape is
adapted for transporting oxygen.

[1 mark]

Figure 1

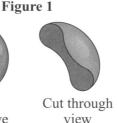

View from above   Cut through view

2.2 Describe and explain **one** other
way in which this cell is adapted
for carrying oxygen.

[2 marks]

2.3 Name the other main type of blood cell, and state its function.

[2 marks]

Blood cells are carried in the bloodstream inside blood vessels.

2.4 Capillaries are one type of blood vessel.
Outline how the structure of a capillary enables it to carry out its function.

[4 marks]

2.5 Blood flows through different types of blood vessels at different rates.
The volume of blood that passed through an artery in 2.5 minutes was 1.155 l.
Calculate the rate of blood flow through the artery in ml/min.

[2 marks]

Exam Questions

3 **Figure 2** shows the human heart and four blood vessels, as seen from the front. The left ventricle has been labelled.

Figure 2

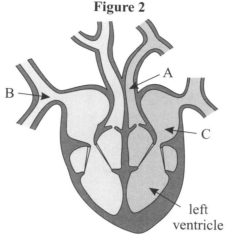

3.1 Name the parts labelled **A**, **B** and **C**.

[1 mark]

3.2 Describe the function of the left ventricle.

[1 mark]

3.3 What is the function of the valves in the heart?

[1 mark]

3.4* Describe how deoxygenated blood from the body passes through the heart to reach the lungs.

[4 marks]

4 A student did an experiment to compare the elasticity of arteries and veins. He dissected out an artery and a vein from a piece of fresh meat. He then took a 5 cm length of each vessel, hung different masses on it, and measured how much it stretched. His results are shown in **Table 1**.

Table 1

Mass added (g)	Length of blood vessel (mm)	
	Artery	Vein
0	50	50
5	51	53
10	53	56
15	55	59
20	56	-

4.1 Suggest **one** way in which the student could tell which was the artery and which was the vein when he was dissecting the meat.

[1 mark]

4.2 Which vessel stretched more easily?
Suggest why this was.

[1 mark]

Cardiovascular Disease

Cardiovascular disease is a term used to describe diseases of the heart or blood vessels, for example coronary heart disease. This page tells you all about how stents are used to combat coronary heart disease.

Coronary Heart Disease is Life-Threatening

Coronary heart disease is when the coronary arteries that supply the blood to the muscle of the heart get blocked by layers of fatty material building up.

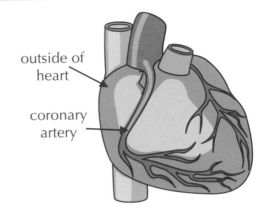

This causes the arteries to become narrow, so blood flow is restricted and there's a lack of oxygen to the heart muscle — this can result in a heart attack.

Stents Keep Arteries Open

1) Stents are tubes that are inserted inside arteries. They keep them open, making sure blood can pass through to the heart muscles. This keeps the person's heart beating (and the person alive).

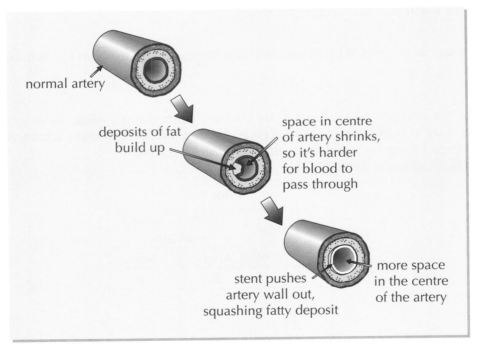

2) Stents are a way of lowering the risk of a heart attack in people with coronary heart disease. They are effective for a long time and the recovery time from the surgery is relatively quick.

3) On the down side, there is a risk of complications during the operation (e.g. heart attack) and a risk of infection from surgery. There is also the risk of patients developing a blood clot near the stent — this is called thrombosis.

Coronary heart disease is a type of cardiovascular disease

Coronary heart disease is caused by the arteries being blocked by fatty material — if the heart muscle can't get enough oxygen, then it can't work properly. And if the heart can't work properly, well, you're in trouble.

Cardiovascular Disease

You've read about stents, so now it's time for a second treatment for coronary heart disease — statins.

Statins Reduce Cholesterol in the Blood

1) Cholesterol is an essential lipid that your body produces and needs to function properly. However, too much of a certain type of cholesterol (known as 'bad' or LDL cholesterol) can cause health problems.

2) Having too much of this 'bad' cholesterol in the bloodstream can cause fatty deposits to form inside arteries, which can lead to coronary heart disease.

3) Statins are drugs that can reduce the amount of 'bad' cholesterol present in the bloodstream. This slows down the rate of fatty deposits forming.

Statins Have Advantages and Disadvantages

Advantages

1) By reducing the amount of 'bad' cholesterol in the blood, statins can reduce the risk of strokes, coronary heart disease and heart attacks.

2) As well as reducing the amount of 'bad' cholesterol, statins can increase the amount of a beneficial type of cholesterol (known as 'good' or HDL cholesterol) in your bloodstream. This type can remove 'bad' cholesterol from the blood.

3) Some studies suggest that statins may also help prevent some other diseases.

Disadvantages

1) Statins are a long-term drug that must be taken regularly. There's the risk that someone could forget to take them.

2) Statins can sometimes cause negative side effects, e.g. headaches. Some of these side effects can be serious, e.g. kidney failure, liver damage and memory loss.

3) The effect of statins isn't instant. It takes time for their effect to kick in.

An Artificial Heart Can Pump Blood Around the Body

1) If a patient has heart failure, doctors may perform a heart transplant (or heart and lungs transplant if the lungs are also diseased) using donor organs from people who have recently died. However, if donor organs aren't available right away or they're not the best option, doctors may fit an artificial heart.

2) Artificial hearts are mechanical devices that pump blood for a person whose own heart has failed. They're usually only used as a temporary fix, to keep a person alive until a donor heart can be found or to help a person recover by allowing the heart to rest and heal. In some cases though they're used as a permanent fix, which reduces the need for a donor heart.

3) The main advantage of artificial hearts is that they're less likely to be rejected by the body's immune system than a donor heart. This is because they're made from metals or plastics, so the body doesn't recognise them as 'foreign' and attack in the same way as it does with living tissue.

4) But surgery to fit an artificial heart (as with transplant surgery) can lead to bleeding and infection. Also, artificial hearts don't work as well as healthy natural ones — parts of the heart could wear out or the electrical motor could fail. Blood doesn't flow through artificial hearts as smoothly, which can cause blood clots and lead to strokes. The patient has to take drugs to thin their blood and make sure this doesn't happen, which can cause problems with bleeding if they're hurt in an accident.

Replacing a person's heart is major surgery, which has risks.

Cardiovascular Disease

One final page on cardiovascular disease. Having a heart transplant or getting an artificial heart fitted aren't the only surgeries for cardiovascular disease. Surgeons can do things like replacing just the valves in a heart.

Faulty Heart Valves Can Be Replaced

1) The valves in the heart can be damaged or weakened by heart attacks, infection or old age.

2) The damage may cause the valve tissue to stiffen, so it won't open properly. Or a valve may become leaky, allowing blood to flow in both directions rather than just forward. This means that blood doesn't circulate as effectively as normal.

3) Severe valve damage can be treated by replacing the valve.

4) Replacement valves can be ones taken from humans or other mammals (e.g. cows or pigs) — these are biological valves. Or they can be man-made — these are mechanical valves.

5) Replacing a valve is a much less drastic procedure than a whole heart transplant. But fitting artificial valves is still major surgery and there can still be problems with blood clots.

Artificial Blood Can Keep You Alive In An Emergency

1) When someone loses a lot of blood, e.g. in an accident, their heart can still pump the remaining red blood cells around (to get oxygen to their organs), as long as the volume of their blood can be topped up.

2) Artificial blood is a blood substitute, e.g. a salt solution ("saline"), which is used to replace the lost volume of blood. It's safe (if no air bubbles get into the blood) and can keep people alive even if they lose ⅔ of their red blood cells. This may give the patient enough time to produce new blood cells. If not, the patient will need a blood transfusion.

3) Ideally, an artificial blood product would replace the function of the red blood cells, so that there's no need for a blood transfusion. Scientists are currently working on products that can do this.

An artificial blood product that carries oxygen would replace the need for a blood transfusion from another person. This would have advantages such as decreasing the risk of diseases being passed on.

EXAM TIP

Don't lose heart...

You could be asked to evaluate treatments for cardiovascular disease. Don't panic — just use any information you're given and your own knowledge to weigh up the advantages and disadvantages. Make sure your answer doesn't just focus on one side — e.g. don't just talk about the advantages and ignore the disadvantages — and don't forget to include a justified conclusion.

Warm-Up & Exam Questions

Hopefully I've persuaded you by now that it's a good idea to try these questions. Believe me, when you're sitting with your real exam paper in front of you, you'll feel so much better knowing that you've already been through loads of practice questions. So off you go...

Warm-Up Questions

1) Which vessels are affected in coronary heart disease?
2) a) What device can be used to keep an artery open?
   b) Give three risks associated with getting one of these devices fitted.
3) What is an artificial heart?

Exam Questions

1   Coronary heart disease is the main cause of death worldwide. **Figure 1** shows a cross-section of a blood vessel in someone with coronary heart disease.

Figure 1

1.1   Name the substance labelled **X** on **Figure 1**.

[1 mark]

1.2   Explain how the presence of this substance can affect oxygen delivery to the heart muscle.

[2 marks]

2   A patient is taken into hospital. They are diagnosed as having a leaky heart valve.

2.1   Explain why a leaky valve could cause a health problem.

[2 marks]

The doctor decides that a surgeon should replace the valve.

2.2   Name and describe the **two** types of valve that the surgeon might use.

[4 marks]

2.3   Suggest **one** disadvantage of replacing the faulty valve.

[1 mark]

3   Some people with cardiovascular disease take statins. These are drugs that need to be taken every day.

3.1   Outline why statins are sometimes used in the treatment of coronary heart disease.

[2 marks]

3.2   Suggest **one** disadvantage to a patient of taking statins.

[1 mark]

Health and Disease

Try as we might, it's unlikely that we'll be in tip-top condition for all of our lives — disease tends to get us all at some point. There are lots of different types of diseases we could get...

Diseases are a **Major Cause** of **Ill Health**

Health is the state of physical and mental wellbeing.
Diseases are often responsible for causing ill health.

Diseases Can be **Communicable** or **Non-Communicable**

1) Communicable diseases are those that can spread from person to person or between animals and people. They can be caused by things like bacteria, viruses, parasites and fungi. They're sometimes described as contagious or infectious diseases. Measles and malaria are examples of communicable diseases. There's more about them on pages 76-79.

2) Non-communicable diseases are those that cannot spread between people or between animals and people. They generally last for a long time and get worse slowly. Asthma, cancer and coronary heart disease (see page 58) are examples of non-communicable diseases.

Different Types of Disease Sometimes Interact

Sometimes diseases can interact and cause other physical and mental health issues that don't immediately seem related. Here are a few examples:

1) People who have problems with their immune system (the system that your body uses to help fight off infection — see p.82) have an increased chance of suffering from communicable diseases such as influenza (flu), because their body is less likely to be able to defend itself against the pathogen that causes the disease.

Pathogen is just the fancy term for a microorganism that can cause a disease when it infects its host.

2) Some types of cancer can be triggered by infection by certain viruses. For example, infection with some types of hepatitis virus can cause long-term infections in the liver, where the virus lives in the cells. This can lead to an increased chance of developing liver cancer. Another example is infection with HPV (human papilloma virus), which can cause cervical cancer in women.

3) Immune system reactions in the body caused by infection by a pathogen can sometimes trigger allergic reactions such as skin rashes or worsen the symptoms of asthma for asthma sufferers.

4) Mental health issues such as depression can be triggered when someone is suffering from severe physical health problems, particularly if they have an impact on the person's ability to carry out everyday activities or if they affect the person's life expectancy.

Communicable diseases can spread...

...but non-communicable diseases can't. Remember that — it's really important.

Health and Disease

Ill health isn't just about having a disease — there are plenty of other causes.
And then there's the cost of ill health to consider too — there might be more to it than you'd first thought...

Other Factors Can Also Affect Your Health

There are plenty of factors other than diseases that can also affect your health. For example:

1) Whether or not you have a good, balanced diet that provides your body with everything it needs, and in the right amounts. A poor diet can affect your physical and mental health.

2) The stress you are under — being constantly under lots of stress can lead to health issues.

3) Your life situation — for example, whether you have easy access to medicines to treat illness, or whether you have access to things that can prevent you from getting ill in the first place, e.g. being able to buy healthy food or access condoms to prevent the transmission of some sexually transmitted diseases.

Non-Communicable Diseases Can Be Costly

The Human Cost

1) The human cost of non-communicable diseases is obvious. Tens of millions of people around the world die from non-communicable diseases per year.

2) People with these diseases may have a lower quality of life or a shorter lifespan. This not only affects the sufferers themselves, but their loved ones too.

The Financial Cost

1) It's also important to think about the financial cost.

2) The cost to the NHS of researching and treating these diseases is huge — and it's the same for other health services and organisations around the world.

3) Families may have to move or adapt their home to help a family member with a disease, which can be costly.

4) Also, if the family member with the disease has to give up work or dies, the family's income will be reduced.

5) A reduction in the number of people able to work can also affect a country's economy.

Lots of things affect health, and ill health can be costly

A human cost is the effect something has on humans. A financial cost is to do with how much spending something results in. When you're studying biology, you'll come across lots of things that have a human cost or a financial cost (or both). Some things can have quite far-reaching knock-on effects.

Risk Factors for Non-Communicable Diseases

You've probably heard the term 'risk factor' before. These next couple of pages have lots of info on them. There's nothing too tricky, but there's quite a bit to read — take it slowly and make sure it goes in.

Risk Factors Increase Your Chance of Getting a Disease

1) Risk factors are things that are linked to an increase in the likelihood that a person will develop a certain disease during their lifetime. They don't guarantee that someone will get the disease.

2) Risk factors are often aspects of a person's lifestyle (e.g. how much exercise they do).

3) They can also be the presence of certain substances in the environment (e.g. air pollution) or substances in your body (e.g. asbestos fibres — asbestos was a material used in buildings until it was realised that the fibres could build up in your airways and cause diseases such as cancer later in life).

4) Many non-communicable diseases are caused by several different risk factors interacting with each other rather than one factor alone.

5) Lifestyle factors can have different impacts locally, nationally and globally. E.g. in developed countries, non-communicable diseases are more common as people generally have a higher income and can buy high-fat food. Nationally, people from deprived areas are more likely to smoke, have a poor diet and not exercise. This means the incidence of cardiovascular disease, obesity and Type 2 diabetes is higher in those areas. Your individual choices affect the local incidence of disease.

Some Risk Factors Can Cause a Disease Directly

Some risk factors are able to directly cause a disease. For example:

Smoking has been proven to directly cause cardiovascular disease, lung disease and lung cancer. It damages the walls of arteries and the cells in the lining of the lungs.

It's thought that obesity can directly cause Type 2 diabetes by making the body less sensitive or resistant to insulin, meaning that it struggles to control the concentration of glucose in the blood.

There's more about Type 2 diabetes on page 115.

Risk Factors for Non-Communicable Diseases

Here are a few <u>more risk factors</u> that can <u>directly</u> cause <u>disease</u>:

1) Drinking <u>too much alcohol</u> has been shown to cause <u>liver disease</u>. The liver <u>breaks down</u> alcohol, but the reaction can <u>damage</u> its <u>cells</u>.

2) Liver cells may also be damaged when <u>toxic chemicals</u> leak from the <u>gut</u> due to damage to the <u>intestines</u> caused by alcohol.

3) Too much alcohol can affect <u>brain function</u> too. It can <u>damage</u> the <u>nerve cells</u> in the brain, causing the brain to <u>lose volume</u>.

<u>Smoking</u> when pregnant <u>reduces</u> the amount of <u>oxygen</u> the baby receives in the womb and can cause <u>lots</u> of <u>health problems</u> for the <u>unborn baby</u>. Drinking <u>alcohol</u> has <u>similar</u> effects. Alcohol can <u>damage</u> the <u>baby's cells</u>, affecting its <u>development</u> and causing a <u>wide range</u> of health issues.

There's more about cancer coming up on the next page.

Cancer can be directly caused by <u>exposure</u> to certain <u>substances</u> or <u>radiation</u>. Things that cause cancer are known as <u>carcinogens</u>. Carcinogens work in <u>different</u> ways. For example, some <u>damage</u> a cell's <u>DNA</u> in a way that makes the cell more likely to <u>divide uncontrollably</u>. <u>Ionising radiation</u> (e.g. from X-rays) is an example of a <u>carcinogen</u>.

Risk Factors Can be **Identified** Using **Correlation**

1) Risk factors are identified by scientists looking for <u>correlations</u> in data. However, <u>correlation doesn't always equal cause</u>.

2) Some risk factors <u>aren't</u> capable of directly causing a disease, but are <u>related</u> to <u>another</u> risk factor that <u>is</u>.

3) For example:

See pages 10 and 13 for more about correlations.

A <u>lack of exercise</u> and a <u>high fat diet</u> are heavily linked to an increased chance of <u>cardiovascular disease</u>, but they can't cause the disease directly. It's the resulting <u>high blood pressure</u> and <u>high 'bad' cholesterol levels</u> (see p.59) that can <u>actually cause</u> it.

It's hard to avoid all risk factors of disease...

...but remember that risk factors that <u>cause disease</u> don't mean you'll <u>definitely</u> get the disease — they just increase the chance of it happening. Also, remember that <u>not all</u> risk factors <u>cause</u> disease. Many are just <u>correlated</u> with the disease, meaning there is a relationship between them.

Cancer

The more we understand about cancer, the better our chances of avoiding and beating it. Hoorah.

Cancer is Caused by **Uncontrolled Cell Growth and Division**

This uncontrolled growth and division is a result of changes that occur to the cells and results
in the formation of a tumour (a growth of abnormal cells). Not all tumours are cancerous.
They can be benign or malignant:

Benign

1) This is where the tumour grows
   until there's no more room.

2) The tumour stays in one place (usually
   within a membrane) rather than
   invading other tissues in the body.

3) This type isn't normally dangerous,
   and the tumour isn't cancerous.

Malignant

1) This is where the tumour grows and spreads
   to neighbouring healthy tissues.

2) Cells can break off and spread to other parts of
   the body by travelling in the bloodstream.

3) The malignant cells then invade healthy tissues
   elsewhere in the body and form secondary tumours.

4) Malignant tumours are dangerous and
   can be fatal — they are cancers.

Risk Factors Can **Increase** the **Chance** of **Some Cancers**

Anyone can develop cancer. Having risk factors doesn't mean that you'll definitely get cancer.
It just means that you're at an increased risk of developing the disease. Cancer survival rates have
increased due to medical advances such as improved treatment, being able to diagnose cancer
earlier and increased screening for the disease.

Risk Factors Can Be Associated With **Lifestyle**

Scientists have identified lots of lifestyle risk factors for various types of cancer. For example:

1) Smoking — It's a well known fact that smoking is linked to lung cancer,
   but research has also linked it to other types of cancer too, including
   mouth, bowel, stomach and cervical cancer.

2) Obesity — Obesity has been linked to many different cancers, including bowel, liver
   and kidney cancer. It's the second biggest preventable cause of cancer after smoking.

3) UV exposure — People who are often exposed to UV radiation from the Sun have an
   increased chance of developing skin cancer. People who live in sunny climates and people
   who spend a lot of time outside are at higher risk of the disease. People who frequently use
   sun beds are also putting themselves at higher risk of developing skin cancer.

4) Viral infection — Infection with some viruses has been shown to increase the chances of
   developing certain types of cancer. For example, infection with hepatitis B and hepatitis C
   viruses can increase the risk of developing liver cancer. The likelihood of becoming infected
   with these viruses sometimes depends on lifestyle — e.g. they can be spread between people
   through unprotected sex or sharing needles.

Risk Factors Can Also Be Associated With **Genetics**

Sometimes you can inherit faulty genes that make you more susceptible to cancer.   For example:

Mutations in the BRCA genes have been linked to an
increased likelihood of developing breast and ovarian cancer.

Warm-Up & Exam Questions

It's time for some more questions — don't just assume that you've remembered everything you just read on the past few pages. Give these a go, and then go back over anything that you struggled with.

Warm-Up Questions

1) What is meant by 'health'?
2) What does it mean if a disease is 'communicable'?
3) Give an example of a national financial cost associated with non-communicable diseases.
4) Give an example of a type of risk factor other than an aspect of a person's lifestyle.

Exam Questions

1 Many diseases have risk factors. **Grade 4-6**

1.1 What is meant by the term risk factor?

[1 mark]

1.2 Give **one** risk factor for lung disease.

[1 mark]

1.3 Name **one** carcinogen that is a risk factor for cancer.

[1 mark]

2 Cancer results from a tumour. **Grade 4-6**

2.1 What causes tumours to form? Tick **one** box.

- [ ] Uncontrolled cell division.
- [ ] Slow cell division.
- [ ] Cell division stopping.
- [ ] Cells dying.

[1 mark]

2.2 Name the type of tumour that causes cancer.

[1 mark]

2.3 Explain how secondary tumours form in the body.

[2 marks]

3 Diseases can be communicable or non-communicable. **Grade 6-7**

3.1 What is meant by a non-communicable disease?

[1 mark]

3.2 Influenza is a communicable disease.
Why might someone who has a problem with their immune system have an increased chance of suffering from influenza?

[1 mark]

Plant Cell Organisation

You saw on pages 40-41 how animals keep their <u>specialised cells</u> neat and tidy — plants are in on the act too.

Plant Cells Are Organised Into Tissues And Organs

<u>Plants</u> are made of <u>organs</u> like <u>stems</u>, <u>roots</u> and <u>leaves</u>. Plant organs work together to make <u>organ systems</u>. These can perform the various tasks that a plant needs to carry out to survive and grow — for example, <u>transporting substances</u> around the plant. Plant organs are made of <u>tissues</u>. Examples of plant tissues are:

1) <u>Epidermal tissue</u> — this <u>covers</u> the whole plant.
2) <u>Palisade mesophyll tissue</u> — this is the part of the leaf where most <u>photosynthesis</u> happens.
3) <u>Spongy mesophyll tissue</u> — this is also in the leaf, and contains big <u>air spaces</u> to allow   *For more on*
 gases to <u>diffuse</u> in and out of cells.   *photosynthesis,*
4) <u>Xylem</u> and <u>phloem</u> — they <u>transport</u> things like <u>water</u>, <u>mineral ions</u> and <u>food</u>   *see page 91.*
 around the plant (through the roots, stems and leaves — see next page for more).
5) <u>Meristem tissue</u> — this is found at the <u>growing tips</u> of <u>shoots</u> and <u>roots</u> and is able to <u>differentiate</u> (change) into lots of <u>different types</u> of plant cell, allowing the plant to <u>grow</u>.

The Leaf is an Organ Made Up of Several Types of Tissue

Leaves contain <u>epidermal</u>, <u>mesophyll</u>, <u>xylem</u> and <u>phloem</u> tissues.

Mesophyll just means 'middle of a leaf'.

Here's how the <u>structures</u> of the tissues that make up the leaf are <u>related</u> to their <u>function</u>:

1) The epidermal tissues are covered with a <u>waxy cuticle</u>, which helps to <u>reduce water loss</u> by evaporation.
2) The <u>upper epidermis</u> is <u>transparent</u> so that light can pass through it to the <u>palisade layer</u>.
3) The <u>palisade layer</u> has lots of <u>chloroplasts</u> (the little structures where photosynthesis takes place). This means that they're near the top of the leaf where they can get the most <u>light</u>.
4) The <u>xylem</u> and <u>phloem</u> form a network of vascular bundles, which <u>deliver water</u> and other <u>nutrients</u> to the entire leaf and take away the <u>glucose</u> produced by photosynthesis. They also help <u>support</u> the structure.
5) The <u>tissues</u> of leaves are also adapted for efficient <u>gas exchange</u> (see page 35). E.g. the <u>lower epidermis</u> is full of little holes called <u>stomata</u>, which let CO_2 diffuse directly into the leaf. The opening and closing of stomata is controlled by <u>guard cells</u> in response to environmental conditions. The <u>air spaces</u> in the <u>spongy mesophyll</u> tissue <u>increase</u> the rate of diffusion of gases.

Transpiration and Translocation

Flowering plants have <u>two</u> separate types of vessel — <u>xylem</u> and <u>phloem</u> — for transporting stuff around. <u>Both</u> types of vessel go to <u>every part</u> of the plant, but they are totally <u>separate</u>.

Phloem Tubes Transport Food:

1) Made of columns of <u>elongated</u> living cells with small <u>pores in the end walls</u> to allow <u>cell sap</u> to flow through.

Cell sap is a liquid that's made up of the substances being transported and water.

2) They transport <u>food substances</u> (mainly dissolved <u>sugars</u>) made in the leaves to the rest of the plant for <u>immediate use</u> (e.g. in growing regions) or for <u>storage</u>.

3) The transport goes in <u>both directions</u>.

4) This process is called <u>translocation</u>.

Xylem Tubes Take Water Up:

1) Made of <u>dead cells</u> joined end to end with <u>no</u> end walls between them and a hole down the middle. They're strengthened with a material called <u>lignin</u>.

2) They carry <u>water</u> and <u>mineral</u> ions from the <u>roots</u> to the <u>stem</u> and <u>leaves</u>.

3) The movement of water <u>from</u> the <u>roots</u>, <u>through</u> the <u>xylem</u> and <u>out</u> of the <u>leaves</u> is called the <u>transpiration stream</u> (see next page).

Water and minerals

REVISION TIP

Xylem vessels carry water, phloem vessels carry sugars

Make sure you don't get your phloem <u>mixed up</u> with your xylem. To help you to learn which is which, you could remember that phl<u>o</u>em transports substances in b<u>o</u>th directions, but xylem only transports things upwards — x<u>y</u> to the sk<u>y</u>. It might just bag you a mark or two on exam day...

Transpiration

If you don't water a house plant for a few days it starts to go all droopy. Plants need <u>water</u>.

Transpiration is the Loss of Water from the Plant

1) Transpiration is caused by the <u>evaporation</u> and <u>diffusion</u> (see page 29) of water from a plant's surface. Most transpiration happens at the <u>leaves</u>.

2) This evaporation creates a slight <u>shortage</u> of water in the leaf, and so more water is drawn up from the rest of the plant through the <u>xylem vessels</u> to replace it.

3) This in turn means more water is drawn up from the <u>roots</u>, and so there's a constant <u>transpiration stream</u> of water through the plant.

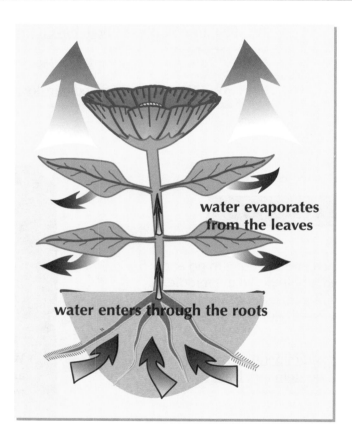

water evaporates from the leaves

water enters through the roots

Head back to page 23 to see how root hair cells are adapted for taking up water.

Transpiration is just a <u>side-effect</u> of the way leaves are adapted for <u>photosynthesis</u>. They have to have <u>stomata</u> in them so that gases can be exchanged easily (see page 35). Because there's more water <u>inside</u> the plant than in the <u>air outside</u>, the water escapes from the leaves through the stomata by diffusion.

Transpiration involves evaporation and diffusion

A big tree loses about a <u>thousand litres</u> of water from its leaves <u>every single day</u> — it's a fact. That's as much water as the average person drinks in a whole year, so the <u>roots</u> have to be very effective at drawing in water from the soil. Which is why they have all those root <u>hairs</u>, you see.

The Rate of Transpiration

The <u>rate of transpiration</u> varies according to the <u>environmental conditions</u>...

Transpiration Rate is Affected by Four Main Things

Light Intensity

1) The <u>brighter</u> the light, the <u>greater</u> the transpiration rate.
2) <u>Stomata</u> begin to <u>close</u> as it gets darker. Photosynthesis can't happen in the dark, so they don't need to be open to let <u>CO_2</u> in. When the stomata are closed, very little water can escape.

Temperature

1) The <u>warmer</u> it is, the <u>faster</u> transpiration happens.
2) When it's warm the water particles have <u>more energy</u> to evaporate and diffuse out of the stomata.

Air Flow

1) The <u>better</u> the air flow around a leaf (e.g. stronger wind), the <u>greater</u> the transpiration rate.
2) If air flow around a leaf is <u>poor</u>, the water vapour just <u>surrounds the leaf</u> and doesn't move away. This means there's a <u>high concentration</u> of water particles outside the leaf as well as inside it, so <u>diffusion</u> doesn't happen as quickly.
3) If there's <u>good</u> air flow, the water vapour is <u>swept away</u>, maintaining a <u>low concentration</u> of water in the air outside the leaf. Diffusion then happens quickly, from an area of higher concentration to an area of lower concentration.

Humidity

1) The <u>drier</u> the air around a leaf, the <u>faster</u> transpiration happens.
2) This is like what happens with air flow. If the air is <u>humid</u> there's a lot of water in it already, so there's not much of a <u>difference</u> between the inside and the outside of the leaf.
3) Diffusion happens <u>fastest</u> if there's a <u>really high concentration</u> in one place, and a <u>really low concentration</u> in the other.

Measuring Transpiration and Stomata

Sorry, more on <u>transpiration</u>. But then it's a quick dash through <u>stomata</u> and out of the other end of the topic.

A **Potometer** can be Used to **Estimate Transpiration Rate**

1) You can estimate the <u>rate of transpiration</u> by measuring the <u>uptake of water</u> by a plant.
2) This is because you can assume that <u>water uptake</u> by the plant is directly related to <u>water loss</u> by the leaves (transpiration).
3) Set up the apparatus as in the diagram, and then record the <u>starting position</u> of the air bubble.
4) Start a stopwatch and record the <u>distance moved</u> by the bubble per unit time, e.g. per hour.
5) Keep the <u>conditions constant</u> throughout the experiment, e.g. the <u>temperature</u> and <u>air humidity</u>.

reservoir of water

As the plant takes up water, the air bubble moves along the scale.

Tap is shut off during experiment.

Water moves this way.

Bubble moves this way.

capillary tube with a scale

Beaker of water.

This piece of apparatus is called a potometer. Setting it up is quite tough — there are some tips on page 182.

Guard Cells Are Adapted to **Open and Close Stomata**

guard cell

stoma
(plural — stomata)

1) They have a kidney shape which <u>opens</u> and <u>closes</u> the <u>stomata</u> (page 35) in a leaf.
2) When the plant has <u>lots</u> of water the guard cells fill with it and go plump and <u>turgid</u>. This makes the stomata <u>open</u> so <u>gases</u> can be exchanged for <u>photosynthesis</u>.
3) When the plant is <u>short</u> of water, the guard cells lose water and become <u>flaccid</u>, making the stomata <u>close</u>. This helps stop too much water vapour <u>escaping</u>.
4) <u>Thin</u> outer walls and <u>thickened</u> inner walls make the opening and closing work.
5) They're also <u>sensitive to light</u> and <u>close at night</u> to save water without losing out on photosynthesis.
6) You usually find <u>more</u> stomata on the <u>undersides</u> of leaves than on the top. The <u>lower surface</u> is <u>shaded</u> and <u>cooler</u> — so <u>less water</u> is <u>lost</u> through the stomata than if they were on the upper surface.
7) Guard cells are therefore adapted for <u>gas exchange</u> and <u>controlling water loss</u> within a <u>leaf</u>.

The opening and closing of stomata is important for plants to survive

Different leaves will have different <u>distributions</u> of <u>stomata</u>. You can peel the epidermal tissue off some leaves and then mount them on <u>microscope slides</u> (see page 19) to <u>compare</u> them.

Warm-Up & Exam Questions

Just a few simple Warm-Up Questions and a few slightly harder Exam Questions stand between you and mastering cell organisation and transport in plants...

Warm-Up Questions

1) Describe the characteristics of meristem tissue.
2) Which layer of plant tissue contains lots of chloroplasts?
3) True or false? Substances pass in both directions through xylem vessels.
4) State the four main factors that affect the rate of transpiration in plants.

Exam Questions

1   Leaves contain many types of tissue.   (Grade 4-6)

Which type of plant tissue contains air spaces for the diffusion of gases?
Tick **one** box.

☐   epidermal tissue

☐   palisade mesophyll tissue

☐   spongy mesophyll tissue

☐   meristem tissue

[1 mark]

2   Plants absorb water and mineral ions through their root hair cells.   (Grade 4-6)

2.1   Name the vessels that transport water and mineral ions from the roots of a plant to the leaves.

[1 mark]

2.2   Describe the structure of the vessels you named in **2.1**.

[3 marks]

2.3   Name the process of water transport through a plant.

[1 mark]

3   Aphids are insects which feed on plant cell sap. Cell sap is the name   (Grade 6-7)
given to the liquids carried around the plant in transport vessels.

3.1   The cell sap the aphids feed on contains sugars.
What type of transport vessel does the cell sap come from?

[1 mark]

3.2   Explain how the structure of these transport vessels is adapted to their function.

[2 marks]

3.3   Name the movement of cell sap through the plant's transport vessels.

[1 mark]

Exam Questions

4 A student used a rose plant in his garden to carry out some investigations.

4.1 The student cut several stems from the plant and put them in a glass vase on his kitchen windowsill.
He added a layer of oil to the surface of the water to prevent evaporation.
Over the next few days, he noticed that the level of water in the vase gradually decreased.
How would the reduction of water in the vase differ if the kitchen was not as warm?
Explain your answer.

[3 marks]

4.2* The student investigated the appearance of guard cells on the underside of a rose leaf at different
times on a humid day. He took a leaf from his rose plant at 10 am, 4 pm and 11 pm and immediately
examined it under a microscope. He drew diagrams to show the appearance of the guard cells at each
time, as shown in **Figure 1**.

Figure 1

A **B** **C**

Suggest which diagram (A-C), shows the appearance of the guard cells observed at 11 pm.
Explain your answer.

[4 marks]

5 A student was investigating transpiration in basil plants under different conditions.
She used twelve plants, three plants in each of the four different conditions.
The plants were weighed before and after the experiment. She calculated the
% loss in the mass per day and recorded her results in **Table 1**.

Table 1

plant	in a room (% loss in mass)	next to a fan (% loss in mass)	by a lamp (% loss in mass)	next to a fan and by a lamp (% loss in mass)
1	5	8	10	13
2	5	9	11	15
3	4	11	9	13
mean	4.7	9.3		13.6

5.1 Calculate the mean % loss in plant mass for the three plants by a lamp.

[2 marks]

5.2 Explain why the plants located next to a fan lost more mass than those in a still room.

[3 marks]

5.3 The student then covered the undersides of the leaves with petroleum jelly.
Suggest how this would affect the rate of transpiration from the leaves.

[2 marks]

5.4 Suggest how you could alter the student's experiment to investigate the effects of humidity
on the rate of transpiration in basil plants.

[2 marks]

Revision Summary for Topic 2

Well, that's <u>Topic 2</u> finished. Now it's time to test how much you've taken in...
- Try these questions and <u>tick off each one</u> when you <u>get it right</u>.
- When you've done <u>all the questions</u> under a heading and are <u>completely happy</u> with it, tick it off.

Cell Organisation (p.40-41) ☐
1) What is a tissue? ☑
2) Give an example of a human organ system. ☑

The Role of Enzymes and Food Tests (p.42-48) ☐
3) Why can enzymes be described as biological catalysts? ☑
4) What does it mean when an enzyme has been 'denatured'? ☑
5) Describe how you could investigate the effect of pH on the rate of amylase activity. ☑
6) List the three places where amylase is made in the human body. ☑
7) What is the role of lipases? ☑
8) Where is bile stored? ☑
9) Name the solution that you would use to test for the presence of lipids in a food sample. ☑

The Lungs and Circulatory System (p.51-55) ☐
10) Explain the role that alveoli play in gas exchange. ☑
11) Explain why the circulatory system in humans is described as a 'double circulatory system'. ☑
12) Name the four chambers of the heart. ☑
13) How are arteries adapted to carry blood away from the heart? ☑
14) Why do red blood cells not have a nucleus? ☑
15) Name the pigment in red blood cells. ☑
16) What is the function of plasma? ☑

Diseases and Risk Factors (p.58-66) ☐
17) Give two advantages of statins. ☐
18) What name is given to a replacement heart valve that has been man-made? ☐
19) Give a factor other than disease that can affect health. ☐
20) Give an example of where different types of disease might interact in the body. ☐
21) Give one risk factor for Type 2 diabetes. ☐
22) Which type of tumour is not cancerous? ☐

Plant Cell Organisation and Transport (p.68-72) ☐
23) List the tissues that make up a leaf. ☐
24) Explain how the structure of the upper epidermal tissue in a leaf is related to its function. ☐
25) What is the function of phloem? ☐
26) What is transpiration? ☐
27) How could you measure the rate of transpiration? ☐
28) Name the type of cell that helps open and close stomata. ☐

Communicable Disease

If you're hoping I'll ease you gently into this new topic... no such luck. Straight on to the <u>baddies</u> of biology.

There Are **Several Types** of **Pathogen**

1) Pathogens are <u>microorganisms</u> that enter the body and cause <u>disease</u>.
2) They cause <u>communicable</u> (infectious) diseases — diseases that can <u>easily spread</u> (see p.62).
3) Both <u>plants</u> and <u>animals</u> can be infected by pathogens.
4) Pathogens can be <u>bacteria</u> or <u>viruses</u> (see below), or <u>protists</u> or <u>fungi</u> (see next page).

1. **Bacteria** Are Very Small **Living Cells**

1) Bacteria are <u>very small cells</u> (about 1/100th the size of your body cells), which can reproduce rapidly inside your body.

2) They can make you <u>feel ill</u> by <u>producing toxins</u> (poisons) that <u>damage your cells and tissues</u>.

2. **Viruses** Are **Not** Cells — They're Much Smaller

1) Viruses are <u>not cells</u>. They're <u>tiny</u>, about 1/100th the size of a bacterium.

2) Like bacteria, they can <u>reproduce rapidly</u> inside your body.

3) They live inside your cells and <u>replicate themselves</u> using the cells' <u>machinery</u> to produce many <u>copies</u> of themselves.

4) The cell will usually then <u>burst</u>, releasing all the new viruses.

5) This <u>cell damage</u> is what makes you feel ill.

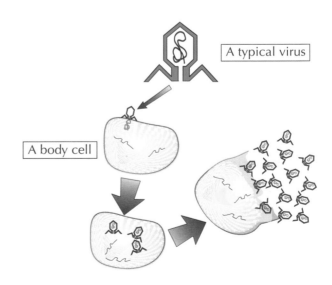

A typical virus

A body cell

Communicable Disease

3. Protists are Single-Celled Eukaryotes

1) There are lots of different types of protists. But they're all eukaryotes (see page 16) and most of them are single-celled.
2) Some protists are parasites. Parasites live on or inside other organisms and can cause them damage. They are often transferred to the organism by a vector, which doesn't get the disease itself — e.g. an insect that carries the protist.

4. Fungi Come in Different Shapes

1) Some fungi are single-celled.
2) Others have a body which is made up of hyphae (thread-like structures).
3) These hyphae can grow and penetrate human skin and the surface of plants, causing diseases.
4) The hyphae can produce spores, which can be spread to other plants and animals.

Pathogens Can Be Spread in Different Ways

Pathogens can be spread in many ways. Here are just a few...

Water
1) Some pathogens can be picked up by drinking or bathing in dirty water.
2) E.g. cholera is a bacterial infection that's spread by drinking water contaminated with the diarrhoea of other sufferers.

Air
1) Pathogens can be carried in the air and can then be breathed in.
2) Some airborne pathogens are carried in the air in droplets produced when you cough or sneeze — e.g. the influenza virus that causes flu is spread this way.

Direct Contact
1) Some pathogens can be picked up by touching contaminated surfaces, including the skin.
2) E.g. athlete's foot is a fungus which makes skin itch and flake off. It's most commonly spread by touching the same things as an infected person, e.g. shower floors and towels.

Watch yourself, there are a lot of nasties out there...

Plants need to be worried too, as you'll find out. It's strange to think such small things can have such massive effects on your body, but bacteria and viruses in particular can multiply extremely quickly.

Viral and Fungal Diseases

There are heaps of diseases caused by <u>viruses</u> or <u>fungi</u> — here are four of them...

Measles, HIV and TMV are Viral Diseases

1. Measles

1) <u>Measles</u> is spread by <u>droplets</u> from an infected person's sneeze or cough.
2) People with measles develop a <u>red skin rash</u>, and they show signs of a <u>fever</u> (a high temperature).
3) Measles can be very serious, or even fatal, if there are <u>complications</u>. For example, measles can sometimes lead to <u>pneumonia</u> (a lung infection) or a brain infection called <u>encephalitis</u>.
4) Most people are <u>vaccinated</u> against measles when they're young.

2. HIV

1) <u>HIV</u> is a <u>virus</u> spread by <u>sexual contact</u>, or by exchanging <u>bodily fluids</u> such as blood. This can happen when people <u>share needles</u> when taking drugs.
2) HIV initially causes <u>flu-like symptoms</u> for a few weeks. Usually, the person doesn't then experience any symptoms for several years. During this time, HIV can be controlled with <u>antiretroviral drugs</u>. These stop the virus <u>replicating</u> in the body.
3) The virus attacks the <u>immune cells</u> (see page 82).
4) If the body's immune system is badly damaged, it <u>can't cope</u> with <u>other infections</u> or <u>cancers</u>. At this stage, the virus is known as <u>late stage HIV</u> infection, or <u>AIDS</u>.

3. Tobacco Mosaic Virus

1) <u>Tobacco mosaic virus</u> (<u>TMV</u>) is a <u>virus</u> that affects many species of <u>plants</u>, e.g. <u>tomatoes</u>.
2) It causes a mosaic pattern on the leaves of the plants — parts of the leaves become <u>discoloured</u>.
3) The discolouration means the plant can't carry out <u>photosynthesis</u> as well, so the virus affects <u>growth</u>.

Photosynthesis is important for plant growth because it produces glucose — see page 91.

Rose Black Spot is a Fungal Disease

1) <u>Rose black spot</u> is a <u>fungus</u> that causes <u>purple or black spots</u> to develop on the <u>leaves</u> of <u>rose plants</u>. The leaves can then turn <u>yellow</u> and <u>drop off</u>.
2) This means that less <u>photosynthesis</u> can happen, so the plant doesn't <u>grow</u> very well.
3) It spreads through the environment in <u>water</u> or by the <u>wind</u>.
4) Gardeners can treat the disease using <u>fungicides</u> and by <u>stripping</u> the plant of its <u>affected leaves</u>. These leaves then need to be <u>destroyed</u> so that the fungus can't spread to other rose plants.

Protist and Bacterial Diseases

Sorry — I'm afraid there are some more diseases to learn about here. This time, there's one disease caused by a protist and a couple caused by <u>bacteria</u>. I don't know about you, but I'm starting to feel a bit itchy...

Malaria is a Disease Caused by a Protist

1) Part of the malarial protist's <u>life cycle</u> takes place inside a mosquito.
2) The mosquitoes are <u>vectors</u> (see page 77) — they <u>pick up</u> the malarial protist when they <u>feed</u> on an <u>infected animal</u>.
3) Every time the mosquito feeds on another animal, it <u>infects it</u> by inserting the protist into the animal's blood vessels.
4) Malaria causes <u>repeating</u> episodes of <u>fever</u>. It can be <u>fatal</u>.
5) People can be protected from mosquitoes using <u>insecticides</u> and <u>mosquito nets</u>.

There's more on protists on page 77.

Salmonella and **Gonorrhea** Are Two **Bacterial Diseases**

1. *Salmonella*

1) *Salmonella* is a type of <u>bacteria</u> that causes <u>food poisoning</u>.
2) Infected people can suffer from <u>fever</u>, <u>stomach cramps</u>, <u>vomiting</u> and <u>diarrhoea</u>.
3) These symptoms are caused by the <u>toxins</u> that the bacteria produce (see page 76).
4) You can get *Salmonella* food poisoning by eating <u>food</u> that's been <u>contaminated</u> with *Salmonella* bacteria, e.g. eating chicken that caught the disease whilst it was alive, or eating food that has been contaminated by being prepared in unhygienic conditions.

2. Gonorrhoea

1) <u>Gonorrhoea</u> is a <u>sexually transmitted disease</u> (STD).
2) STDs are passed on by <u>sexual contact</u>, e.g. having unprotected sex.
3) Gonorrhoea is caused by <u>bacteria</u>.
4) A person with gonorrhoea will get <u>pain</u> when they <u>urinate</u>. Another symptom is a thick yellow or green <u>discharge</u> from the <u>vagina</u> or the <u>penis</u>.
5) Gonorrhoea was originally treated with an <u>antibiotic</u> called <u>penicillin</u>, but this has become trickier now because strains of the bacteria have become <u>resistant</u> to it (see page 85).
6) To prevent the <u>spread</u> of gonorrhoea, people can be treated with <u>antibiotics</u> and should use <u>barrier methods</u> of contraception (see page 120), such as <u>condoms</u>.

Hang in there, this stuff is pretty gross, but it's nearly over...

Try drawing out a <u>table</u> with columns for 'disease', 'type of organism it's caused by', 'symptoms' and 'how it's spread', then fill it in for all the diseases on this page and the previous one. See how much you can write down <u>without</u> looking back at the page.

Preventing Disease

Pathogens can make life very <u>difficult</u>, but there are lots of things we can do to <u>protect</u> ourselves...

The **Spread** of Disease Can Be **Reduced** or **Prevented**

There are things that we can do to <u>reduce</u>, and even <u>prevent</u>, the spread of disease. For example:

1. Being **Hygienic**

Using <u>simple hygiene measures</u> can prevent the spread of disease.

Doing things like <u>washing your hands</u> thoroughly before preparing food or after you've sneezed can stop you infecting another person.

2. **Destroying Vectors**

1) By <u>getting rid</u> of the <u>organisms</u> that spread disease, you can prevent the disease from being <u>passed on</u>.
2) Vectors that are <u>insects</u> can be killed using <u>insecticides</u> or by <u>destroying</u> their <u>habitat</u> so that they can no longer breed.

The <u>spread</u> of malaria (see previous page) can be reduced by stopping <u>mosquitoes</u> from <u>breeding</u>.

3. **Isolating** Infected Individuals

If you <u>isolate</u> someone who has a communicable disease, it <u>prevents</u> them from <u>passing it on</u> to anyone else.

4. **Vaccination**

<u>Vaccinating</u> people and animals against communicable diseases means that they <u>can't</u> develop the infection and then <u>pass it on</u> to someone else.

There's more about how vaccination works on page 83.

For example, in the UK, most <u>poultry</u> (e.g. chickens and turkeys) is given a <u>vaccination</u> against *Salmonella*. This is to control the <u>spread</u> of the disease.

There you go, basic hygiene can be a real life saver...

There are <u>lots of ways</u> to prevent the spread of diseases and often the method used <u>depends</u> on the disease. As well as the methods on this page, don't forget about the different ways of preventing the spread of the diseases you learnt about on the <u>previous two pages</u> — e.g. using condoms.

Warm-Up & Exam Questions

Have a go at these questions to test whether you know about each of the diseases covered on the previous pages — their symptoms, how they are transmitted and how their spread can be limited.

Warm-Up Questions

1) What is meant by a communicable disease?
2) List three viral diseases.
3) What symptom of measles is shown on the skin?
4) What effect does rose black spot disease have on plants?
5) How is gonorrhoea transmitted between individuals?
6) How can vaccinations help to limit the spread of a disease?

Exam Questions

1 Diseases are often recognised by their symptoms.

1.1 Describe the initial symptoms of HIV infection.

[1 mark]

1.2 Give **two** symptoms of gonorrhoea.

[2 marks]

1.3 A person has food poisoning caused by *Salmonella*. Give **two** symptoms that they may have.

[2 marks]

2 Viruses are a type of pathogen. They can infect every type of living organism.

2.1 What is meant by the term 'pathogen'?

[1 mark]

2.2 The leaves of a tobacco plant can become discoloured if it is infected by a particular virus. Name the virus that affects tobacco plants in this way and describe what effect the discolouration of the leaves can have on a plant.

[2 marks]

2.3 HIV is a virus that can infect humans. Outline how HIV can be spread.

[2 marks]

3 The methods used to prevent the spread of a disease depend on how the disease is transmitted.

3.1 It is important for chefs to wash their hands thoroughly before cooking. Suggest why.

[1 mark]

3.2 Explain why hand washing may not be helpful in limiting the spread of malaria.

[2 marks]

3.3 Suggest and explain **one** reason why efforts to limit the spread of malaria often focus on the mosquito.

[1 mark]

Fighting Disease

The human body has some pretty neat features when it comes to <u>fighting disease</u>.

Your Body Has a Pretty Sophisticated Defence System

1) The human body has got features that stop a lot of nasties getting inside in the first place.
2) The <u>skin</u> acts as a <u>barrier</u> to pathogens. It also secretes <u>antimicrobial substances</u> which kill pathogens.
3) <u>Hairs</u> and <u>mucus</u> in your nose <u>trap</u> particles that could contain pathogens.
4) The <u>trachea</u> and <u>bronchi</u> (breathing pipework — see page 51) secrete <u>mucus</u> to trap pathogens.
5) The trachea and bronchi are lined with <u>cilia</u>. These are hair-like structures, which <u>waft the mucus</u> up to the back of the throat where it can be <u>swallowed</u>.
6) The <u>stomach</u> produces <u>hydrochloric acid</u>. This kills pathogens that make it that far from the mouth.

These are the body's non-specific defence systems.

Your Immune System Can Attack Pathogens

1) If pathogens do make it into your body, your <u>immune system</u> kicks in to destroy them.
2) The most important part of your immune system is the <u>white blood cells</u>. They travel around in your blood and crawl into every part of you, constantly patrolling for microbes. When they come across an invading microbe they have three lines of attack.

1. Consuming Them

White blood cells can <u>engulf</u> foreign cells and <u>digest</u> them. This is called <u>phagocytosis</u>.

2. Producing Antibodies

1) Every invading pathogen has unique molecules (called <u>antigens</u>) on its surface.
2) When some types of white blood cell come across a <u>foreign antigen</u> (i.e. one they don't recognise), they will start to produce <u>proteins</u> called <u>antibodies</u> to lock onto the invading cells so that they can be <u>found</u> and <u>destroyed</u> by other white blood cells. The antibodies produced are specific to that type of antigen — they won't lock on to any others.
3) Antibodies are then produced <u>rapidly</u> and carried around the body to find all similar bacteria or viruses.
4) If the person is infected with the same pathogen again the white blood cells will rapidly produce the antibodies to kill it — the person is <u>naturally immune</u> to that pathogen and won't get ill.

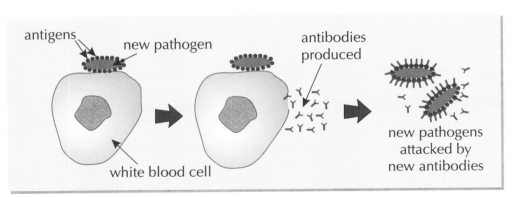

The white blood cells that produce antibodies are also known as B-lymphocytes.

3. Producing Antitoxins
These counteract toxins produced by the <u>invading bacteria</u>.

Fighting Disease — Vaccination

Vaccinations have changed the way we fight disease. We don't always have to deal with the problem once it's happened — we can <u>prevent</u> it happening in the first place.

Vaccination — Protects from Future Infections

1) When you're infected with a new <u>pathogen</u>, it takes your white blood cells a few days to <u>learn</u> how to deal with it. But by that time, you can be pretty <u>ill</u>.

2) <u>Vaccinations</u> involve injecting small amounts of <u>dead</u> or <u>inactive</u> pathogens. These carry <u>antigens</u>, which cause your body to produce <u>antibodies</u> to attack them — even though the pathogen is <u>harmless</u> (since it's dead or inactive).

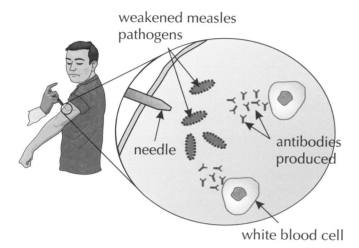

weakened measles pathogens

needle

antibodies produced

white blood cell

The MMR vaccine contains <u>weakened</u> versions of the viruses that cause <u>measles</u>, <u>mumps</u> and <u>rubella</u> (German measles) all in one vaccine.

3) But if live pathogens of the same type appear after that, the white blood cells can <u>rapidly</u> mass-produce antibodies to kill off the pathogen.

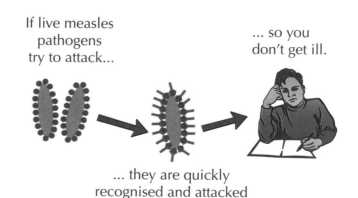

If live measles pathogens try to attack...

... so you don't get ill.

... they are quickly recognised and attacked by antibodies...

Practice exam questions are a lot like vaccinations...

We expose you to some <u>harmless questions</u> (the vaccine) that you learn how to recognise and answer, then when you're confronted with the <u>real exam</u> (the full strength pathogen), you've got the necessary <u>knowledge</u> (antibodies) to answer (kill) them. Gosh, you'd best get revising...

Fighting Disease — Vaccination

Having a whole range of <u>vaccinations</u> is pretty much standard now, so children today are <u>much less likely</u> to catch the kinds of diseases that they might have in the past. That doesn't mean that vaccination is without its problems though...

There are **Pros** and **Cons** of **Vaccination**

Pros:

1) Vaccines have helped <u>control</u> lots of communicable diseases that were once <u>common</u> in the UK (e.g. polio, measles, whooping cough, rubella, mumps, tetanus...).

> Because of vaccinations, <u>smallpox</u> no longer occurs at all, and <u>polio</u> infections have fallen by 99%.

2) Big outbreaks of disease — called <u>epidemics</u> — can be prevented if a <u>large percentage</u> of the population is vaccinated. That way, even the people who aren't vaccinated are <u>unlikely</u> to catch the disease because there are <u>fewer</u> people able to pass it on. But if a significant number of people <u>aren't</u> vaccinated, the disease can <u>spread</u> quickly through them and lots of people will be <u>ill</u> at the same time.

Cons:

1) Vaccines don't always work — sometimes they <u>don't</u> give you <u>immunity</u>.

2) You can sometimes have a <u>bad reaction</u> to a vaccine (e.g. swelling, or maybe something more serious like a fever or seizures). But bad reactions are very <u>rare</u>.

Prevention is better than cure...

WORKING SCIENTIFICALLY

Deciding whether to have a vaccination means <u>balancing risks</u> — the risk of catching the disease if you don't have a vaccine, against the risk of having a bad reaction if you do. As always, you need to look at the <u>evidence</u>. For example, if you get measles (the disease), there's about a 1 in 15 chance that you'll get complications (e.g. pneumonia) — and about 1 in 500 people who get measles actually die. However, the number of people who have a problem with the vaccine is more like 1 in 1 000 000.

Fighting Disease — Drugs

You've probably had to take some sort of <u>medicine</u> if you've been ill, e.g. cough remedies, painkillers. And you're about to find out why it's important to only take <u>antibiotics</u> when you really need them.

Some Drugs Just **Relieve Symptoms** — Others **Cure** the Problem

1) <u>Painkillers</u> (e.g. aspirin) are drugs that relieve pain. However, they don't actually tackle the <u>cause</u> of the disease or kill pathogens, they just help to reduce the <u>symptoms</u>.

2) Other drugs do a similar kind of thing — reduce the <u>symptoms</u> without tackling the underlying <u>cause</u>. For example, lots of "cold remedies" don't actually <u>cure</u> colds.

A flu virus

3) <u>Antibiotics</u> (e.g. penicillin) work differently — they actually <u>kill</u> (or prevent the growth of) the bacteria causing the problem without killing your own body cells. <u>Different antibiotics</u> kill <u>different types</u> of bacteria, so it's important to be treated with the <u>right one</u>.

4) But antibiotics <u>don't destroy viruses</u> (e.g. <u>flu</u> or <u>cold</u> viruses). Viruses reproduce <u>using your own body cells</u>, which makes it very difficult to develop drugs that destroy just the virus without killing the body's cells.

5) The use of antibiotics has greatly reduced the number of deaths from communicable diseases caused by <u>bacteria</u>.

Bacteria Can Become **Resistant** to **Antibiotics**

1) Bacteria can <u>mutate</u> — sometimes the mutations cause them to be <u>resistant</u> to (not killed by) an <u>antibiotic</u>.

2) If you have an <u>infection</u>, some of the bacteria might be <u>resistant</u> to antibiotics.

3) This means that when you <u>treat</u> the infection, only the <u>non-resistant</u> strains of bacteria will be <u>killed</u>.

4) The individual <u>resistant</u> bacteria will <u>survive</u> and <u>reproduce</u>, and the population of the resistant strain will <u>increase</u>. This is an example of natural selection (see page 142).

5) This resistant strain could cause a <u>serious infection</u> that <u>can't</u> be treated by antibiotics. E.g. <u>MRSA</u> (methicillin-resistant *Staphylococcus aureus*) causes serious wound infections and is resistant to the powerful antibiotic <u>methicillin</u>.

6) To <u>slow down</u> the <u>rate</u> of development of <u>resistant strains</u>, it's important for doctors to <u>avoid</u> <u>over-prescribing</u> antibiotics. So you <u>won't</u> get them for a <u>sore throat</u>, only for something more serious.

7) It's also important that you <u>finish</u> the <u>whole course</u> of antibiotics and don't just stop once you feel better.

Antibiotic resistance is inevitable...

Antibiotic resistance is <u>scary</u>. Bacteria reproduce quickly, and so are pretty <u>fast at evolving</u> to deal with threats (e.g. antibiotics). If we were back in the situation where we had no way to treat bacterial infections, it'd be a bit of a nightmare. So do your bit, and <u>finish your courses</u> of antibiotics.

Fighting Disease — Drugs

New drugs against diseases don't just appear out of nowhere. There's a very lengthy process which a new drug has to go through before it can be used in humans (more on that on the next page). First of all, though, a new drug has to be discovered — this is where plants and microorganisms come in...

Many Drugs Originally Came From Plants

1) Plants produce a variety of chemicals to defend themselves against pests and pathogens.

2) Some of these chemicals can be used as drugs to treat human diseases or relieve symptoms.

3) A lot of our current medicines were discovered by studying plants used in traditional cures. For example:

> 1) Aspirin is used as a painkiller and to lower fever. It was developed from a chemical found in willow.
> 2) Digitalis is used to treat heart conditions. It was developed from a chemical found in foxgloves.

4) Some drugs were extracted from microorganisms. For example:

> 1) Alexander Fleming was clearing out some Petri dishes containing bacteria.
> 2) He noticed that one of the dishes of bacteria also had mould on it and the area around the mould was free of the bacteria.
> 3) He found that the mould (called *Penicillium notatum*) on the Petri dish was producing a substance that killed the bacteria — this substance was penicillin.

5) These days, drugs are made on a large scale in the pharmaceutical industry — they're synthesised by chemists in labs.

6) However, the process still might start with a chemical extracted from a plant.

Good old mould — saving lives since 1928...

Drug development is a big industry. A lot of money and time goes into developing new and better drugs, but it can all start with something as humble as a plant or a microorganism.

Developing Drugs

New drugs are constantly being developed. But before they can be given to the general public, they have to go through a thorough <u>testing</u> procedure. This is what usually happens...

There are **Three Main Stages** in Drug Testing

1) In preclinical testing, drugs are tested on <u>human cells and tissues</u> in the lab.

> However, you can't use human cells and tissues to test drugs that affect <u>whole</u> or <u>multiple</u> body systems, e.g. testing a drug for blood pressure must be done on a whole animal because it has an intact circulatory system.

2) The next step in preclinical testing is to test the drug on <u>live animals</u>.

> 1) This is to test <u>efficacy</u> (whether the drug <u>works</u> and produces the effect you're looking for), to find out about its <u>toxicity</u> (how harmful it is) and to find the best <u>dosage</u> (the concentration that should be given, and how often it should be given).
>
> 2) The law in Britain states that any new drug must be tested on <u>two</u> different <u>live mammals</u>. Some people think it's <u>cruel</u> to test on animals, but others believe this is the <u>safest</u> way to make sure a drug isn't dangerous before it's given to humans.

But some people think that animals are so different from humans that testing on animals is pointless.

3) If the drug <u>passes</u> the tests on animals then it's tested on <u>human volunteers</u> in a <u>clinical trial</u>.

> 1) First, the drug is tested on <u>healthy</u> volunteers. This is to make sure that it doesn't have any <u>harmful side effects</u> when the body is working normally. At the start of the trial, a <u>very low dose</u> of the drug is given and this is gradually increased.
>
> 2) If the results of the tests on healthy volunteers are good, the drugs can be tested on people suffering from the <u>illness</u>. The <u>optimum dose</u> is found — this is the dose of drug that is the <u>most effective</u> and has <u>few side effects</u>.
>
> 3) To test how well the drug works, patients are <u>randomly</u> put into <u>two groups</u>. One is given the <u>new drug</u>, the other is given a <u>placebo</u> (a substance that's like the drug being tested but doesn't do anything). This is so the <u>doctor</u> can see the actual difference the drug makes — it allows for the <u>placebo effect</u> (when the patient expects the treatment to work and so <u>feels better</u>, even though the treatment isn't doing anything).
>
> 4) Clinical trials are <u>blind</u> — the patient in the study <u>doesn't know</u> whether they're getting the drug or the placebo. In fact, they're often <u>double-blind</u> — neither the patient nor the <u>doctor</u> knows until all the <u>results</u> have been gathered. This is so the doctors <u>monitoring</u> the patients and <u>analysing</u> the results aren't <u>subconsciously influenced</u> by their knowledge.
>
> 5) The results of drug testing and drug trials aren't published until they've been through <u>peer review</u>. This helps to prevent <u>false claims</u>.

Peer review is when other scientists check that the work is valid and has been carried out rigorously — see page 1.

The placebo effect doesn't work with revision...

... you can't just expect to get a good mark and then magically get it. I know, I know, there's a lot of information to take in on this page, but just <u>read it through slowly</u>. There's nothing too tricky here — it's just a case of going over it <u>again</u> and <u>again</u> until you've got it all firmly lodged in your memory.

Warm-Up & Exam Questions

It's easy to think you've learnt everything in the section until you try the Warm-Up Questions.
Don't panic if there's a bit you've forgotten, just go back over that bit until it's firmly fixed in your brain.

Warm-Up Questions

1) How is the skin adapted to defend against the entry of pathogens?
2) What is the role of the immune system?
3) From what organism was the drug digitalis sourced originally?
4) What is meant by the efficacy of a drug?
5) What is a placebo?
6) Why are placebos used in drug trials?

Exam Questions

1   There are many different lines of defence in the human body (Grade 4-6) that help to prevent pathogens from entering the blood.

1.1   What is the role of the hairs and mucus in the nose?

[1 mark]

1.2   How do the cilia in the trachea and bronchi help to defend the body?

[1 mark]

1.3   What does the stomach produce to kill pathogens?

[1 mark]

2   A scientist is carrying out a clinical trial. (Grade 6-7)

2.1   What is a drug tested on in a clinical trial? Tick **one** box.

☐ human cells

☐ human volunteers

☐ live animals

☐ human tissue

[1 mark]

2.2   The clinical trial is double blind. Explain what this means.

[2 marks]

2.3   Apart from the toxicity of the drug, give **two** other factors that scientists research during drug testing.

[2 marks]

2.4   The results from drug testing are assessed by peer review.
Explain what this means and why it is done.

[2 marks]

Exam Questions

3 White blood cells play an important role in defence against pathogens, including the production of antibodies and antitoxins.

3.1 Apart from producing antibodies and antitoxins, give **one** other method that white blood cells use to defend the body against pathogens.

[1 mark]

3.2 Explain why the production of antibodies is specific to a certain disease.

[1 mark]

4 The development of antibiotics has helped to save many lives.
However, the overuse of antibiotics may be a threat to global health in the future.
Penicillin is an example of an antibiotic.

4.1 Name the organism that penicillin originates from.

[1 mark]

4.2 Explain why the overuse of antibiotics may be a threat to global health in the future.

[2 marks]

4.3 Infection with rhinovirus causes the common cold.
Explain why antibiotics such as penicillin are not used to treat a cold.

[1 mark]

5 Rubella is a communicable viral disease.

The rubella virus is spread in droplets through the air when an infected person coughs, sneezes or talks. The virus causes several symptoms including fever and painful joints. Fortunately, the spread of the disease can be reduced by vaccination.

5.1 Suggest a drug that patients with rubella may be given to relieve their symptoms.

[1 mark]

5.2 Explain why it might be difficult to develop a drug which destroys rubella in the body.

[2 marks]

5.3* Explain how being vaccinated against rubella can prevent a person from catching the disease and suggest why vaccinating a large proportion of the population reduces the risk of someone who hasn't been vaccinated from catching rubella.

[6 marks]

5.4 Suggest **one** reason why some individuals may choose not to receive a vaccination against a disease.

[1 mark]

Revision Summary for Topic 3

Well, that wraps up <u>Topic 3</u> — time to put yourself to the test and find out <u>how much you really know</u>.
* Try these questions and <u>tick off each one</u> when you <u>get it right</u>.
* When you've done <u>all the questions</u> under a heading and are <u>completely happy</u> with it, tick it off.

Types of Disease (p.76-80) ☑

1) How can bacteria make us feel ill? ☐
2) How do viruses cause cell damage? ☐
3) Give one way that fungi can cause disease. ☐
4) Give three ways that pathogens can be spread between people. ☐
5) How is the measles virus spread? ☐
6) Name the fungal disease that causes a mosaic pattern on the leaves of tomato plants. ☐
7) How are mosquitoes involved in the spread of malaria? ☐
8) What type of pathogen causes *Salmonella* food poisoning? ☐
9) How can the spread of gonorrhoea be prevented? ☐
10) How can destroying vectors help to prevent the spread of disease? ☐
11) Why might a person with a disease be isolated? ☐

Fighting Disease (p.82-87) ☑

12) What do the trachea and bronchi have that help to defend the body against pathogens? ☐
13) What is the name for the molecules which antibodies lock onto on the surface of a pathogen? ☐
14) What are antitoxins? ☐
15) What is injected into the body during a vaccination? ☐
16) How does antibiotic resistance arise in a population of bacteria? ☐
17) Which plant does the painkiller aspirin originate from? ☐
18) Name the scientist who discovered penicillin. ☐
19) What two things are drugs tested on in preclinical testing? ☐
20) What is meant by a drug's toxicity? ☐

Photosynthesis

First, photosynthesis equations. Then onto how plants use glucose...

Photosynthesis Produces Glucose Using Light

1) Photosynthesis uses energy to change carbon dioxide and water into glucose and oxygen.
2) It takes place in chloroplasts in green plant cells — they contain pigments like chlorophyll that absorb light.
3) Energy is transferred to the chloroplasts from the environment by light.
4) Photosynthesis is endothermic — this means energy is transferred from the environment in the process.
5) The word equation for photosynthesis is:

$$\text{carbon dioxide} + \text{water} \xrightarrow{\text{light}} \text{glucose} + \text{oxygen}$$

6) Here's the symbol equation too:

$$6CO_2 + 6H_2O \xrightarrow{\text{light}} C_6H_{12}O_6 + 6O_2$$

Plants Use Glucose in Five Main Ways...

1) For respiration — This transfers energy from glucose (see p.100) which enables the plants to convert the rest of the glucose into various other useful substances.

2) Making cellulose — Glucose is converted into cellulose for making strong plant cell walls (see p.17).

3) Making amino acids — Glucose is combined with nitrate ions (absorbed from the soil) to make amino acids, which are then made into proteins.

4) Stored as oils or fats — Glucose is turned into lipids (fats and oils) for storing in seeds.

5) Stored as starch — Glucose is turned into starch and stored in roots, stems and leaves, ready for use when photosynthesis isn't happening, like in the winter. Starch is insoluble, which makes it much better for storing than glucose — a cell with lots of glucose in would draw in loads of water and swell up.

'Photo' means light and 'synthesis' means putting together...

...so photosynthesis means 'putting together using light'. And of course the thing being put together is glucose. Well, I guess that's one way of remembering it... (Maybe just learn the word equation instead.)

The Rate of Photosynthesis

The rate of photosynthesis is affected by the intensity of <u>light</u>, the concentration of <u>CO_2</u>, and the <u>temperature</u>. Plants also need <u>water</u> for photosynthesis, but when a plant is so short of water that it becomes the <u>limiting factor</u> in photosynthesis, it's already in such <u>trouble</u> that this is the least of its worries.

Limiting Factors Affect the Rate of Photosynthesis

1) Any of these three factors can become the <u>limiting factor</u> — this just means that it's stopping photosynthesis from happening any <u>faster</u>.

2) These factors have a <u>combined effect</u> on the rate of photosynthesis, but which factor is limiting at a particular time depends on the <u>environmental conditions</u>:

- at <u>night</u> it's pretty obvious that <u>light</u> is the limiting factor,
- in <u>winter</u> it's often the <u>temperature</u>,
- if it's warm enough and bright enough, the amount of <u>CO_2</u> is usually limiting.

3) <u>Chlorophyll</u> can also be a <u>limiting factor</u> of photosynthesis.

The <u>amount of chlorophyll</u> in a plant can be affected by <u>disease</u> (e.g. infection with the tobacco mosaic virus) or <u>environmental stress</u>, such as a <u>lack of nutrients</u>. These factors can cause <u>chloroplasts</u> to become <u>damaged</u> or to <u>not</u> make <u>enough chlorophyll</u>. This means the rate of photosynthesis is <u>reduced</u> because they <u>can't absorb</u> as much <u>light</u>.

Not Enough Light Slows Down the Rate of Photosynthesis

1) Light provides the <u>energy</u> needed for photosynthesis.

2) As the <u>light level</u> is raised, the rate of photosynthesis <u>increases steadily</u> — but only up to a <u>certain point</u>.

3) Beyond that, it <u>won't</u> make any difference — as light intensity increases, the rate will <u>no longer increase</u>. This is because it'll be either the <u>temperature</u> or the <u>CO_2 level</u> which is now the limiting factor, not light.

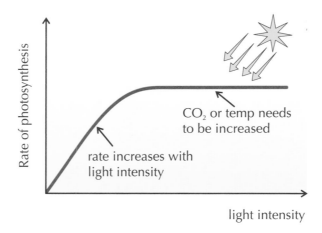

4) In the lab, you can change the light intensity by <u>moving a lamp</u> closer to or further away from your plant (see page 95 for this experiment).

5) But if you just plot the rate of photosynthesis against "distance of lamp from the plant", you get a <u>weird-shaped graph</u>. To get a graph like the one above you either need to <u>measure</u> the light intensity at the plant using a <u>light meter</u> or do a bit of nifty maths with your results.

The Rate of Photosynthesis

Too Little **Carbon Dioxide** Also Slows it Down

CO_2 is one of the <u>raw materials</u> needed for photosynthesis.

1) As with light intensity, the amount of <u>CO_2</u> will only increase the rate of photosynthesis up to a point.
2) After this, the graph <u>flattens out</u> — as the amount of CO_2 increases, the rate <u>no longer increases</u>. This shows that CO_2 is no longer the <u>limiting factor</u>.
3) As long as <u>light</u> and <u>CO_2</u> are in plentiful supply then the factor limiting photosynthesis must be <u>temperature</u>.

The **Temperature** has to be Just Right

Temperature affects the rate of photosynthesis because it affects the <u>enzymes</u> involved.

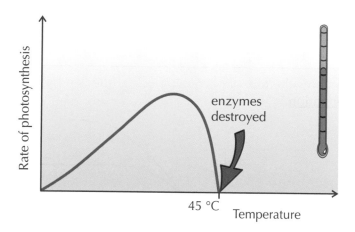

1) Usually, if the temperature is the <u>limiting factor</u> it's because it's <u>too low</u> — the <u>enzymes</u> needed for photosynthesis work more <u>slowly</u> at low temperatures.
2) But if the plant gets <u>too hot</u>, the enzymes it needs for photosynthesis and its other reactions will be <u>damaged</u>.
3) This happens at about <u>45 °C</u> (which is pretty hot for outdoors, although <u>greenhouses</u> can get that hot if you're not careful).

Graphs, graphs and more graphs...

It's really vital that you've got your head around <u>limiting factors</u>, particularly the <u>graphs</u>. I say this because on the next page you're going to have to tackle graphs that have <u>more than one</u> limiting factor — so there's <u>no point</u> moving on until you're completely happy with dealing with just one on its own first.

The Rate of Photosynthesis

Now that you know all about <u>limiting factors</u>, it's time to take it to the next level...

One Graph May Show the Effect of Many Limiting Factors

You could get a graph that shows <u>more than one</u> limiting factor on the rate of photosynthesis, for example:

The graph shows how the rate of photosynthesis is affected by <u>light intensity</u> and <u>temperature</u>.

1) At the start, both of the lines show that as the light intensity <u>increases</u>, the rate of photosynthesis <u>increases steadily</u>.
2) But the lines <u>level off</u> when <u>light</u> is <u>no longer</u> the limiting factor. The line at <u>25 °C</u> levels off at a <u>higher point</u> than the one at 15 °C, showing that <u>temperature</u> must have been a <u>limiting factor</u> at 15 °C.

The graph shows how the rate of photosynthesis is affected by <u>light intensity</u> and <u>CO_2 concentration</u>.

1) Again, both the lines <u>level off</u> when <u>light</u> is <u>no longer</u> the limiting factor.
2) The line at the <u>higher CO_2 concentration of 0.4%</u> levels off at a <u>higher point</u> than the one at 0.04%. This means <u>CO_2 concentration</u> must have been a <u>limiting factor</u> at 0.04% CO_2. The limiting factor here <u>isn't temperature</u> because it's the <u>same</u> for both lines (25 °C).

Make sure you know how to read from graphs

In the exam, you might have to describe what's going on in a graph of limiting factors. <u>Don't panic</u> — just look at the graph <u>carefully</u>, making sure you pay attention to the <u>axes</u>, as well as any additional <u>labels</u>, to see how the factors shown are affecting the <u>rate of photosynthesis</u>.

Measuring the Rate of Photosynthesis

It's practical time again. This one lets you see how changing <u>light intensity</u> affects the <u>rate of photosynthesis</u>.

Oxygen Production Shows the Rate of Photosynthesis

<u>Canadian pondweed</u> can be used to measure the effect of <u>light intensity</u> on the <u>rate of photosynthesis</u>. The rate at which the pondweed produces <u>oxygen</u> corresponds to the rate at which it's photosynthesising — the <u>faster</u> the rate of oxygen production, the <u>faster</u> the rate of photosynthesis.

Here's how the experiment works:

1) A source of <u>white light</u> is placed at a <u>specific distance</u> from the pondweed.

2) The pondweed is left to photosynthesise for a <u>set amount of time</u>. As it photosynthesises, the oxygen released will collect in the <u>capillary tube</u>.

3) At the end of the experiment, the <u>syringe</u> is used to draw the gas bubble in the tube up alongside a ruler and the <u>length</u> of the <u>gas bubble</u> is <u>measured</u>. This is <u>proportional</u> to the <u>volume of O$_2$</u> produced.

4) For this experiment, any <u>variables</u> that could affect the results should be <u>controlled</u>, e.g. the <u>temperature</u> and <u>time</u> the pondweed is left to photosynthesise.

5) The experiment is <u>repeated</u> twice with the <u>light source</u> at the <u>same</u> distance and the <u>mean</u> volume of O$_2$ produced is calculated.

6) Then the whole experiment is repeated with the <u>light source</u> at <u>different distances</u> from the pondweed.

You can compare the results at different light intensities by giving the rate as the length of the bubble per unit time, e.g. cm/min.

The apparatus above can be altered to measure the effect of <u>temperature</u> or <u>CO$_2$</u> on photosynthesis. For example:

1) The test tube of pondweed can be put into a <u>water bath</u> at a <u>set temperature</u>, or a measured amount of <u>sodium hydrogencarbonate</u> can be dissolved in the water (which <u>gives off</u> CO$_2$).
2) The experiment can then be repeated with different temperatures of water / concentrations of sodium hydrogencarbonate.

Canadian pondweed is not native to the UK, so it must be disposed of carefully after the experiment — it shouldn't be released into the environment.

Measuring the Rate of Photosynthesis

This page is all about the <u>inverse square law</u>. It can be a bit tricky to get your head around, so focus...

The **Inverse Square Law** Links **Light Intensity** and **Distance**

1) In the experiment on the previous page, when the <u>lamp</u> is <u>moved away</u> from the pondweed, the amount of <u>light</u> that reaches the pondweed <u>decreases</u>.

2) You can say that as the <u>distance increases</u>, the <u>light intensity decreases</u>.
   In other words, distance and light intensity are <u>inversely proportional</u> to each other.

3) However, it's not quite as simple as that. It turns out that light intensity decreases in <u>proportion</u> to the <u>square</u> of the distance. This is called the <u>inverse square law</u> and is written out like this:

This is the 'proportional to' symbol.

Putting one over the distance shows the <u>inverse</u>.

$$\text{light intensity} \propto \frac{1}{\text{distance (d)}^2}$$

The distance is <u>squared</u>.

4) The inverse square law means that if you <u>halve</u> the <u>distance</u>, the <u>light intensity</u> will be <u>four times greater</u> and if you <u>divide</u> the distance by <u>three</u>, the light intensity will be <u>nine times greater</u>.

5) Likewise, if you <u>double</u> the distance, the light intensity will be <u>four times smaller</u> and if you <u>treble</u> the distance, the light intensity will be <u>nine times smaller</u>.

6) You can use $1/d^2$ as a measure of light intensity.

EXAMPLE: Use the inverse square law to calculate the light intensity when the lamp is 10 cm from the pondweed.

1) <u>Use the formula</u> $\frac{1}{d^2}$.

$$\text{light intensity} = \frac{1}{d^2}$$

2) Fill in the <u>values</u> you know — you're given the distance, so put that in.

$$\text{light intensity} = \frac{1}{10^2}$$

3) Calculate the <u>answer</u>.

$$= 0.01 \text{ a.u.}$$

'a.u.' stands for 'arbitrary units'.

As one thing goes up, the other goes down...

That's what <u>inverse proportion</u> is all about. To take it a step further, they go up and down at the same rate. So here, as distance <u>decreases</u>, light intensity <u>increases</u> — but rather confusingly, the light intensity increases <u>in proportion</u> to the <u>square</u> of the distance. Phew, that's made my brain hurt a bit.

Ideal Conditions for Photosynthesis

Growing plants outdoors can be <u>very difficult</u>, especially on a <u>large scale</u> — it's almost impossible to control the weather and other conditions. But there's a way around that...

You can **Artificially Create** the **Ideal Conditions** for **Farming**

1) The most common way to artificially create the <u>ideal environment</u> for plants is to grow them in a <u>greenhouse</u>.

2) Greenhouses help to <u>trap</u> the Sun's <u>heat</u>, and make sure that the <u>temperature</u> doesn't become <u>limiting</u>. In winter a farmer or gardener might use a <u>heater</u> as well to keep the temperature at the ideal level. In summer it could get <u>too hot</u>, so they might use <u>shades</u> and <u>ventilation</u> to cool things down.

3) <u>Light</u> is always needed for photosynthesis, so commercial farmers often supply <u>artificial light</u> after the Sun goes down to give their plants more quality photosynthesis time.

Greenhouses are used to grow plants, including food crops, flowers and tobacco plants.

4) Farmers and gardeners can also increase the level of <u>carbon dioxide</u> in the greenhouse. A fairly common way is to use a <u>paraffin heater</u> to heat the greenhouse. As the paraffin burns, it makes carbon dioxide as a <u>by-product</u>.

5) Keeping plants <u>enclosed</u> in a greenhouse also makes it easier to keep them free from <u>pests</u> and <u>diseases</u>. The farmer can add <u>fertilisers</u> to the soil as well, to provide all the <u>minerals</u> needed for healthy growth.

6) Sorting all this out <u>costs money</u> — but if the farmer can keep the conditions <u>just right</u> for photosynthesis, the plants will grow much <u>faster</u> and a <u>decent crop</u> can be harvested much more <u>often</u>, which can then be <u>sold</u>. It's important that a farmer supplies just the <u>right amount</u> of heat, light, etc. — enough to make the plants grow well, but <u>not</u> more than the plants <u>need</u>, as this would just be <u>wasting money</u>.

Greenhouses control the growing environment

Farmers use <u>greenhouses</u> to make sure crops get the <u>right amount</u> of <u>carbon dioxide</u>, <u>light</u> and <u>heat</u>. They can alter the conditions using paraffin heaters, artificial light and ventilation. This ensures nothing becomes a <u>limiting factor</u> for photosynthesis, which means a <u>good crop</u> is produced.

98

Warm-Up & Exam Questions

Time for a break in the topic and some questions. Do them now, whilst all that learning is fresh in your mind. Using that knowledge will help you to remember it all, and that's what this game is all about.

Warm-Up Questions

1) What does the chemical symbol $C_6H_{12}O_6$ represent?
2) What is meant by a limiting factor for the rate of photosynthesis?
3) Explain why the rate of photosynthesis decreases if the temperature is too high.
4) What could you measure to show the rate of photosynthesis?
5) Write down the inverse square law for light intensity.
6) Why might a farmer want to increase the rate of photosynthesis in her greenhouse of tomatoes?

Exam Questions

1 Photosynthesis produces glucose using light. **(Grade 4-6)**

1.1 Complete the word equation for photosynthesis.

carbon dioxide + ... $\xrightarrow{\text{light}}$ glucose + ...

[2 marks]

1.2 Plants use some of the glucose they produce to make a substance which strengthens their cell walls. Which of the following strengthens cells walls?
Tick **one** box.

☐ cellulose ☐ oils ☐ starch ☐ fats

[1 mark]

1.3 Give **two** others way that plants use the glucose they produce in photosynthesis.

[2 marks]

PRACTICAL

2 A student did an experiment to see how the rate of photosynthesis depends on light intensity. **(Grade 4-6)** **Figure 1** shows some of her apparatus.

2.1 How can the student measure the rate of photosynthesis?

[1 mark]

2.2 State the dependent variable and the independent variable in this experiment.

[2 marks]

2.3 State **one** factor that should be kept constant during this experiment.

[1 mark]

Figure 1

gas bubbles

LIGHT SOURCE →

pond plant

Exam Questions

3 A student investigated the effect of different concentrations of carbon dioxide on the rate of photosynthesis of his Swiss cheese plant. The results are shown in **Figure 2**.

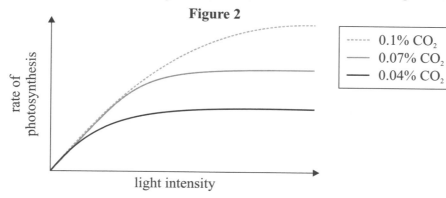

Figure 2

3.1 Describe the effect that increasing the concentration of CO_2 has on the rate of photosynthesis as light intensity increases.

[2 marks]

3.2 Explain why all the lines on the graph level off eventually.

[1 mark]

4 **Figure 3** shows a variegated leaf. It is partly green and partly white. Chlorophyll is present in the green parts of the leaf but not the white parts.

Figure 3

A student did an experiment in which part of the leaf was covered with black paper, as shown in **Figure 4**. The leaf was then exposed to light for four hours and was then tested for starch.

Figure 4

4.1 Complete **Figure 4** by shading in the part(s) of the leaf that you would expect to contain **starch**.

[1 mark]

4.2 Explain your answer to **4.1**.

[2 marks]

5 A student is investigating the effect of light intensity on the rate of photosynthesis by placing a lamp at various distances from a plant and measuring the rate of photosynthesis. Use the inverse square law to calculate the light intensity when the lamp is 7.5 cm from the plant. Give your answer in arbitrary units (a.u.) to 2 significant figures.

[2 marks]

Respiration

You need energy to keep your body going. Energy comes from food, and it's transferred by respiration.

Respiration is NOT "Breathing In and Out"

Respiration involves many reactions. These are really important reactions, as respiration transfers the energy that the cell needs to do just about everything — this energy is used for all living processes.

1) Respiration is not breathing in and breathing out, as you might think.

2) Respiration is the process of transferring energy from the breakdown of glucose (sugar) — and it goes on in every cell in your body continuously.

3) It happens in plants too. All living things respire.
    It's how they transfer energy from their food to their cells.

> RESPIRATION is the process of TRANSFERRING ENERGY FROM GLUCOSE, which goes on IN EVERY CELL.

4) Respiration is exothermic — it transfers energy to the environment.

Respiration Transfers Energy for All Kinds of Things

Here are three examples of how organisms use the energy transferred by respiration:

1) To build up larger molecules from smaller ones (like proteins from amino acids).

2) In animals it's used to allow the muscles to contract (so they can move about).

3) In mammals and birds the energy is used to keep their body temperature steady in colder surroundings. (Unlike other animals, mammals and birds keep their bodies constantly warm.)

Respiration releases energy from glucose

So... respiration is a pretty important thing. Cyanide is a really nasty toxin that stops respiration by stopping enzymes involved in the process from working — so it's pretty poisonous (it can kill you). Your brain, heart and liver are affected first because they have the highest energy demands... nice.

Metabolism

Metabolism is going on <u>all of the time</u>. Right now. And now. Even now.
Okay, you get the picture. Time to read all about it.

Metabolism is ALL the Chemical Reactions in an Organism

1) In a <u>cell</u> there are <u>lots</u> of <u>chemical reactions</u> happening <u>all the time</u>, which are controlled by <u>enzymes</u>.

Enzymes are biological catalysts — see p.42.

2) Many of these reactions are <u>linked together</u> to form <u>bigger reactions</u>:

3) In some of these reactions, <u>larger molecules</u> are <u>made</u> from smaller ones. For example:

> 1) Lots of small <u>glucose</u> molecules are <u>joined together</u> in reactions to form <u>starch</u> (a storage molecule in plant cells), <u>glycogen</u> (a storage molecule in animal cells) and <u>cellulose</u> (a component of plant cell walls).

> 2) <u>Lipid</u> molecules are each made from <u>one molecule</u> of <u>glycerol</u> and <u>three fatty acids</u>.

> 3) <u>Glucose</u> is combined with <u>nitrate ions</u> to make <u>amino acids</u>, which are then made into <u>proteins</u>.

4) In other reactions, larger molecules are <u>broken down</u> into smaller ones. For example:

> 1) <u>Glucose</u> is broken down in <u>respiration</u>. Respiration transfers energy to power <u>all</u> the reactions in the body that <u>make molecules</u>.

> 2) <u>Excess protein</u> is <u>broken down</u> in a <u>reaction</u> to produce <u>urea</u>. Urea is then <u>excreted</u> in <u>urine</u>.

5) The <u>sum</u> (total) of <u>all</u> of the <u>reactions</u> that happen in a <u>cell</u> or the <u>body</u> is called its <u>metabolism</u>.

It's still going on now

<u>Enzymes</u> are key to metabolism, so if you need a reminder about them, now is a good time to head back to page 42. Even if you <u>are</u> happy with enzymes, don't move on just yet — check you've taken in everything on this page before you flip over to continue on through the world of respiration. It's all important stuff.

Aerobic and Anaerobic Respiration

There are two types of respiration — aerobic and anaerobic.

Aerobic Respiration Needs Plenty of Oxygen

1) Aerobic respiration is respiration using oxygen.
   It's the most efficient way to transfer energy from glucose.
2) Aerobic respiration goes on all the time in plants and animals.
3) Most of the reactions in aerobic respiration happen inside mitochondria (see page 16).
4) Here are the word and symbol equations for aerobic respiration:

$$\text{glucose} + \text{oxygen} \longrightarrow \text{carbon dioxide} + \text{water}$$

$$C_6H_{12}O_6 + 6O_2 \longrightarrow 6CO_2 + 6H_2O$$

Anaerobic Respiration is Used if There's Not Enough Oxygen

When you do vigorous exercise and your body can't supply enough oxygen to your muscles,
they start doing anaerobic respiration as well as aerobic respiration.

1) "Anaerobic" just means "without oxygen". It's the incomplete breakdown of glucose, making lactic acid.
2) Here's the word equation for anaerobic respiration in muscle cells:

$$\text{glucose} \longrightarrow \text{lactic acid}$$

3) Anaerobic respiration does not transfer nearly as much energy as aerobic respiration.
   This is because glucose isn't fully oxidised (because it doesn't combine with oxygen).
4) So, anaerobic respiration is only useful in emergencies, e.g. during exercise when it
   allows you to keep on using your muscles for a while longer.

Anaerobic Respiration in Plants and Yeast is Slightly Different

1) Plants and yeast cells can respire without oxygen too, but they produce ethanol (alcohol)
   and carbon dioxide instead of lactic acid.
2) Here's the word equation for anaerobic respiration in plants and yeast cells:

$$\text{glucose} \longrightarrow \text{ethanol} + \text{carbon dioxide}$$

Yeast are
single-celled
organisms.

3) Anaerobic respiration in yeast cells is called fermentation.
4) In the food and drinks industry, fermentation by yeast is of great value
   because it's used to make bread and alcoholic drinks, e.g. beer and wine.
5) In bread-making, it's the carbon dioxide from fermentation that makes bread rise.
6) In beer and wine-making, it's the fermentation process that produces alcohol.

Exercise

When you <u>exercise</u>, your body responds in a number of helpful ways...

When You **Exercise** You **Respire More**

1) Muscles need <u>energy</u> from respiration to <u>contract</u>. When you exercise, some of your muscles contract more frequently than normal so you need <u>more energy</u>. This energy comes from <u>increased respiration</u>.

2) The increase in respiration in your cells means you need to get <u>more oxygen</u> into them.

3) Your <u>breathing rate</u> and <u>breath volume increase</u> to get more oxygen into the blood, and your <u>heart rate increases</u> to get this oxygenated blood around the body faster. This <u>removes CO_2</u> more quickly at the same time.

4) When you do <u>really vigorous exercise</u> (like sprinting) your body can't supply <u>oxygen</u> to your muscles quickly enough, so they start <u>respiring anaerobically</u> (see the previous page).

5) This is <u>NOT the best way to transfer energy from glucose</u> because <u>lactic acid</u> builds up in the muscles, which gets <u>painful</u>.

6) Long periods of exercise also cause <u>muscle fatigue</u> — the muscles get <u>tired</u> and then <u>stop contracting efficiently</u>.

Remember, lactic acid is formed from the incomplete oxidation of glucose.

Anaerobic Respiration Leads to an **Oxygen Debt**

1) After resorting to anaerobic respiration, when you stop exercising you'll have an "<u>oxygen debt</u>".

2) An oxygen debt is the <u>amount of extra oxygen</u> your body needs to <u>react</u> with the <u>build up</u> of <u>lactic acid</u> and <u>remove</u> it from the cells. Oxygen reacts with the lactic acid to form harmless CO_2 and <u>water</u>.

3) In other words you have to "<u>repay</u>" the oxygen that you didn't get to your muscles in time, because your <u>lungs</u>, <u>heart</u> and <u>blood</u> couldn't keep up with the <u>demand</u> earlier on.

4) This means you have to keep breathing hard for a while <u>after you stop</u>, to get <u>more oxygen</u> into your blood, which is transported to the muscle cells.

5) The <u>pulse</u> and <u>breathing rate</u> stay high whilst there are <u>high levels</u> of <u>lactic acid</u> and CO_2.

6) Your body also has another way of coping with the high level of lactic acid — the <u>blood</u> that enters your muscles <u>transports</u> the <u>lactic acid</u> to the <u>liver</u>. In the liver, the lactic acid is <u>converted</u> back to <u>glucose</u>.

You Can Investigate The **Effect of Exercise** on **The Body**

1) You can measure <u>breathing rate</u> by <u>counting breaths</u>, and <u>heart rate</u> by <u>taking the pulse</u>.

2) To take the pulse, you put two fingers on the inside of your <u>wrist</u> or your <u>neck</u> and count the number of pulses in <u>1 minute</u>.

3) E.g. you could take your <u>pulse</u> after:

- <u>sitting down</u> for 5 minutes,
- then after 5 minutes of <u>gentle walking</u>,
- then again after 5 minutes of <u>slow jogging</u>,
- then again after <u>running</u> for 5 minutes.

You could then <u>plot</u> your results in a bar chart.

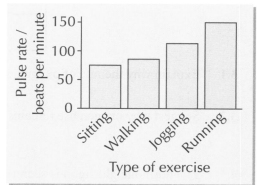

4) Your pulse rate will <u>increase</u> the more <u>intense</u> the exercise is, as your body needs to get <u>more oxygen</u> to the <u>muscles</u> and take more <u>carbon dioxide away</u> from the muscles.

5) To <u>reduce</u> the effect of any <u>random errors</u> on your results, do it as a <u>group</u> and plot the <u>average pulse rate</u> for each exercise.

There's more about random error on page 7.

Warm-Up & Exam Questions

You know the drill by now — work your way through the Warm-Up questions, then the Exam Questions.

Warm-Up Questions

1) Give two examples of how animals use the energy transferred by respiration.
2) What is metabolism?
3) What are the reactants of aerobic respiration?
4) What is the process of anaerobic respiration in yeast called?
5) State three changes that take place in the body during vigorous exercise.

Exam Questions

1 Respiration is a process carried out by all living cells.
It can take place aerobically or anaerobically.

1.1 Give **two** differences between aerobic and anaerobic respiration.

[2 marks]

1.2 Write the word equation for aerobic respiration.

[2 marks]

2 In the human body, respiration may be aerobic or anaerobic at different times.

2.1 Write down the word equation for anaerobic respiration in humans.

[1 mark]

2.2 Explain why the body uses anaerobic respiration during vigorous exercise.

[2 marks]

3 **Figure 1** shows the rate of oxygen use by a person before, during and after a period of exercise.

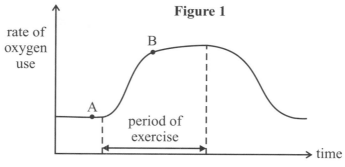

3.1 Explain why the rate of oxygen consumption is higher at **B** than at **A**.

[2 marks]

3.2 Suggest why oxygen use remains high, even after the period of exercise ends.

[1 mark]

4 The hormone glucagon is secreted by the pancreas. It stimulates the conversion of glycogen to glucose in the liver. Suggest why the blood glucagon level increases during vigorous exercise.

[2 marks]

Revision Summary for Topic 4

Well, it's all over for <u>Topic 4</u> folks — but I know how much you'll miss it, so here are some questions on it...
- Try these questions and <u>tick off each one</u> when you <u>get it right</u>.
- When you've done <u>all the questions</u> under a heading and are <u>completely happy</u> with it, tick it off.

Photosynthesis (p.91-97) ☑

1) Where in a plant cell does photosynthesis take place? ☑
2) How is energy transferred to a plant from its environment for photosynthesis? ☑
3) What is an endothermic reaction? ☑
4) Name the products of photosynthesis. ☑
5) What type of molecule is formed from combining glucose molecules with nitrate ions? ☑
6) Why do plants store glucose as starch? ☑
7) What effect would a low carbon dioxide concentration have on the rate of photosynthesis? ☑
8) What effect would a very low temperature have on the rate of photosynthesis? ☑
9) Describe a method that could be used to measure the effect of light intensity on the rate of photosynthesis. ☑
10) In the inverse square law, how are light intensity and distance linked? ☑
11) Give one way that the temperature can be decreased in a greenhouse. ☑
12) Give one way that the level of carbon dioxide can be increased in a greenhouse. ☑

Respiration and Metabolism (p.100-103) ☑

13) What is respiration? ☑
14) What is an exothermic reaction? ☑
15) What process transfers energy to make new molecules in cells? ☑
16) Give three examples of metabolic reactions. ☑
17) Name the products of aerobic respiration. ☑
18) What is produced by anaerobic respiration in muscle cells? ☑
19) What is the word equation for anaerobic respiration in yeast cells? ☑
20) Name two products of the food and drink industry that fermentation is needed for. ☑
21) What happens to muscles when they become fatigued? ☑
22) In what organ is lactic acid converted back to glucose? ☑

Homeostasis

Homeostasis — a word that strikes fear into the heart of many a GCSE student. But it's really not that bad at all. This page is a brief <u>introduction</u> to the topic, so you need to <u>nail all of this</u> before you can move on.

Homeostasis — Maintaining a **Stable Internal Environment**

1) The conditions inside your body need to be kept <u>steady</u>, even when the <u>external environment changes</u>.

2) This is really important because your <u>cells</u> need the <u>right conditions</u> in order to <u>function properly</u>, including the right conditions for <u>enzyme action</u> (see p.43).

3) <u>Homeostasis</u> is all about the <u>regulation</u> of the conditions inside your body (and cells) to <u>maintain a stable internal environment</u>, in response to <u>changes</u> in both internal and external conditions.

4) You have loads of <u>automatic control systems</u> in your body that regulate your internal environment — these include both <u>nervous</u> and <u>hormonal</u> communication systems. For example, there are control systems that maintain your <u>body temperature</u>, your <u>blood glucose</u> level (see page 114) and your <u>water content</u>.

5) All your automatic control systems are made up of <u>three main components</u> which work together to maintain a steady condition — cells called <u>receptors</u>, <u>coordination centres</u> (including the brain, spinal cord and pancreas) and <u>effectors</u>.

Negative Feedback **Counteracts Changes**

Your automatic control systems keep your internal environment stable using a mechanism called <u>negative feedback</u>. When the level of something (e.g. water or temperature) gets <u>too high</u> or <u>too low</u>, your body uses negative feedback to bring it back to <u>normal</u>.

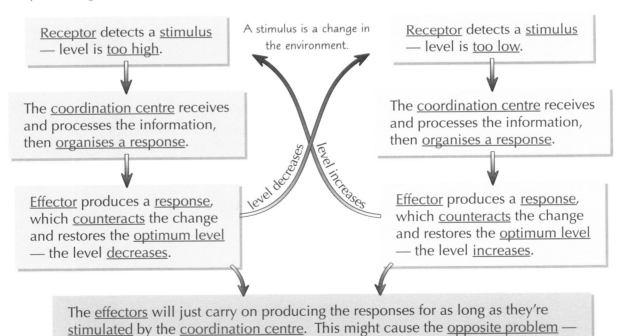

This process happens without you thinking about it — it's all <u>automatic</u>.

The Nervous System

The <u>nervous system</u> means that humans can <u>react to their surroundings</u> and <u>coordinate their behaviour</u>.

The **Nervous System Detects** and **Reacts** to **Stimuli**

1) Organisms need to <u>respond to stimuli</u> (changes in the environment) in order to <u>survive</u>.

2) A <u>single-celled</u> organism can just <u>respond</u> to its environment, but the cells of <u>multicellular</u> organisms need to <u>communicate</u> with each other first.

3) So as multicellular organisms evolved, they developed <u>nervous</u> and <u>hormonal communication systems</u>.

The **Nervous System** is made up of **Different Parts**

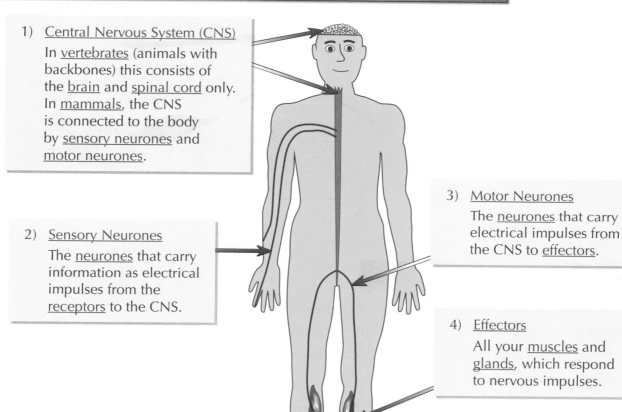

1) <u>Central Nervous System (CNS)</u>

In <u>vertebrates</u> (animals with backbones) this consists of the <u>brain</u> and <u>spinal cord</u> only. In <u>mammals</u>, the CNS is connected to the body by <u>sensory neurones</u> and <u>motor neurones</u>.

2) <u>Sensory Neurones</u>

The <u>neurones</u> that carry information as electrical impulses from the <u>receptors</u> to the CNS.

3) <u>Motor Neurones</u>

The <u>neurones</u> that carry electrical impulses from the CNS to <u>effectors</u>.

4) Effectors

All your <u>muscles</u> and <u>glands</u>, which respond to nervous impulses.

Receptors and **Effectors** can form part of **Complex Organs**

1) <u>Receptors</u> are the cells that <u>detect stimuli</u>.

2) There are many <u>different types</u> of receptors, such as <u>taste</u> receptors on the tongue and <u>sound</u> receptors in the ears.

3) Receptors can form part of <u>larger</u>, <u>complex organs</u>, e.g. the <u>retina</u> of the <u>eye</u> is covered in <u>light receptor cells</u>.

The retina is the inner layer of tissue at the back of the eye.

4) <u>Effectors respond</u> to nervous impulses and bring about a change.

5) Muscles and glands are known as <u>effectors</u> — they respond in different ways. <u>Muscles contract</u> in response to a nervous impulse, whereas <u>glands secrete hormones</u>.

The Nervous System

The **Central Nervous System** (CNS) **Coordinates** the **Response**

The CNS is a <u>coordination centre</u> — it receives information from the <u>receptors</u> and then <u>coordinates a response</u> (decides what to do about it). The response is carried out by <u>effectors</u>.

For example, a small bird is eating some seed...

1) ...when, out of the corner of its eye, it spots a cat skulking towards it (this is the <u>stimulus</u>).

2) The <u>receptors</u> in the bird's eye are <u>stimulated</u>.

3) <u>Sensory neurones</u> carry the information <u>from</u> the <u>receptors</u> to the <u>CNS</u>.

4) The CNS <u>decides</u> what to do about it.

5) The CNS sends information to the muscles in the bird's wings (the <u>effectors</u>) along <u>motor neurones</u>.

6) The muscles contract and the bird flies away to safety.

| Stimulus | Receptor | Sensory neurone | CNS | Motor neurone | Effector | Response |

Light receptors in the retina

Synapses Connect Neurones

1) The <u>connection</u> between <u>two neurones</u> is called a <u>synapse</u>.

2) The nerve signal is transferred by <u>chemicals</u> which <u>diffuse</u> (move) across the gap.

3) These chemicals then set off a <u>new electrical signal</u> in the <u>next</u> neurone.

chemicals released

End of neurone

Nerve impulse

neurone

Don't let the thought of exams play on your nerves...

Don't forget that it's only <u>large animals</u> like mammals and birds that have <u>complex nervous systems</u>. <u>Simple animals</u> like jellyfish <u>don't</u> — everything they do is a <u>reflex response</u> (see next page).

Reflexes

Neurones transmit information <u>very quickly</u> to and from the brain, and your brain <u>quickly decides</u> how to respond to a stimulus. But <u>reflexes</u> are even quicker...

Reflexes Help Prevent Injury

1) <u>Reflexes</u> are <u>rapid</u>, <u>automatic</u> responses to certain stimuli that <u>don't involve</u> the <u>conscious</u> part of the brain — they can reduce the chances of being injured.

> • For example, if someone shines a <u>bright light</u> in your eyes, your <u>pupils</u> automatically get smaller so that less light gets into the eye — this stops it getting <u>damaged</u>.

> • Or if you get a shock, your body releases the <u>hormone</u> adrenaline automatically — it doesn't wait for you to <u>decide</u> that you're shocked.

2) The passage of information in a reflex (from receptor to effector) is called a <u>reflex arc</u>.

The Reflex Arc Goes Through the Central Nervous System

1) The neurones in reflex arcs go through the <u>spinal cord</u> or through an <u>unconscious part of the brain</u>.

2) When a <u>stimulus</u> (e.g. a painful bee sting) is detected by receptors, <u>impulses</u> are sent along a <u>sensory neurone</u> to the CNS.

3) When the impulses reach a <u>synapse</u> between the sensory neurone and a relay neurone, they trigger chemicals to be released (see previous page). These chemicals cause impulses to be sent along the <u>relay neurone</u>.

4) When the impulses reach a <u>synapse</u> between the relay neurone and a motor neurone, the same thing happens. Chemicals are released and cause impulses to be sent along the <u>motor neurone</u>.

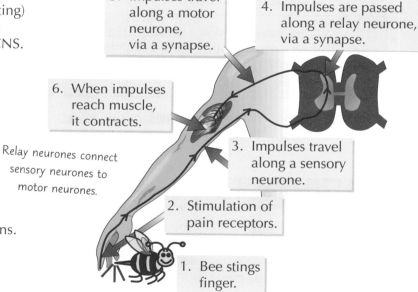

5. Impulses travel along a motor neurone, via a synapse.

4. Impulses are passed along a relay neurone, via a synapse.

6. When impulses reach muscle, it contracts.

Relay neurones connect sensory neurones to motor neurones.

3. Impulses travel along a sensory neurone.

2. Stimulation of pain receptors.

1. Bee stings finger.

5) The impulses then travel along the motor neurone to the <u>effector</u> (in this example it's a muscle).

6) The <u>muscle</u> then <u>contracts</u> and moves your hand away from the bee.

7) Because you don't have to think about the response (which takes time) it's <u>quicker</u> than normal responses.

Don't get all twitchy — just learn it...

Reflexes <u>bypass</u> your <u>conscious brain</u> completely when a <u>quick response</u> is <u>essential</u> — your body just gets on with things. If you had to stop and think first, you'd end up a lot more sore (or worse).

Investigating Reaction Time

Reaction time is the time it takes to <u>respond to a stimulus</u> — it's often <u>less</u> than a <u>second</u>. It can be <u>affected</u> by factors such as <u>age</u>, <u>gender</u> or <u>drugs</u>.

You Can Measure **Reaction Time**

<u>Caffeine</u> is a drug that can <u>speed up</u> a person's reaction time. The <u>effect of caffeine</u> on reaction time can be <u>measured</u> like this...

1) The person being tested should sit with their arm resting on the edge of a table (this should stop them moving their arm up or down during the test).

2) Hold a <u>ruler</u> vertically between their thumb and forefinger. Make sure that the <u>zero end</u> of the ruler is <u>level</u> with their thumb and finger. Then <u>let go</u> without giving any warning.

3) The person being tested should try to <u>catch the ruler</u> as quickly as they can — as soon as they see it fall.

4) Reaction time is measured by the <u>number</u> on the ruler where it's caught — the further down it's caught (i.e. the higher the number), the slower their reaction time.

5) <u>Repeat</u> the test several times then calculate the <u>mean distance</u> that the ruler fell.

6) The person being tested should then have a <u>caffeinated drink</u> (e.g. 300 ml of cola). After <u>ten minutes</u>, repeat steps 1 to 5.

With a little bit of maths, it's possible to work out the reaction time in seconds using the mean distance.

7) You need to <u>control any variables</u> to make sure that this is a fair test.

> For example, you should use the <u>same person</u> to catch the ruler each time, and that person should always use the <u>same hand</u> to catch the ruler. Also, the ruler should always be dropped from the <u>same height</u>, and you should make sure that the person being tested has not had <u>any caffeine</u> (or anything else that may affect their reaction time) before the start of the experiment.

8) Too much caffeine can cause <u>unpleasant side-effects</u>, so the person being tested should avoid drinking <u>any more caffeine</u> for the rest of the day after the experiment is completed.

Reaction Time Can Be Measured Using a **Computer**

1) Simple <u>computer tests</u> can also be used to measure reaction time.

> For example, the person being tested has to <u>click the mouse</u> (or <u>press a key</u>) as soon as they see a stimulus on the screen, e.g. a box <u>change colour</u>.

2) Computers can give a <u>more precise</u> reaction time because they remove the possibility of <u>human error</u> from the measurement.

3) As the computer can record the reaction time in <u>milliseconds</u>, it can also give a more <u>accurate</u> measurement.

4) Using a computer can also remove the possibility that the person can <u>predict</u> when to respond — using the ruler test, the catcher may learn to <u>anticipate</u> the drop by reading the tester's <u>body language</u>.

 ## As with any practical, you need to control the variables...

It's important that you measure a person's reaction time <u>before</u> they've had a caffeinated drink, as well as after — otherwise you won't be able to tell what effect the caffeine has had (if any).

Warm-Up & Exam Questions

Welcome to some questions. There are quite a few of them, but that's because they're pretty important...

Warm-Up Questions

1) What is homeostasis?
2) State three things that are controlled by homeostasis in the human body.
3) What name is given to the connection between two neurones?
4) Name the three types of neurone in a reflex arc.
5) State one factor that affects human reaction time.

Exam Questions

PRACTICAL

1   A student is taking part in an experiment to test reaction times. Every time a red triangle appears on the computer screen in front of her, she has to click the mouse.

1.1   Suggest what the stimulus, receptors and effectors are in this experiment.

[3 marks]

1.2   The student took the test three times. Her reaction time in test 1 was 328 ms. Her reaction time in test 2 was 346 ms. Her mean reaction time was 343 ms. Calculate her reaction time for test 3.

[2 marks]

2   Young babies have several reflexes not usually present in adults. For example, if an object is placed in the palm of a newborn baby's hand, the baby will move their fingers to grasp the object. The reflex arc for this reflex is shown in **Figure 1**.

Figure 1

2.1   Name the structure labelled **X** on **Figure 1**.

[1 mark]

2.2   State the type of effector in this response and describe its action.

[2 marks]

2.3   Explain how an electrical impulse in one neurone is able to pass to the next neurone.

[2 marks]

2.4   If an object is placed in the palm of a baby over 6 months old, it can choose whether it wants to grasp hold of the object. Describe **one** way in which the pathway of nervous impulses involved in grasping an object differs between a newborn baby and a baby older than 6 months.

[1 mark]

The Endocrine System

The other way to send information around the body (apart from along nerves) is by using <u>hormones</u>.

Hormones Are Chemical Messengers Sent in the Blood

1) <u>Hormones</u> are <u>chemical molecules</u> released directly into the <u>blood</u>.

2) They are carried in the blood to other parts of the body, but only affect particular cells in particular organs (called <u>target organs</u>).

3) Hormones control things in organs and cells that need <u>constant adjustment</u>.

4) Hormones are produced in (and secreted by) various <u>glands</u>, called <u>endocrine glands</u>. These glands make up your <u>endocrine system</u>.

5) Hormones tend to have relatively <u>long-lasting</u> effects.

Endocrine Glands Are Found in Different Places in The Body

PITUITARY GLAND

1) The pituitary gland produces <u>many hormones</u> that regulate <u>body conditions</u>.

2) It is sometimes called the '<u>master gland</u>' because these hormones act on <u>other glands</u>, directing them to <u>release hormones</u> that bring about <u>change</u>.

THYROID

This produces <u>thyroxine</u>, which is involved in regulating things like the <u>rate of metabolism</u>, <u>heart rate</u> and <u>temperature</u>.

ADRENAL GLAND

This produces <u>adrenaline</u>, which is used to prepare the body for a '<u>fight or flight</u>' response (see page 122).

OVARIES (females only)

Produce <u>oestrogen</u>, which is involved in the <u>menstrual cycle</u> (see page 118).

PANCREAS

This produces <u>insulin</u>, which is used to regulate the <u>blood glucose level</u> (see page 114).

TESTES (males only)

Produce <u>testosterone</u>, which controls <u>puberty</u> and <u>sperm production</u> in males (see page 117).

Comparing Nerves and Hormones

Now you know that there are <u>two</u> ways information can be sent round the body
— via the <u>nervous</u> or <u>hormonal</u> systems — here's a recap of the differences between them...

Hormones and Nerves Carry Messages in Different Ways

<u>Hormones</u> and <u>nerves</u> do similar jobs — they both <u>carry information</u> and <u>instructions</u> around the body. But there are some important <u>differences</u> between them:

Nerves

1) Very <u>FAST</u> action.

2) Act for a very <u>SHORT TIME</u>.

3) Act on a very <u>PRECISE AREA</u>.

Hormones

1) <u>SLOWER</u> action.

2) Act for a <u>LONG TIME</u>.

3) Act in a more <u>GENERAL</u> way.

If you're not sure whether a response is nervous or hormonal, have a think about the <u>speed</u> of the reaction and <u>how long it lasts</u>.

If the Response is Really Quick, It's Probably Nervous

Some information needs to be passed to effectors <u>really quickly</u> (e.g. <u>pain</u> signals, or information from your eyes telling you about the <u>lion</u> heading your way), so it's no good using hormones to carry the message — they're <u>too slow</u>.

If a Response Lasts For a Long Time, It's Probably Hormonal

For example, when you get a <u>shock</u>, a hormone called <u>adrenaline</u> is released into the body (causing the fight-or-flight response, where your body is hyped up ready for action). You can tell it's a <u>hormonal response</u> (even though it kicks in pretty quickly) because you feel a bit wobbly for a while <u>afterwards</u>.

Nerves, hormones — no wonder revision makes me tense...

Hormones control various organs and cells in the body, though they tend to control things that <u>aren't immediately life-threatening</u> (so things like <u>sexual development</u>, <u>blood sugar level</u>, <u>water content</u>, etc.).

Controlling Blood Glucose

You should remember from page 106 that homeostasis is all about maintaining a stable internal environment. Blood glucose is controlled as part of homeostasis — insulin and glucagon are the two hormones involved.

Insulin and Glucagon Control Blood Glucose Level

1) Eating foods containing carbohydrate puts glucose (a type of sugar) into the blood from the gut.
2) The normal metabolism of cells removes glucose from the blood.
3) Vigorous exercise removes much more glucose from the blood.
4) Excess glucose can be stored as glycogen in the liver and in the muscles.
5) The level of glucose in the blood must be kept steady. Changes are monitored and controlled by the pancreas, using the hormones insulin and glucagon, in a negative feedback cycle:

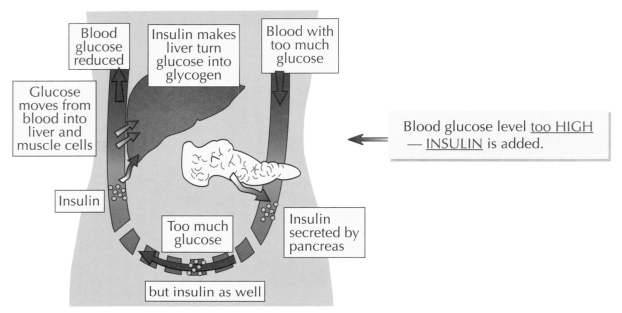

So insulin removes glucose from the blood.

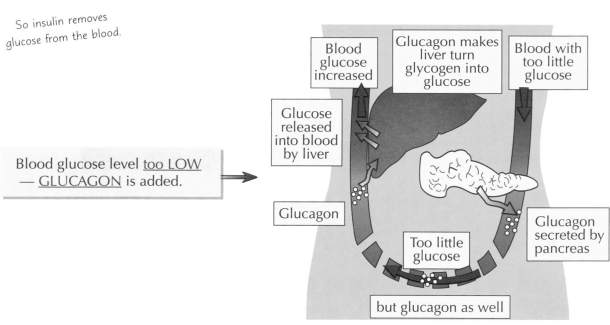

And people used to think the pancreas was just a cushion... (true)

This stuff can seem a bit confusing at first, but if you learn those two diagrams, it should get a bit easier.

Diabetes

Sometimes, homeostasis goes wrong. <u>Diabetes</u> is an example of this.

With **Diabetes**, You **Can't Control** Your **Blood Sugar Level**

<u>Diabetes</u> is a condition that affects your ability to <u>control</u> your blood sugar level. There are <u>two types</u>:

Type 1 Diabetes — **Little** or **No Insulin** is Made

1) <u>Type 1 diabetes</u> is where the <u>pancreas</u> produces <u>little</u> or <u>no insulin</u>.

2) This means a person's blood glucose level can <u>rise</u> to a level that can <u>kill them</u>.

3) People with Type 1 diabetes need <u>insulin therapy</u> — this usually involves several <u>injections</u> of insulin throughout the day, most likely at mealtimes. This makes sure that <u>glucose</u> is <u>removed</u> from the blood quickly once the food has been <u>digested</u>, stopping the level getting too high. It's a <u>very effective treatment</u>.

4) The amount of insulin that needs to be injected depends on the person's <u>diet</u> and how <u>active</u> they are.

5) As well as insulin therapy, people with Type 1 diabetes need to think about <u>limiting the intake</u> of food rich in <u>simple carbohydrates</u>, e.g. sugars (which cause the blood glucose to rise rapidly) and taking <u>regular exercise</u> (which helps to <u>remove excess glucose</u> from the blood).

Type 2 Diabetes — **Insulin Resistance**

1) <u>Type 2</u> diabetes is where a person becomes <u>resistant to their own insulin</u> (they still produce insulin, but their body's cells <u>don't respond</u> properly to the hormone).

2) This can also cause a person's <u>blood sugar level</u> to <u>rise</u> to a dangerous level.

3) Being <u>overweight</u> can <u>increase</u> your chance of <u>developing</u> Type 2 diabetes, as <u>obesity</u> is a major <u>risk factor</u> in the development of the disease.

4) Type 2 diabetes can be controlled by eating a <u>carbohydrate-controlled diet</u> and getting regular <u>exercise</u>.

Be prepared to interpret graphs in the exam

You could be asked to interpret a graph showing the <u>effects of insulin</u> on the <u>blood sugar levels</u> of <u>people with and without diabetes</u>. Don't panic — just study the graph carefully (including the <u>axes labels</u>) so you know exactly what it's showing you. Then apply your blood sugar knowledge.

Warm-Up & Exam Questions

Right then, another lot of pages down. Now there's just the small matter of answering some questions...

1) How do hormones travel to their target organs?
2) Name five endocrine glands found in the male human body.
3) What does insulin do?
4) What is Type 2 diabetes?

Exam Questions

1   **Figure 1** shows how the blood glucose level is regulated in humans. Grade 6-7

Figure 1

1.1   Identify organs A and B in **Figure 1**.

[2 marks]

1.2   Apart from organ B releasing glucose, suggest **one** reason why the blood glucose level could rise.

[1 mark]

1.3   With reference to **Figure 1**, explain what goes wrong with the regulation
of blood glucose level in people with Type 1 diabetes.

[3 marks]

1.4   Describe what the hormone glucagon does.

[1 mark]

2   Hypopituitarism is a condition in which the pituitary gland stops secreting one or more
of the pituitary hormones, or doesn't secrete enough of these hormones. People with
hypopituitarism may experience tiredness and weight gain. They may also feel the
cold more. These symptoms are all linked to low thyroid hormone levels.

Suggest and explain why someone with hypopituitarism may experience these symptoms.

[3 marks]

3   Glycogen synthase is an enzyme which helps to convert glucose into glycogen in the body.

3.1   Glycogen synthase is present in the liver.
Give **one** other location in the body where glycogen synthase is also likely to be present.

[1 mark]

3.2   Some people do not have enough functioning glycogen synthase in their liver.
When these people eat, their blood sugar level can become extremely high. Suggest why.

[3 marks]

Puberty and the Menstrual Cycle

The monthly <u>release of an egg</u> from a woman's ovaries is part of the <u>menstrual cycle</u>.

Hormones Promote Sexual Characteristics at Puberty

At <u>puberty</u>, your body starts releasing <u>sex hormones</u> that trigger off <u>secondary sexual characteristics</u> (such as the development of <u>facial hair</u> in men and <u>breasts</u> in women) and cause <u>eggs</u> to <u>mature</u> in women.

- In <u>men</u>, the main reproductive hormone is <u>testosterone</u>.
  It's produced by the <u>testes</u> and stimulates <u>sperm production</u>.

- In <u>women</u>, the main reproductive hormone is <u>oestrogen</u>. It's produced by the <u>ovaries</u>.
  As well as bringing about <u>physical changes</u>, oestrogen is also involved in the <u>menstrual cycle</u>.

The Menstrual Cycle Has Four Stages

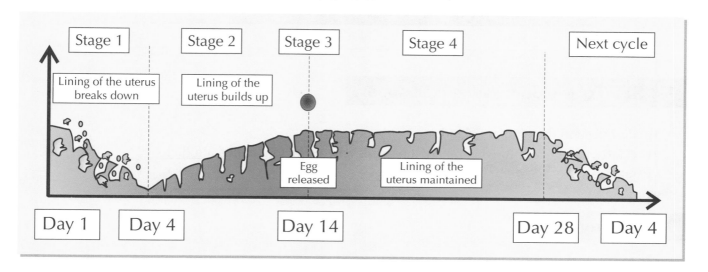

Stage 1

<u>Day 1 — menstruation starts</u>. The uterus lining breaks down for about four days.

Stage 2

<u>The uterus lining builds up again</u>, from day 4 to day 14, into a thick spongy layer full of blood vessels, ready to receive a fertilised egg.

Stage 3

<u>An egg develops and is released</u> from the ovary at day 14 — this is called <u>ovulation</u>.

Stage 4

<u>The wall is then maintained</u> for about 14 days until day 28. If no fertilised egg has landed on the uterus wall by day 28, the spongy lining starts to break down and the whole cycle starts again.

Puberty and the Menstrual Cycle

There's <u>more than one</u> hormone involved in the menstrual cycle...

The **Menstrual Cycle** is **Controlled** by **Four Hormones**

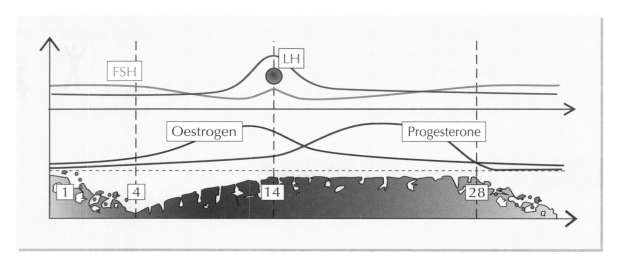

1. **FSH** (Follicle-Stimulating Hormone)

1) Produced in the <u>pituitary gland</u>.
2) Causes an <u>egg to mature</u> in one of the ovaries, in a structure called a <u>follicle</u>.
3) <u>Stimulates</u> the <u>ovaries</u> to produce <u>oestrogen</u>.

2. **Oestrogen**

1) Produced in the <u>ovaries</u>.
2) Causes the lining of the uterus to <u>grow</u>.
3) <u>Stimulates</u> the release of <u>LH</u> (which causes the release of an egg) and <u>inhibits</u> release of <u>FSH</u>.

3. **LH** (Luteinising Hormone)

1) Produced by the <u>pituitary gland</u>.
2) Stimulates the <u>release of an egg</u> at day 14 (<u>ovulation</u>).

4. **Progesterone**

1) Produced in the <u>ovaries</u> by the remains of the <u>follicle</u> after ovulation.
2) <u>Maintains</u> the lining of the uterus during the <u>second half</u> of the cycle. When the level of progesterone <u>falls</u>, the lining <u>breaks down</u>.
3) <u>Inhibits</u> the release of <u>LH</u> and <u>FSH</u>.

Examiners love a good menstrual cycle graph...

Female or not, learn this page... till you know <u>what hormone does what</u> and understand the <u>graph</u> above.

Controlling Fertility

<u>Pregnancy</u> can happen if sperm reaches the ovulated egg. <u>Contraception</u> tries to <u>stop</u> this happening.

Hormones Can Be Used to **Reduce Fertility**

1) <u>Oestrogen</u> can be used to <u>prevent</u> the <u>release</u> of an <u>egg</u> — so it can be used as a method of <u>contraception</u>.

2) This may seem kind of strange (since naturally oestrogen helps stimulate the <u>release</u> of eggs). But if oestrogen is taken <u>every day</u> to keep the level of it <u>permanently high</u>, it <u>inhibits</u> the production of <u>FSH</u>, and after a while <u>egg development</u> and <u>production stop</u> and stay stopped.

3) <u>Progesterone</u> also reduces fertility, e.g. by stimulating the production of <u>thick mucus</u> which <u>prevents</u> any <u>sperm</u> getting through and reaching an egg.

Oestrogen and **Progesterone** Can Be Taken in a **Pill**

1) <u>The pill</u> is an oral contraceptive containing <u>oestrogen</u> and <u>progesterone</u> (known as the <u>combined oral contraceptive pill</u>).

2) It's <u>over 99% effective</u> at preventing pregnancy, but it can cause <u>side effects</u> like headaches and nausea and it <u>doesn't protect</u> against <u>sexually transmitted diseases</u>.

There's also a <u>progesterone-only pill</u> — it has <u>fewer side effects</u> than the pill, and is just as effective.

Other Contraceptives Also **Contain Hormones**

Here are some examples:

1) The <u>contraceptive patch</u> contains <u>oestrogen</u> and <u>progesterone</u> (the same as the combined pill). It's a small (5 cm × 5 cm) patch that's stuck to the <u>skin</u>. Each patch lasts <u>one week</u>.

2) The <u>contraceptive implant</u> is inserted <u>under the skin</u> of the arm. It releases a <u>continuous</u> amount of <u>progesterone</u>, which stops the ovaries releasing eggs, makes it hard for sperm to swim to the egg, and stops any fertilised egg implanting in the uterus. An implant can last for <u>three years</u>.

3) The <u>contraceptive injection</u> also contains <u>progesterone</u>. Each dose lasts <u>2 to 3 months</u>.

4) An <u>intrauterine device</u> (IUD) is a <u>T-shaped</u> device that is inserted into the <u>uterus</u> to <u>kill sperm</u> and <u>prevent implantation</u> of a fertilised egg. There are <u>two</u> main types — <u>plastic</u> IUDs that release <u>progesterone</u> and <u>copper</u> IUDs that prevent the sperm <u>surviving</u> in the uterus.

So oestrogen and progesterone can be used to prevent pregnancy...

As you probably already know, hormonal contraceptives are <u>not</u> the <u>only contraceptives</u> you can use. You'll find out about non-hormonal methods on the next page — but get this lot <u>learnt</u> first.

Controlling Fertility

Not everyone wants to avoid getting pregnant — hormones can also be used to increase fertility. First up though, a bit on non-hormonal methods of contraception...

Barriers Stop Egg and Sperm Meeting

1) Non-hormonal forms of contraception are designed to stop the sperm from getting to the egg.

2) Condoms are worn over the penis during intercourse to prevent the sperm entering the vagina. There are also female condoms that are worn inside the vagina. Condoms are the only form of contraception that will protect against sexually transmitted diseases.

3) A diaphragm is a shallow plastic cup that fits over the cervix (the entrance to the uterus) to form a barrier. It has to be used with spermicide (a substance that disables or kills the sperm).

4) Spermicide can be used alone as a form of contraception, but it is not as effective (only about 70-80%).

There are More Drastic Ways to Avoid Pregnancy

1) Sterilisation — this involves cutting or tying the fallopian tubes (which connect the ovaries to the uterus) in a female, or the sperm duct (the tube between the testes and penis) in a male. This is a permanent procedure. However, there is a very small chance that the tubes can rejoin.

2) 'Natural methods' — Pregnancy may be avoided by finding out when in the menstrual cycle the woman is most fertile and avoiding sexual intercourse on those days. It's popular with people who think that hormonal and barrier methods are unnatural, but it's not very effective.

3) Abstinence — The only way to be completely sure that sperm and egg don't meet is to not have intercourse.

Hormones Can Be Used to Increase Fertility

1) Some women have levels of FSH (follicle-stimulating hormone) that are too low to cause their eggs to mature. This means that no eggs are released and the women can't get pregnant.

2) The hormones FSH and LH can be given to women as a fertility drug to stimulate ovulation.

3) The use of hormones to increase fertility has one big pro:

It helps a lot of women to get pregnant when previously they couldn't... pretty obvious.

4) There are some cons though:

1) It doesn't always work — some women may have to do it many times, which can be expensive.

2) Too many eggs could be stimulated, resulting in unexpected multiple pregnancies (twins, triplets, etc.).

The winner of best contraceptive ever — just not doing it...

You might be asked to evaluate the different hormonal and non-hormonal methods of contraception in your exam. If you do, make sure you weigh up and write about both the pros and the cons of each method.

Controlling Fertility

If the use of FSH and LH alone can't help a woman to get pregnant, <u>IVF</u> may be considered...

IVF Can Also Help Couples to Have Children

If a woman cannot get pregnant using medication, she may chose to try <u>IVF</u> ("*in vitro* fertilisation").

1) IVF involves collecting <u>eggs</u> from the woman's ovaries and fertilising them in a <u>lab</u> using the man's <u>sperm</u>.

2) IVF treatment can also involve a technique called <u>Intra-Cytoplasmic Sperm Injection (ICSI)</u>, where the sperm is <u>injected</u> directly into an egg. It's useful if the man has a very low sperm count.

3) The fertilised eggs are then grown into <u>embryos</u> in a laboratory incubator.

4) Once the embryos are <u>tiny balls of cells</u>, one or two of them are <u>transferred</u> to the woman's uterus to improve the chance of <u>pregnancy</u>.

5) <u>FSH</u> and <u>LH</u> are given before egg collection to <u>stimulate several eggs to mature</u> (so more than one egg can be collected).

6) IVF has a pretty obvious <u>benefit</u>:

> Fertility treatment can give an infertile couple <u>a child</u>.

7) But there are also <u>downsides</u> to IVF:

> 1) <u>Multiple births</u> can happen if more than one embryo grows into a baby — these are <u>risky</u> for the mother and babies (there's a higher risk of miscarriage, stillbirth...).
>
> 2) The success rate of IVF is <u>low</u> — the average success rate in the UK is about 26%. This makes the process incredibly <u>stressful</u> and often <u>upsetting</u>, especially if it ends in <u>multiple failures</u>.
>
> 3) As well as being <u>emotionally stressful</u>, the process is also <u>physically stressful</u> for the woman. Some women have a strong <u>reaction</u> to the hormones — e.g. <u>abdominal pain</u>, <u>vomiting</u>, <u>dehydration</u>.

Advances in Technology Have Improved IVF

1) Advances in <u>microscope techniques</u> have helped to improve the techniques (and therefore the <u>success rate</u>) of IVF.

2) Specialised <u>micro-tools</u> have been developed to use on the eggs and sperm under the microscope. They're also used to <u>remove</u> single cells from the embryo for <u>genetic testing</u> (to check that it is <u>healthy</u> — see page 137).

3) More recently, the development of <u>time-lapse imaging</u> (using a microscope and camera built into the incubator) means that the growth of the embryos can be <u>continuously monitored</u> to help identify those that are more likely to result in a <u>successful pregnancy</u>.

Some People Are Against IVF

1) The process of IVF often results in <u>unused</u> embryos that are eventually destroyed. Because of this, some people think it is <u>unethical</u> because each embryo is a <u>potential human life</u>.

2) The <u>genetic testing</u> of embryos before implantation also raises ethical issues as some people think it could lead to the selection of <u>preferred characteristics</u>, such as gender or eye colour.

Adrenaline and Thyroxine

You've met a lot of human hormones so far, but <u>two more</u> won't hurt...

Adrenaline Prepares You for "Fight or Flight"

1) <u>Adrenaline</u> is a hormone released by the <u>adrenal glands</u>, which are <u>just above the kidneys</u> (see p.112).

2) Adrenaline is released in response to <u>stressful or scary situations</u> — your brain detects fear or stress and sends <u>nervous impulses</u> to the adrenal glands, which respond by secreting adrenaline.

3) It gets the body ready for '<u>fight or flight</u>' by triggering mechanisms that <u>increase</u> the supply of <u>oxygen</u> and <u>glucose</u> to cells in the <u>brain</u> and <u>muscles</u>. E.g. adrenaline <u>increases heart rate</u>.

Hormone Release can be Affected by Negative Feedback

Your body can <u>control</u> the levels of hormones (and other substances) in the blood using <u>negative feedback systems</u>. When the body detects that the level of a substance has gone <u>above or below</u> the <u>normal level</u>, it <u>triggers a response</u> to bring the level <u>back to normal</u> again. Here's an example of just that:

Thyroxine Regulates Metabolism

1) <u>Thyroxine</u> is a hormone released by the <u>thyroid gland</u>, which is in the <u>neck</u> (see p.112).

2) It plays an important role in regulating the <u>basal metabolic rate</u> — the speed at which chemical reactions in the body occur while the body is at <u>rest</u>. Thyroxine is also important for loads of processes in the body, such as stimulating <u>protein synthesis</u> for <u>growth</u> and <u>development</u>.

3) Thyroxine is released in response to <u>thyroid stimulating hormone</u> (TSH), which is released from the <u>pituitary gland</u>.

4) A <u>negative feedback system</u> keeps the amount of thyroxine in the blood at the right level — when the level of thyroxine in the blood is <u>higher than normal</u>, the secretion of <u>TSH</u> from the pituitary gland is <u>inhibited</u> (stopped). This <u>reduces</u> the amount of <u>thyroxine</u> released from the thyroid gland, so the level in the blood <u>falls</u> back towards <u>normal</u>.

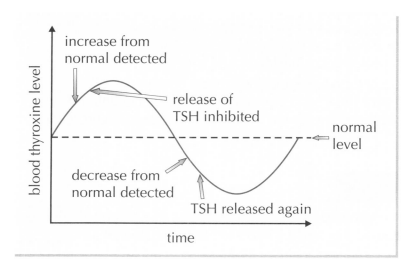

Thyroxine is made in the thyroid gland from iodine and amino acids.

Warm-Up & Exam Questions

If these questions don't get your adrenaline pumping, I don't know what will. Better get started...

Warm-Up Questions

1) Name the hormone that stimulates an egg to mature in the ovary.
2) Name three forms of contraception that reduce fertility using progesterone, not oestrogen.
3) Give one drawback to using hormones to increase fertility.
4) What is the role of FSH and LH during IVF?
5) Name the gland that releases thyroxine.

Exam Questions

1   The menstrual cycle is controlled by several different hormones.

1.1 What effect does oestrogen have on the release of FSH?

[1 mark]

1.2 Which hormone is responsible for maintaining the uterus lining?

[1 mark]

1.3 On what day of the menstrual cycle is the egg released?

[1 mark]

2   The combined oral contraceptive pill contains oestrogen and progesterone.

2.1 Explain how taking oestrogen can prevent pregnancy.

[2 marks]

2.2 Progesterone can prevent pregnancy by preventing ovulation.
         Explain **one** other way in which taking progesterone can prevent pregnancy.

[2 marks]

The combined pill is taken once a day in a '21 day pill, 7 day no pill' cycle. One of the problems with the combined pill is that women may forget to take it on the days they are supposed to.

2.3 Suggest an alternative method of hormonal contraception that may be more suitable for a woman who is worried about remembering to take the combined pill. Explain your choice.

[2 marks]

2.4 A couple in their late 30s who have already had three children are looking for a more permanent method of contraception. Suggest **one** method of contraception that may be suitable for them.

[1 mark]

3   A dog suddenly runs towards a cat across the street, which frightens the cat.

Explain what would happen to the cat's heart rate when it sees the dog and explain why this response is beneficial.

[5 marks]

124

Revision Summary for Topic 5

Congratulations, you've made it to the end of Topic 5 — now for some questions to make sure you've been paying attention...

- Try these questions and tick off each one when you get it right.
- When you've done all the questions under a heading and are completely happy with it, tick it off.

Homeostasis and the Nervous System (p.106-110) ☑

1) What is a stimulus? ☐
2) Explain how negative feedback helps to maintain a stable internal environment. ☐
3) What makes up the central nervous system and what does it do? ☐
4) What is a synapse? ☐
5) What is the purpose of a reflex action? ☐
6) What is a reaction time? ☐

Hormones in Humans (p.112-122) ☑

7) What is a hormone? ☐
8) Give two differences between nervous and hormonal responses. ☐
9) Where is excess glucose stored in the body? ☐
10) What effect does the hormone glucagon have on blood glucose level? ☐
11) What is the difference between how Type 1 and Type 2 diabetes are usually controlled? ☐
12) Draw a timeline of the 28 day menstrual cycle.
Label the four stages of the cycle and label when the egg is released. ☐
13) Describe two effects of FSH on the body. ☐
14) Which of the following is a hormonal contraceptive — condom, plastic IUD or diaphragm? ☐
15) Briefly describe how IVF is carried out. ☐
16) What is the role of thyroxine in the body? ☐

DNA

The first step in understanding <u>genetics</u> is getting to grips with <u>DNA</u>.

Chromosomes Are Really Long Molecules of DNA

1) <u>DNA</u> stands for <u>deoxyribonucleic acid</u>. It's the <u>chemical</u> that all of the <u>genetic material</u> in a cell is <u>made</u> up from.

2) It contains <u>coded information</u> — basically all the <u>instructions</u> to put an organism together and <u>make it work</u>.

3) So it's <u>what's in your DNA</u> that determines <u>what inherited characteristics</u> you have.

4) DNA is found in the <u>nucleus</u> of animal and plant cells, in really long structures called <u>chromosomes</u>.

5) <u>Chromosomes</u> normally come in <u>pairs</u>.

6) DNA is a <u>polymer</u>. It's made up of <u>two strands</u> coiled together in the shape of a <u>double helix</u>.

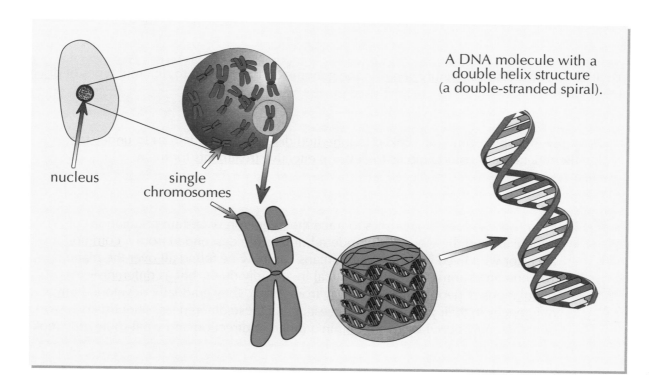

A DNA molecule with a double helix structure (a double-stranded spiral).

nucleus

single chromosomes

Every living organism has DNA

Remember, DNA contains all the <u>instructions</u> to 'build' an organism. The instructions are <u>different</u> for each type of organism on Earth (otherwise all living things would be the same). There's a lot more about <u>DNA</u> and <u>chromosomes</u> coming up in this topic so make sure you understand this page before you move on.

DNA

DNA determines what characteristics an organism has — it's a very important molecule. It's not surprising then that scientists are super keen on understanding more about it.

A Gene Codes for a Specific Protein

1) A gene is a small section of DNA found on a chromosome.
2) Each gene codes for (tells the cells to make) a particular sequence of amino acids which are put together to make a specific protein.
3) Only 20 amino acids are used, but they make up thousands of different proteins.
4) Genes simply tell cells in what order to put the amino acids together.
5) DNA also determines what proteins the cell produces, e.g. haemoglobin, keratin.
6) That in turn determines what type of cell it is, e.g. red blood cell, skin cell.

Every Organism Has a Genome

1) Genome is just the fancy term for the entire set of genetic material in an organism.
2) Scientists have worked out the complete human genome.
3) Understanding the human genome is a really important tool for science and medicine for many reasons.

1) It allows scientists to identify genes in the genome that are linked to different types of disease.

2) Knowing which genes are linked to inherited diseases could help us to understand them better and could help us to develop effective treatments for them.

3) Scientists can look at genomes to trace the migration of certain populations of people around the world. All modern humans are descended from a common ancestor who lived in Africa, but humans can now be found all over the planet. The human genome is mostly identical in all individuals, but as different populations of people migrated away from Africa, they gradually developed tiny differences in their genomes. By investigating these differences, scientists can work out when new populations split off in a different direction and what route they took.

Your genes make you different from everyone else

Working out the human genome was a massive project — it involved scientists from many different parts of the world and took more than ten years to complete. Still, if scientists can use the information to help us understand more about diseases and how to fight them, then I reckon it was well worth all the effort.

Topic 6 — Inheritance, Variation and Evolution

Reproduction

Reproduction is important for all species. It can happen in <u>two</u> different ways...

Sexual Reproduction Produces Genetically Different Cells

1) <u>Sexual reproduction</u> is where genetic information from <u>two</u> organisms (a <u>father</u> and a <u>mother</u>) is combined to produce offspring which are <u>genetically different</u> to either parent.

2) In sexual reproduction, the mother and father produce <u>gametes</u> (sex cells) by <u>meiosis</u> (see next page) — e.g. <u>egg</u> and <u>sperm</u> cells in animals.

3) In humans, each gamete contains <u>23 chromosomes</u> — <u>half</u> the number of chromosomes in a normal cell. (Instead of having <u>two</u> of each chromosome, a <u>gamete</u> has just <u>one</u> of each.)

4) The <u>egg</u> (from the mother) and the <u>sperm</u> cell (from the father) then <u>fuse together</u> (fertilisation) to form a cell with the <u>full number</u> of chromosomes (<u>half from the father</u>, <u>half from the mother</u>).

> <u>SEXUAL REPRODUCTION</u> involves the fusion of male and female gametes.
> Because there are <u>TWO</u> parents, the offspring contain <u>a mixture of their parents' genes</u>.

5) This is why the offspring <u>inherits features</u> from <u>both parents</u> — it's received a <u>mixture</u> of chromosomes from its mum and its dad (and it's the chromosomes that decide how you turn out).

6) This <u>mixture of genetic information</u> produces <u>variation</u> in the offspring.

7) <u>Flowering plants</u> can reproduce in this way <u>too</u>. They also have <u>egg cells</u>, but their version of sperm is known as pollen.

Asexual Reproduction Produces Genetically Identical Cells

1) In <u>asexual reproduction</u> there's only <u>one parent</u> so the offspring are <u>genetically identical</u> to that parent.

2) Asexual reproduction happens by <u>mitosis</u> — an <u>ordinary cell</u> makes a new cell by <u>dividing in two</u> (see page 27).

3) The <u>new cell</u> has <u>exactly the same</u> genetic information (i.e. genes) as the parent cell — it's called a <u>clone</u>.

> In <u>ASEXUAL REPRODUCTION</u> there's only <u>ONE</u> parent. There's <u>no fusion</u> of gametes, <u>no mixing</u> of chromosomes and <u>no genetic variation</u> between parent and offspring. The offspring are <u>genetically identical</u> to the parent — they're <u>clones</u>.

4) <u>Bacteria</u>, <u>some plants</u> and <u>some animals</u> reproduce <u>asexually</u>.

You might need to reproduce these facts in the exam...

The main messages on this page are that: 1) <u>sexual</u> reproduction needs <u>two</u> parents and forms cells that are <u>genetically different</u> to the parents, so there's lots of genetic variation. And 2) <u>asexual</u> reproduction needs just <u>one</u> parent to make <u>genetically identical</u> cells, so there's no genetic variation in the offspring.

Meiosis

If you're wondering how gametes end up with half the number of chromosomes of a normal cell, read on...

Gametes Are Produced by Meiosis

1) As you know from the previous page, gametes only have one copy of each chromosome, so that when gamete fusion takes place, you get the right amount of chromosomes again (two copies of each).

2) To make gametes which only have half the original number of chromosomes, cells divide by meiosis. This process involves two cell divisions. In humans, it only happens in the reproductive organs (the ovaries in females and testes in males).

Meiosis Produces Cells Which Have Half the Normal Number of Chromosomes

Before the cell starts to divide, it duplicates its genetic information, forming two armed chromosomes — one arm of each chromosome is an exact copy of the other arm. After replication, the chromosomes arrange themselves into pairs.

The genetic information is stored in DNA — see p.125.

In the first division in meiosis the chromosome pairs line up in the centre of the cell.

The pairs are then pulled apart so each new cell only has one copy of each chromosome. Some of the father's chromosomes (shown in blue) and some of the mother's chromosomes (shown in red) go into each new cell.

In the second division, the chromosomes line up again in the centre of the cell. The arms of the chromosomes are pulled apart.

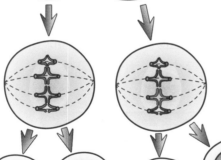

You get four gametes, each with only a single set of chromosomes in it. Each of the gametes is genetically different from the others because the chromosomes all get shuffled up during meiosis and each gamete only gets half of them, at random.

The Cell Produced by Gamete Fusion Replicates Itself

1) After two gametes have fused during fertilisation, the resulting new cell divides by mitosis to make a copy of itself.

There's loads on mitosis on page 27.

2) Mitosis repeats many times to produce lots of new cells in an embryo.

3) As the embryo develops, these cells then start to differentiate (see page 22) into the different types of specialised cell that make up a whole organism.

Now that I have your undivided attention...

Remember, in humans, meiosis only occurs in reproductive organs where gametes are being made.

X and Y Chromosomes

Now for a couple of <u>very important</u> little chromosomes...

Your **Chromosomes** Control Whether You're **Male** or **Female**

1) There are <u>23 pairs</u> of chromosomes in every human body cell (page 26).
2) Of these, <u>22</u> are <u>matched pairs</u> of chromosomes that just control <u>characteristics</u>.
3) The <u>23rd pair</u> are labelled <u>XX</u> or <u>XY</u>.
4) They're the two chromosomes that <u>decide</u> your <u>sex</u> — whether you turn out <u>male</u> or <u>female</u>.

> <u>Males</u> have an <u>X</u> and a <u>Y</u> chromosome: XY
> The <u>Y chromosome</u> causes <u>male characteristics</u>.

> <u>Females</u> have <u>two X chromosomes</u>:   XX
> The <u>XX combination</u> allows
> <u>female characteristics</u> to develop.

X-chromosome   Y-chromosome

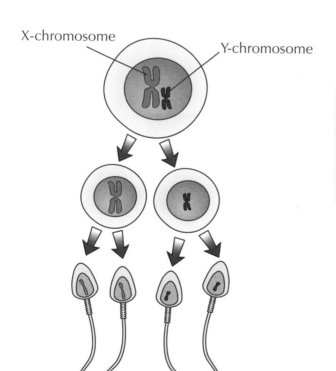

> When making sperm, the X and Y chromosomes are drawn apart in the first division in meiosis. There's a <u>50% chance</u> each sperm cell gets an <u>X chromosome</u> and a <u>50% chance</u> it gets a <u>Y chromosome</u>.

> A similar thing happens when making eggs. But the original cell has two X-chromosomes, so all the eggs have one X-chromosome.

The Y chromosome is physically smaller than the X chromosome

It's possible for people to have one X and two Y chromosomes, or even three X chromosomes, in their cells. But you just need to remember that <u>XX</u> gives female characteristics and <u>XY</u> gives male characteristics.

X and Y Chromosomes

You can work out the <u>probability</u> of offspring being male or female by using a <u>genetic diagram</u>.

Genetic Diagrams Show the Possible Combinations of Gametes

1) To find the <u>probability</u> of getting a boy or a girl, you can draw a <u>genetic diagram</u>.

2) Genetic diagrams are just <u>models</u> that are used to show all the possible genetic <u>outcomes</u> when you <u>cross together</u> different genes or chromosomes.

3) Put the <u>possible gametes</u> (eggs or sperm) from <u>one</u> parent down the side, and those from the <u>other</u> parent along the top.

4) Then in each middle square you <u>fill in</u> the letters from the top and side that line up with that square. The <u>pairs of letters</u> in the middle show the possible combinations of the gametes.

5) There are <u>two XX results</u> and <u>two XY results</u>, so there's the same probability of getting a boy or a girl.

6) Don't forget that this <u>50:50 ratio</u> is only a <u>probability</u> at each pregnancy.

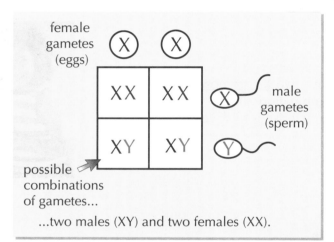

...two males (XY) and two females (XX).

This type of genetic diagram is called a Punnett square.

There's More Than One Type of Genetic Diagram

The other type of genetic diagram looks a bit more complicated, but it shows exactly the same thing.

1) At the top are the <u>parents</u>.

2) The middle circles show the <u>possible gametes</u> that are formed. One gamete from the female combines with one gamete from the male (during fertilisation).

3) The criss-cross lines show <u>all</u> the <u>possible</u> ways the X and Y chromosomes <u>could</u> combine. The <u>possible combinations</u> of the offspring are shown in the bottom circles.

4) Remember, only <u>one</u> of these possibilities would <u>actually happen</u> for any one offspring.

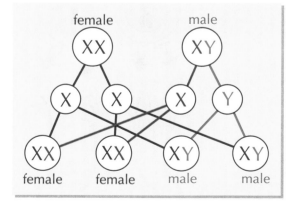

These diagrams aren't as scary as they look...

Most genetic diagrams you'll see in exams concentrate on a <u>gene</u>, instead of a <u>chromosome</u>. But the principle's the same. Don't worry — there are loads of other examples on pages 133-136.

Warm-Up & Exam Questions

It's time to see how much you picked up about meiosis, reproduction and sex chromosomes...

Warm-Up Questions

1) What is a gene?
2) Suggest why there is variation in the offspring of sexual reproduction.
3) How many cell divisions take place in meiosis?
4) What combination of sex chromosomes do human females have?

Exam Questions

1 An organism's genetic material is made up of a chemical called DNA. (Grade 4-6)

1.1 Which of the following describes the structure of DNA? Tick **one** box.

☐ A protein made up of two strands. ☐ A polymer made up of two strands.

☐ A protein made up of four strands. ☐ A polymer made up of four strands.

[1 mark]

1.2 Which of the following contains the largest amount of an organism's DNA? Tick **one** box.

☐ A gene ☐ Its genome ☐ A chromosome

[1 mark]

1.3 Explain the relationship between DNA and the proteins produced by an organism.

[3 marks]

2 Some species of worm can produce offspring through a process called fragmentation. In this process, fragments of the parent's body break off and undergo cell division by mitosis to develop into mature, complete organisms. (Grade 4-6)

2.1 What term is used to describe this form of reproduction?

[1 mark]

2.2 Suggest how the chromosomes in the offspring will compare to those of the parent worm.

[1 mark]

3 Mosquitoes have three pairs of chromosomes in their body cells. **Figure 1** shows a mosquito cell which is about to divide by meiosis. (Grade 6-7)

Figure 1

3.1 The cell in **Figure 1** undergoes meiosis. State how many chromosomes will be present in each new cell produced.

[1 mark]

3.2 How many cells will be produced in total when the cell in **Figure 1** undergoes meiosis?

[1 mark]

3.3 Explain how the processes of meiosis and fertilisation lead to genetic variation in the mosquito's offspring.

[3 marks]

Genetic Diagrams

For those of you expecting to see a <u>diagram</u> or two on a page called 'Genetic Diagrams', prepare to be disappointed. You need to understand a bit more about what genetic diagrams <u>show</u> to start with...

Some **Characteristics** are **Controlled** by **Single Genes**

1) What <u>genes</u> you <u>inherit</u> control what <u>characteristics</u> you <u>develop</u>.

2) <u>Different</u> genes control <u>different</u> characteristics. <u>Some</u> characteristics are controlled by a <u>single</u> gene, e.g. <u>mouse fur colour</u> and <u>red-green colour blindness</u> in humans.

3) However, most characteristics are controlled by <u>several genes interacting</u>.

4) All genes exist in different <u>versions</u> called <u>alleles</u> (which are represented by <u>letters</u> in genetic diagrams).

5) You have <u>two</u> versions (alleles) of <u>every gene</u> in your body — <u>one</u> on <u>each chromosome</u> in a pair.

6) If an organism has <u>two alleles</u> for a particular gene that are <u>the same</u>, then it's <u>homozygous</u> for that trait. If its two alleles for a particular gene are <u>different</u>, then it's <u>heterozygous</u>.

7) If the two alleles are <u>different</u>, only one can determine what <u>characteristic</u> is present. The allele for the <u>characteristic that's shown</u> is called the <u>dominant</u> allele (use a capital letter for dominant alleles — e.g. 'C'). The other one is called <u>recessive</u> (and you show these with small letters — e.g. 'c').

8) For an organism to display a <u>recessive</u> characteristic, <u>both</u> its alleles must be <u>recessive</u> (e.g. cc). But to display a <u>dominant</u> characteristic the organism can be <u>either</u> CC or Cc, because the dominant allele <u>overrules</u> the recessive one if the plant/animal/other organism is heterozygous.

9) Your <u>genotype</u> is the combination of <u>alleles</u> you have. Your alleles work at a molecular level to determine what characteristics you have — your <u>phenotype</u>.

There are lots of fancy words to learn on this page...

Make sure you fully understand what all the <u>different terms</u> on this page mean (i.e. genes, alleles, homozygous, heterozygous, dominant, recessive, genotype and phenotype). You'll feel much more comfortable going into the exam knowing that these words aren't going to trip you up.

Genetic Diagrams

Genetic Diagrams Show the **Possible Alleles** of **Offspring**

Suppose you start breeding <u>hamsters</u> with <u>superpowers</u>. The allele which causes hamsters to have superpowers is <u>recessive</u> ("b"), whilst <u>normal</u> (boring) behaviour is due to a <u>dominant</u> allele ("B").

1) A <u>superpowered</u> hamster <u>must</u> have the <u>genotype bb</u>. But a <u>normal</u> hamster could be <u>BB or Bb</u>.

2) Here's what happens if you breed from two <u>homozygous</u> hamsters:

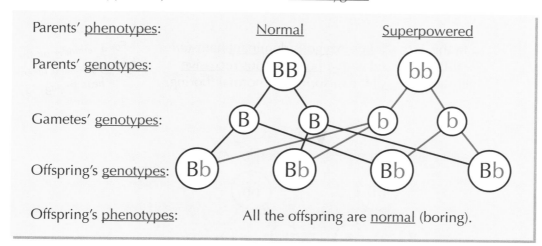

genotype = BB or Bb, phenotype = normal

When you cross two parents to look at just one characteristic, it's called a monohybrid cross.

3) If two of these <u>offspring</u> now <u>breed</u>, you'll get the next generation:

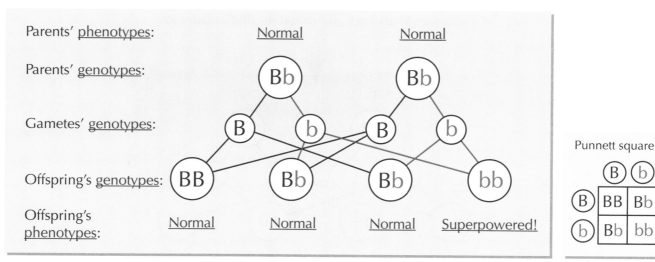

4) That's a <u>3:1 ratio</u> of normal to superpowered offspring in this generation (a <u>1 in 4</u> or <u>25%</u> probability of superpowers).

But remember — genetic diagrams only tell you probabilities. They don't say definitely what'll happen.

Genetic diagrams aren't that scary — you just need to practise them...

You should know how to <u>produce</u> and <u>interpret</u> both of these types of genetic diagram before exam day.

More Genetic Diagrams

In the exam, you could be asked to <u>predict</u> and <u>explain</u> the outcomes of crosses between individuals for each <u>possible combination</u> of <u>dominant</u> and <u>recessive alleles</u> of a gene. You should be able to draw a <u>genetic diagram</u> and <u>work it out</u> — but it'll be easier if you've seen them all before. So here are some more examples.

All the Offspring are Normal

Let's take another look at the <u>superpowered hamster</u> example from page 133:

In this cross, a <u>homozygous dominant</u> hamster (BB) is crossed with a <u>homozygous recessive</u> hamster (bb). <u>All</u> the offspring are normal (boring).

For a reminder on the terms homozygous and heterozygous, head to page 132.

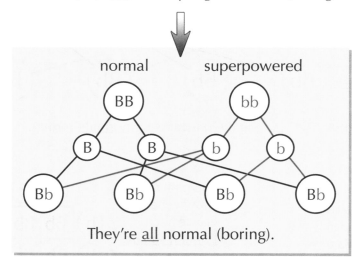

They're <u>all</u> normal (boring).

But, if you crossed a <u>homozygous dominant</u> hamster (BB) with a <u>heterozygous</u> hamster (Bb), you would also get <u>all</u> normal (boring) offspring.

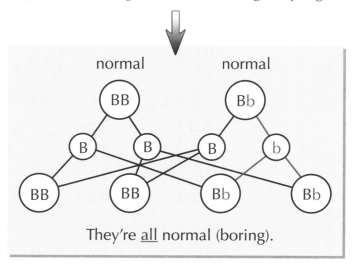

They're <u>all</u> normal (boring).

To find out <u>which</u> it was you'd have to <u>breed the offspring together</u> and see what kind of <u>ratio</u> you got that time — then you'd have a good idea. If it was <u>3:1</u>, it's likely that you originally had BB and bb.

More Genetic Diagrams

One more example of a genetic cross diagram coming up on this page.
Then a little bit about another type of genetic diagram called a <u>family tree</u>...

There's a **1:1 Ratio** in the Offspring

1) A cat with <u>long hair</u> was bred with another cat with <u>short hair</u>.

2) The long hair is caused by a <u>dominant</u> allele 'H', and the short hair by a <u>recessive</u> allele 'h'.

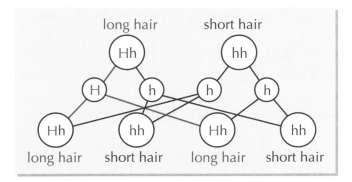

3) The cats had 8 kittens — 4 with long hair and 4 with short hair.

4) This is a <u>1:1</u> ratio — it's what you'd expect when a parent with only <u>one dominant allele</u> (heterozygous — Hh) is crossed with a parent with <u>two recessive alleles</u> (homozygous recessive — hh).

Family Trees Can Show How Characteristics Are **Inherited**

1) Knowing how inheritance works can help you to interpret a <u>family tree</u> — this is one for <u>cystic fibrosis</u> (p.136).

2) From the family tree, you can tell that the allele for cystic fibrosis <u>isn't</u> dominant because plenty of the family <u>carry</u> the allele but <u>don't</u> have the disorder.

3) There is a <u>25%</u> chance that the new baby will have the disorder and a <u>50%</u> chance that it will be a carrier, as both of its parents are carriers but are unaffected. The case of the new baby is just the same as in the genetic diagram on page 136 — so the baby could be <u>unaffected</u> (FF), a <u>carrier</u> (Ff) or <u>have</u> cystic fibrosis (ff).

It's enough to make you go cross-eyed...

In the exam, you might get a family tree showing the inheritance of a <u>dominant</u> allele — in this case, there <u>won't be any carriers</u> shown. If you're struggling to work out a family tree in the exam, try writing the <u>genotype</u> of each person onto it — it might help you to interpret it more easily.

Inherited Disorders

Some disorders can be <u>inherited</u> from your parents. Many of these can be <u>screened</u> for in embryos.

Cystic Fibrosis is Caused by a Recessive Allele

<u>Cystic fibrosis</u> is a <u>genetic disorder</u> of the <u>cell membranes</u>. It <u>results</u> in the body producing a lot of thick sticky <u>mucus</u> in the <u>air passages</u> and in the <u>pancreas</u>.

1) The allele which causes cystic fibrosis is a <u>recessive allele</u>, 'f', carried by about <u>1 person in 25</u>.
2) Because it's recessive, people with only <u>one copy</u> of the allele <u>won't</u> have the disorder — they're known as <u>carriers</u>.
3) For a child to have the disorder, <u>both parents</u> must be either <u>carriers</u> or have the disorder <u>themselves</u>.
4) As the diagram shows, there's a <u>1 in 4 chance</u> of a child having the disorder if <u>both</u> parents are <u>carriers</u>.

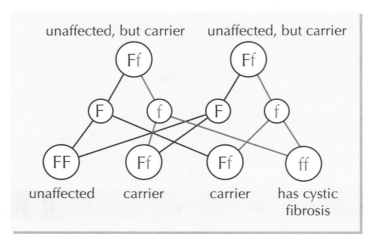

Polydactyly is Caused by a Dominant Allele

<u>Polydactyly</u> is a <u>genetic disorder</u> where a baby's born with <u>extra fingers or toes</u>. It doesn't usually cause any other problems so <u>isn't life-threatening</u>.

1) The disorder is caused by a <u>dominant allele</u>, 'D', and so can be inherited if just <u>one parent</u> carries the defective allele.
2) The <u>parent</u> that <u>has</u> the defective allele <u>will have</u> the condition too since the allele is dominant.
3) As the genetic diagram shows, there's a <u>50% chance</u> of a child having the disorder if <u>one</u> parent has <u>one</u> D allele.

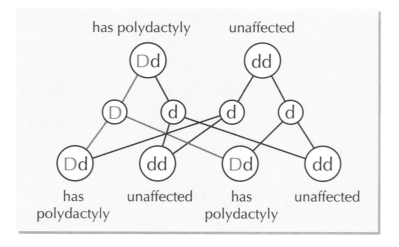

Inherited Disorders

Embryos Can Be Screened for Genetic Disorders

1) During *in vitro* fertilisation (IVF), embryos are fertilised in a laboratory, and then implanted into the mother's womb.

2) Before being implanted, it's possible to remove a cell from each embryo and analyse its genes.

3) Many genetic disorders can be detected in this way, such as cystic fibrosis.

4) It's also possible to get DNA from an embryo in the womb and test that for disorders.

5) There are lots of ethical, social and economic concerns surrounding embryo screening.

6) Embryonic screening is quite controversial because of the decisions it can lead to.

7) For embryos produced by IVF — after screening, embryos with 'bad' alleles would be destroyed.

8) For embryos in the womb — screening could lead to the decision to terminate the pregnancy.

9) Here are some more arguments for and against screening:

For Embryonic Screening

1) It will help to stop people suffering.

2) Treating disorders costs the Government (and the taxpayers) a lot of money.

3) There are laws to stop it going too far. At the moment parents cannot even select the sex of their baby (unless it's for health reasons).

Against Embryonic Screening

1) It implies that people with genetic problems are 'undesirable' — this could increase prejudice.

2) There may come a point where everyone wants to screen their embryos so they can pick the most 'desirable' one, e.g. they want a blue-eyed, blond-haired, intelligent boy.

3) Screening is expensive.

Embryo screening — it's a tricky one...

It's great to think that we might be able to stop people from having inherited disorders that cause suffering, but there are many concerns to think about too. Try writing a balanced argument for and against embryo screening — it's good practice.

Warm-Up & Exam Questions

There's no better preparation for exam questions than doing... err... practice exam questions. Hang on, what's this I see...

Warm-Up Questions

1) What are alleles?
2) What does genotype mean?
3) Why won't someone heterozygous for the cystic fibrosis allele have the disorder?
4) What is polydactyly?
5) Outline what embryo screening involves.

Exam Questions

1   Cystic fibrosis is a genetic disorder caused by recessive alleles.

F = the normal allele   **f** = the faulty allele that leads to cystic fibrosis

Figure 1 is an incomplete Punnett square showing the possible inheritance of cystic fibrosis from one couple.

Figure 1

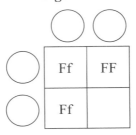

1.1   Complete the Punnett square to show the missing offspring's genotype and the genotypes of the gametes.

[2 marks]

1.2   What proportion of the possible offspring are homozygous?

[1 mark]

1.3   State the phenotypes of the parents.

[2 marks]

2   Fruit flies usually have red eyes. However, there are a small number of white-eyed fruit flies. Having white eyes is a recessive characteristic.

Two fruit flies with red eyes have the heterozygous genotype for this characteristic. They are crossed to produce offspring.

2.1   Draw a genetic diagram to show the possible phenotypes of the offspring.

Use **R** to represent the dominant allele and **r** to represent the recessive allele.

[3 marks]

2.2   State the probability that one of the fruit flies' offspring will have white eyes.

[1 mark]

Exam Questions

3 Polydactyly is a genetic disorder transmitted by the dominant allele **D**. The corresponding recessive allele is **d**. **Figure 2** shows the family pedigree of a family with a history of polydactyly.

Figure 2

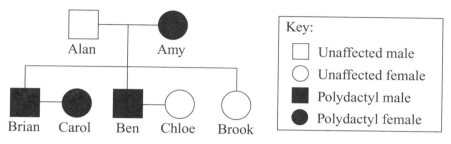

Using the information given above, state what Amy's genotype must be. Explain your answer.

[2 marks]

4 Colour blindness in humans is caused by a recessive allele located on the X chromosome. It is more common in men because men carry only one X chromosome.

A man who is colour blind has a child with a woman who does not have the recessive allele.

4.1 Draw a genetic diagram to show the possible sex of the offspring.

[3 marks]

4.2 The child is a boy. Explain why the boy will not be colour blind.

[1 mark]

4.3 State the probability that a daughter of this couple would be colour blind.

[1 mark]

5 Albinism is a condition characterised by the lack of pigment in the hair and skin. It is caused by the recessive allele **a**. The dominant allele **A** results in normal pigmentation.

5.1 State the possible genotypes of a rabbit that shows no symptoms of albinism.

[1 mark]

A rabbit with albinism mated with a rabbit that showed no symptoms of the condition. 56% of the offspring had albinism.

5.2 Deduce the genotypes of the parent rabbits and the possible genotypes of their offspring. Use a genetic diagram to explain your answer.

[3 marks]

5.3 From your genetic diagram, what percentage of offspring are likely to have albinism?

[1 mark]

5.4 Explain why the percentage of offspring which were born with albinism was not the same as that suggested by your genetic diagram.

[1 mark]

Topic 6 — Inheritance, Variation and Evolution

Variation

You'll probably have noticed that not all people are identical. There are reasons for this.

Organisms of the Same Species Have Differences

1) Different species look... well... different — my dog definitely doesn't look like a daisy.

2) But even organisms of the same species will usually look at least slightly different — e.g. in a room full of people you'll see different colour hair, individually shaped noses, a variety of heights, etc.

3) These differences are called the variation within a species.

4) Variation can be huge within a population.

5) There are two types of variation — genetic variation and environmental variation.

Different Genes Cause Genetic Variation

1) Variation can be genetic — this means it's caused by differences in genotype.

2) Genotype is all of the genes and alleles that an organism has.

3) An organism's genotype affects its phenotype — the characteristics that it displays.

4) An organism's genes are inherited (passed down) from its parents (see page 127).

Characteristics are also Influenced by the Environment

1) It's not only genotype that can affect an organism's phenotype — interactions with its environment (conditions in which it lives) can also influence phenotype.

2) For example:

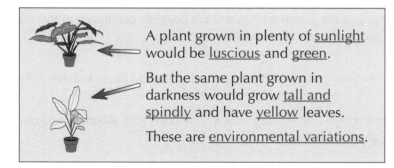

A plant grown in plenty of sunlight would be luscious and green.

But the same plant grown in darkness would grow tall and spindly and have yellow leaves.

These are environmental variations.

Variation

Most Characteristics are Due to Genes AND the Environment

1) Most variation in phenotype is determined by a <u>mixture</u> of <u>genetic</u> and <u>environmental</u> factors.

2) For example, the <u>maximum height</u> that an animal or plant could grow to is determined by its <u>genes</u>. But whether it actually grows that tall depends on its <u>environment</u> (e.g. how much food it gets).

Mutations are Changes to the Genome

1) <u>Occasionally</u>, a gene may <u>mutate</u>. A mutation is a <u>rare</u>, <u>random change</u> in an organism's <u>DNA</u> that can be <u>inherited</u>. Mutations occur <u>continuously</u>.

2) Mutations mean that the gene is <u>altered</u>, which produces a <u>genetic variant</u> (a different form of the gene).

Alleles (see page 132) are genetic variants.

3) As the gene <u>codes</u> for the <u>sequence of amino acids</u> that make up a <u>protein</u>, <u>gene mutations</u> sometimes lead to <u>changes</u> in the <u>protein</u> that it codes for.

4) Most <u>genetic variants</u> have <u>very little</u> or <u>no effect</u> on the <u>protein</u> the gene codes for. Some will change it to such a small extent that its <u>function is unaffected</u>. This means that most mutations have <u>no effect</u> on an organism's <u>phenotype</u>.

5) <u>Some</u> variants have a <u>small influence</u> on the organism's <u>phenotype</u> — they alter the individual's characteristics but only slightly. For example:

> Some characteristics, e.g. eye colour, are controlled by <u>more than one gene</u>. A mutation in <u>one</u> of the genes may <u>change</u> the <u>eye colour</u> a bit, but the difference might not be huge.

6) Very <u>occasionally</u>, variants can have such a <u>dramatic effect</u> that they <u>determine phenotype</u>. For example:

> The genetic disorder, <u>cystic fibrosis</u>, is caused by a mutation that has a <u>huge</u> effect on <u>phenotype</u>. The gene codes for a <u>protein</u> that controls the <u>movement</u> of salt and water into and out of cells. However, the protein produced by the <u>mutated gene</u> doesn't work properly. This leads to <u>excess mucus production</u> in the lungs and digestive system, which can make it difficult to <u>breathe</u> and to <u>digest food</u>.

7) If the <u>environment changes</u>, and the new phenotype makes an <u>individual more suited</u> to the new environment, it can become common <u>throughout</u> the species <u>relatively quickly</u> by natural selection — see the next page.

You can't blame all of your faults on your parents...

Although the <u>genes</u> that you <u>inherit</u> from your parents are really important at determining what <u>characteristics</u> you have, the <u>conditions</u> in which you live usually <u>play a role too</u>.

Evolution

Evolution is very important. Without it we wouldn't have the great variety of life we have on Earth today.

> THEORY OF EVOLUTION: All of today's species have evolved from simple life forms that first started to develop over three billion years ago.

Only the **Fittest Survive**

Charles Darwin came up with a really important theory about evolution, called evolution by natural selection.

1) Darwin knew that organisms in a species show wide variation in their characteristics (phenotypic variation). He also knew that organisms have to compete for limited resources in an ecosystem.

2) Darwin concluded that the organisms with the most suitable characteristics for the environment would be more successful competitors and would be more likely to survive. This idea is called the 'survival of the fittest'.

3) The successful organisms that survive are more likely to reproduce and pass on the genes for the characteristics that made them successful to their offspring.

4) The organisms that are less well adapted would be less likely to survive and reproduce, so they are less likely to pass on their genes to the next generation.

5) Over time, beneficial characteristics become more common in the population and the species changes — it evolves.

New Discoveries Have Helped to **Develop** the Theory

1) Darwin's theory wasn't perfect. Because the relevant scientific knowledge wasn't available at the time, he couldn't give a good explanation for why new characteristics appeared or exactly how individual organisms passed on beneficial adaptations to their offspring.

2) However, the discovery of genetics supported Darwin's idea — it provided an explanation of how organisms born with beneficial characteristics can pass them on (i.e. via their genes) and showed that it is genetic variants (see page 141) that give rise to phenotypes that are suited to the environment.

3) Other evidence was also found by looking at fossils of different ages (the fossil record) — this allows you to see how changes in organisms developed slowly over time.

4) The relatively recent discovery of how bacteria are able to evolve to become resistant to antibiotics also further supports evolution by natural selection.

5) The theory of evolution by natural selection is now widely accepted.

Natural selection — the fittest pass on their genes...

Natural selection's all about the organisms with the best characteristics surviving to pass on their genes so that the whole species ends up adapted to its environment. It doesn't happen overnight though.

Evolution

Species need to <u>continue evolving</u> in order to <u>survive</u>. Sometimes this evolution creates a whole <u>new species</u>, but if a species can't evolve fast enough it might <u>die out</u> completely.

The Development of a **New Species** is Called **Speciation**

1) Over a long period of time, the phenotype of organisms can change <u>so much</u> because of natural selection that a completely <u>new species</u> is formed. This is called <u>speciation</u>.

2) Speciation happens when populations of the same species change enough to become <u>reproductively isolated</u> — this means that they <u>can't interbreed</u> to produce <u>fertile offspring</u>.

Extinction is When **No Individuals** of a Species **Remain**

The fossil record contains many species that <u>don't exist any more</u> — these species are said to be <u>extinct</u>. Species become extinct for these reasons:

1) The <u>environment changes</u> too quickly (e.g. destruction of habitat).

2) A <u>new predator</u> kills them all (e.g. humans hunting them).

3) A <u>new disease</u> kills them all.

4) They can't <u>compete</u> with another (new) species for <u>food</u>.

5) A <u>catastrophic event</u> happens that kills them all (e.g. a volcanic eruption or a collision with an asteroid).

Example — Dodos

1) <u>Dodos</u> are now extinct.

2) Humans not only <u>hunted</u> them, but introduced <u>other animals</u> which ate all their eggs, and we <u>destroyed</u> the forest where they <u>lived</u> — they really didn't stand a chance...

Evolution's happening all the time...

Many species evolve so <u>slowly</u> that there are <u>no significant changes</u> in them within our lifetime. However, some species (e.g. bacteria) <u>reproduce really quickly</u>, so we're able to watch <u>evolution in action</u>.

Warm-Up & Exam Questions

You need to test your knowledge with a few Warm-Up Questions, followed by some Exam Questions...

Warm-Up Questions

1) Explain what is meant by environmental variation.
2) According to the theory of evolution, what have all of today's species evolved from?
3) Give three factors that can lead to a species becoming extinct.

Exam Questions

1   Helen and Stephanie are identical twins.
     This means they have identical DNA.

1.1 Helen weighs 7 kg more than Stephanie.
     Explain whether this is due to genes, environmental factors or both.

[2 marks]

1.2 Stephanie has a birthmark on her shoulder. Helen doesn't.
     State whether birthmarks are caused by genes and explain your answer.

[1 mark]

2   Genetic variation in a population arises partly due to mutations.

2.1 Explain what is meant by genetic variation.

[1 mark]

2.2 Explain how mutations can increase variation in a species.

[3 marks]

2.3 Some mutations are neutral, having no effect on an organism, but some do have an impact.
     Suggest how some mutations may be beneficial.

[2 marks]

3*   **Figure 1** shows a type of stingray. The stingray's appearance mimics a flat rock.
     It spends most of its time on a rocky sea bed.

Figure 1

Describe and explain how the stingray might have evolved to look like this.

[4 marks]

Topic 6 — Inheritance, Variation and Evolution

Selective Breeding

'Selective breeding' sounds like it has the potential to be a tricky topic, but it's actually dead simple. You take the <u>best</u> plants or animals and breed them together to get the best possible <u>offspring</u>. That's it.

Selective Breeding is Very Simple

Selective breeding is when humans <u>artificially select</u> the plants or animals that are going to <u>breed</u> so that the genes for particular characteristics <u>remain</u> in the population. Organisms are <u>selectively bred</u> to develop features that are <u>useful</u> or <u>attractive</u>, for example:

- Animals that produce more <u>meat</u> or <u>milk</u>.
- Crops with <u>disease resistance</u>.
- Dogs with a <u>good</u>, <u>gentle temperament</u>.
- Decorative plants with <u>big</u> or <u>unusual flowers</u>.

This is the basic process involved in <u>selective breeding</u>:

1) From your <u>existing stock</u>, select the ones which have the <u>characteristics</u> you're after.
2) <u>Breed them</u> with each other.
3) Select the <u>best</u> of the <u>offspring</u>, and <u>breed them together</u>.
4) Continue this process over <u>several generations</u>, and the desirable trait gets <u>stronger</u> and <u>stronger</u>. Eventually, <u>all</u> the offspring will have the characteristic.

Selective breeding is also known as 'artificial selection'.

In <u>agriculture</u> (farming), selective breeding can be used to <u>improve yields</u>. E.g. to improve <u>meat yields</u>, a farmer could breed together the <u>cows</u> and <u>bulls</u> with the <u>best characteristics</u> for producing <u>meat</u>, e.g. large size. After doing this for <u>several generations</u> the farmer would get cows with a <u>very high meat yield</u>.

Selective breeding is <u>nothing new</u> — people have been doing it for <u>thousands</u> of years. It's how we ended up with <u>edible crops</u> from <u>wild plants</u> and how we got <u>domesticated animals</u> like cows and dogs.

The **Main Drawback** is a **Reduction** in the **Gene Pool**

1) The main problem with selective breeding is that it reduces the <u>gene pool</u> — the <u>number of different alleles</u> (forms of a gene) in a population. This is because the farmer keeps breeding from the "<u>best</u>" animals or plants — which are all <u>closely related</u>. This is known as <u>inbreeding</u>.

2) Inbreeding can cause <u>health problems</u> because there's more chance of the organisms inheriting <u>harmful genetic defects</u> when the <u>gene pool</u> is <u>limited</u>. Some <u>dog breeds</u> are particularly susceptible to <u>certain defects</u> because of inbreeding — e.g. pugs often have breathing problems.

3) There can also be serious problems if a <u>new disease appears</u>, because there's <u>not much variation</u> in the population. All the stock are <u>closely related</u> to each other, so if one of them is going to be killed by a new disease, the others are <u>also</u> likely to succumb to it.

 Selective Breeding → Reduction in the number of different alleles (forms of a gene) → Less chance of any resistant alleles being present in the population

Selective breeding is just breeding the best to get the best...

Different breeds of <u>dog</u> came from <u>selective breeding</u>. For example, somebody thought 'I really like this small, yappy wolf — I'll breed it with this other one'. After thousands of generations, we got <u>poodles</u>.

Genetic Engineering

Genetic engineering is a relatively new area of science (well, it began in the 1970s). We've already put the technology to good use and it has many more exciting possibilities too...

Genetic Engineering Transfers Genes Between Organisms

The basic idea of genetic engineering is to transfer a gene responsible for a desirable characteristic from one organism's genome into another organism, so that it also has the desired characteristic.

1) A useful gene is isolated (cut) from one organism's genome using enzymes and is inserted into a vector.

2) The vector is usually a virus or a bacterial plasmid (a fancy piece of circular DNA found in bacterial cells), depending on the type of organism that the gene is being transferred to.

3) When the vector is introduced to the target organism, the useful gene is inserted into its cell(s).

4) Scientists use this method to do all sorts of things. For example:

1) Bacteria have been genetically modified to produce human insulin that can be used to treat diabetes.

2) Genetically modified (GM) crops have had their genes modified, e.g. to improve the size and quality of their fruit, or make them resistant to disease, insects and herbicides (chemicals used to kill weeds).

3) Sheep have been genetically engineered to produce substances, like drugs, in their milk that can be used to treat human diseases.

4) Scientists are researching genetic modification treatments for inherited diseases caused by faulty genes, e.g. by inserting working genes into people with the disease. This is called gene therapy.

5) In some cases, the transfer of the gene is carried out when the organism receiving the gene is at an early stage of development (e.g. egg or embryo). This means that the organism develops with the characteristic coded for by the gene.

Genetic engineering has huge potential benefits...

Scientists are creating all sorts of weird and wonderful creatures with their genetic engineering sets. E.g. they have made cats that glow in the dark thanks to a gene taken from a jellyfish. But of course they don't just do it for fun — they're usually aiming to make organisms that benefit humans in some way.

Genetic Engineering

On the face of it, genetic engineering is great.
But like most other things, there are benefits and risks that you need to consider.

Genetic Engineering is a Controversial Topic

1) Genetic engineering is an exciting new area of science, which has the potential for solving many of our problems (e.g. treating diseases, more efficient food production etc.) but not everyone thinks it's a great idea.

2) There are worries about the long-term effects of genetic engineering — that changing an organism's genes might accidentally create unplanned problems, which could get passed on to future generations.

There Are Pros and Cons of GM Crops

Pros:

1) On the plus side, the characteristics chosen for GM crops can increase the yield, making more food.

2) People living in developing nations often lack nutrients in their diets. GM crops could be engineered to contain the nutrient that's missing. For example, 'golden rice' is a GM rice crop that contains beta-carotene — lack of this substance causes blindness.

3) GM crops are already being grown in some places, often without any problems.

Cons:

1) Some people say that growing GM crops will affect the number of wild flowers (and so the population of insects) that live in and around the crops — reducing farmland biodiversity.

2) Not everyone is convinced that GM crops are safe and some people are concerned that we might not fully understand the effects of eating them on human health. E.g. people are worried they may develop allergies to the food — although there's probably no more risk for this than for eating usual foods.

3) A big concern is that transplanted genes may get out into the natural environment. For example, the herbicide resistance gene may be picked up by weeds, creating a new 'superweed' variety.

If only there was a gene to make revision easier...

At the end of the day, it's down to the Government to weigh up all the evidence for the pros and cons before making a decision on how this scientific knowledge is used. All that the scientists can do is make sure the Government has all the information that it needs to make the decision.

Warm-Up & Exam Questions

By doing these Warm-Up Questions, you'll soon find out if you've got the basic facts straight.

Warm-Up Questions

1) Why might a plant nursery use selective breeding?
2) What potential issues can selective breeding cause?
3) Name one useful product that humans have genetically modified bacteria to produce.

Exam Questions

1   Organisms can be genetically modified.
     This means an organism's genes can be altered to alter its characteristics.

1.1 Give **one** function of the enzymes used in genetic engineering.

[1 mark]

1.2 Suggest **one** useful way that plants can be genetically modified.

[1 mark]

1.3 Some people think that it is wrong to genetically modify crop plants.
     Give **two** different objections that people might have.

[2 marks]

2   The characteristics of two varieties of wheat plants are shown in **Table 1**.

Table 1

Variety	Grain yield	Resistance to bad weather
Tall stems	High	Low
Dwarf stems	Low	High

Describe how selective breeding could be used to create a wheat plant with a high grain yield and high resistance to bad weather.

[3 marks]

3   **Figure 1** shows the milk yield for a population of cows over three generations. The peak of each curve shows the average milk yield per generation.

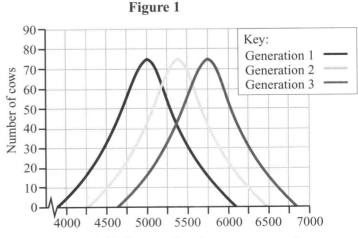

3.1 Do you think that selective breeding is likely to have been used with these cows? Explain your answer.

[1 mark]

3.2 Calculate the percentage increase in the average milk yield per year per cow between generation 1 and generation 3.

[2 marks]

Topic 6 — Inheritance, Variation and Evolution

Fossils

Fossils are great. If they're <u>well-preserved</u>, you can see what oldy-worldly creatures <u>looked</u> like.
They also show how living things have <u>evolved</u>. Although we're not sure how life started in the first place...

Fossils are the Remains of Plants and Animals

Fossils are the <u>remains</u> of organisms from <u>many thousands of years ago</u>, which are found in <u>rocks</u>.
They provide the <u>evidence</u> that organisms lived ages ago. Fossils can tell us a lot about <u>how much</u> or
<u>how little</u> organisms have <u>changed</u> (evolved) over time. Fossils form in rocks in one of <u>three</u> ways:

1) From gradual replacement by minerals

1) Things like <u>teeth</u>, <u>shells</u>, <u>bones</u> etc., which <u>don't decay</u> easily, can last a long time when <u>buried</u>.

2) They're eventually <u>replaced by minerals</u> as they decay, forming a <u>rock-like substance</u> shaped like the original hard part.

3) The surrounding sediments also turn to rock, but the fossil stays <u>distinct</u> inside the rock and eventually someone <u>digs it up</u>.

Most fossils happen this way.

2) From casts and impressions

1) Sometimes, fossils are formed when an organism is <u>buried</u> in a <u>soft</u> material like clay. The clay later <u>hardens</u> around it and the organism decays, leaving a <u>cast</u> of itself. An animal's <u>burrow</u> or a plant's <u>roots</u> (<u>rootlet traces</u>) can be preserved as casts.

2) Things like footprints can also be <u>pressed</u> into these materials when soft, leaving an <u>impression</u> when it hardens.

3) From preservation in places where no decay happens

1) In <u>amber</u> (a clear yellow 'stone' made from fossilised resin) and <u>tar pits</u> there's no <u>oxygen</u> or <u>moisture</u> so <u>decay microbes</u> can't survive.

2) In <u>glaciers</u> it's too <u>cold</u> for the <u>decay microbes</u> to work.

3) <u>Peat bogs</u> are too <u>acidic</u> for <u>decay microbes</u>.

A fully preserved man they named 'Pete Marsh' was found in a bog.

But No One Knows How Life Began

Fossils show how much or how little different organisms have changed (<u>evolved</u>) as life has developed on Earth over millions of years. But where did the <u>first</u> living thing come from...

1) There are various <u>hypotheses</u> suggesting how life first came into being, but no one really <u>knows</u>.

2) Maybe the first life forms came into existence in a primordial <u>swamp</u> (or under the <u>sea</u>) here on <u>Earth</u>. Maybe simple organic molecules were brought to Earth on <u>comets</u> — these could have then become more <u>complex</u> organic molecules, and eventually very simple <u>life forms</u>.

3) These hypotheses can't be supported or disproved because there's a <u>lack</u> of good, <u>valid</u> evidence:

- Many early forms of life were <u>soft-bodied</u>, and soft tissue tends to decay away <u>completely</u> — so the fossil record is <u>incomplete</u>.

- Fossils that did form millions of years ago may have been <u>destroyed</u> by <u>geological activity</u>, e.g. the movement of tectonic plates may have crushed fossils already formed in the rock.

Don't get bogged down by all this information...

It's a bit mind-boggling really how fossils can still exist even <u>millions of years</u> after the organism died.
They really are fascinating things, and scientists have learned a whole lot from studying them in detail.

Antibiotic-Resistant Bacteria

The discovery of <u>antibiotics</u> was a huge benefit to medicine — but they might <u>not</u> be a <u>permanent solution</u>.

Bacteria can Evolve and Become Antibiotic-Resistant

1) Like all organisms, bacteria sometimes develop <u>random mutations</u> (changes) in their DNA. These can lead to <u>changes</u> in the bacteria's characteristics, e.g. being less affected by a particular antibiotic. This can lead to <u>antibiotic-resistant strains</u> forming as the <u>gene</u> for antibiotic resistance becomes <u>more common</u> in the population.

2) To make matters worse, because bacteria are so <u>rapid</u> at <u>reproducing</u>, they can <u>evolve</u> quite <u>quickly</u>.

The gene for antibiotic resistance becomes more common in the population because of natural selection — see page 142 for more.

3) For the bacterium, the ability to resist antibiotics is a big <u>advantage</u>. It's better able to survive, even in a host who's being treated to get rid of the infection, and so it lives for longer and <u>reproduces</u> many more times. This <u>increases</u> the <u>population size</u> of the antibiotic-resistant strain.

4) Antibiotic-resistant strains are a problem for people who become <u>infected</u> with these bacteria because they aren't immune to the new strain and there is no effective treatment. This means that the infection <u>easily spreads</u> between people. Sometimes drug companies can come up with a <u>new</u> antibiotic that's effective, but '<u>superbugs</u>' that are resistant to most known antibiotics are becoming more common.

5) <u>MRSA</u> is a relatively common '<u>superbug</u>' that's really hard to get rid of. It often affects people in <u>hospitals</u> and can be <u>fatal</u> if it enters their bloodstream.

Antibiotic Resistance is Becoming More Common

1) For the last few decades, we've been able to deal with <u>bacterial infections</u> pretty easily using <u>antibiotics</u>. The <u>death rate</u> from infectious bacterial diseases (e.g. pneumonia) has <u>fallen</u> dramatically.

2) But the problem of <u>antibiotic resistance</u> is getting <u>worse</u> — partly because of the <u>overuse</u> and <u>inappropriate use</u> of antibiotics, e.g. doctors prescribing them for <u>non-serious conditions</u> or infections caused by <u>viruses</u>.

Antibiotics don't kill viruses — see p.85.

3) The more <u>often</u> antibiotics are used, the <u>bigger</u> the problem of <u>antibiotic resistance</u> becomes, so it's important that doctors <u>only</u> prescribe antibiotics when they <u>really need</u> to:

It's not that antibiotics actually <u>cause</u> resistance — they create a situation where naturally resistant bacteria have an <u>advantage</u> and so increase in numbers.

4) It's also important that you take <u>all</u> the antibiotics a doctor prescribes for you:

Taking the <u>full course</u> makes sure that <u>all</u> the bacteria are <u>destroyed</u>, which means that there are <u>none</u> left to mutate and develop into <u>antibiotic-resistant strains</u>.

5) In <u>farming</u>, antibiotics can be given to animals to <u>prevent</u> them becoming <u>ill</u> and to make them <u>grow faster</u>. This can lead to the development of <u>antibiotic-resistant bacteria</u> in the animals which can then spread to humans, e.g. during meat preparation and consumption. Increasing concern about the <u>overuse</u> of antibiotics in agriculture has led to some countries <u>restricting their use</u>.

6) The increase in antibiotic resistance has encouraged drug companies to work on developing <u>new</u> antibiotics that are <u>effective</u> against the resistant strains. Unfortunately, the <u>rate of development</u> is <u>slow</u>, which means we're <u>unlikely</u> to be able to keep up with the <u>demand</u> for new drugs as <u>more</u> antibiotic-resistant strains develop and spread. It's also a very <u>costly</u> process.

Classification

It seems to be a basic human urge to want to <u>classify</u> things — that's the case in <u>biology</u> anyway...

Classification is Organising Living Organisms into Groups

1) Traditionally, organisms have been <u>classified</u> according to a system first proposed in the 1700's by <u>Carl Linnaeus</u>, which <u>groups</u> living things according to their <u>characteristics</u> and the <u>structures</u> that make them up.

2) In this system (known as the <u>Linnaean system</u>), living things are first divided into <u>kingdoms</u> (e.g. the plant kingdom).

3) The kingdoms are then <u>subdivided</u> into smaller and smaller groups — <u>phylum</u>, <u>class</u>, <u>order</u>, <u>family</u>, <u>genus</u>, <u>species</u>.

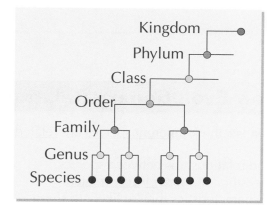

Classification Systems Change Over Time

1) As knowledge of the <u>biochemical processes</u> taking place inside organisms developed and <u>microscopes improved</u> (which allowed us to find out more about the <u>internal structures</u> of organisms), scientists put forward <u>new</u> models of classification.

2) In 1990, Carl Woese proposed the <u>three-domain system</u>. Using evidence gathered from <u>new chemical analysis techniques</u> such as RNA sequence analysis, he found that in some cases, species thought to be <u>closely related</u> in traditional classification systems are in fact <u>not</u> as closely related as first thought.

3) In the three-domain system, organisms are first of all split into <u>three large groups</u> called <u>domains</u>:

> 1) ARCHAEA — Organisms in this domain are <u>primitive bacteria</u>. They're often found in <u>extreme places</u> such as hot springs and salt lakes.

> 2) BACTERIA — This domain contains <u>true bacteria</u> like *E. coli* and *Staphylococcus*. Although they often look similar to Archaea, there are lots of <u>biochemical differences</u> between them.

> 3) EUKARYOTA — This domain includes a <u>broad range</u> of organisms including <u>fungi</u> (page 77), <u>plants</u>, <u>animals</u> and <u>protists</u> (page 77).

4) These are then <u>subdivided</u> into smaller groups — kingdom, phylum, class, order, family, genus, species.

Classification

A bit of a <u>Latin</u> lesson for you now. And a diagram of a <u>funny looking tree</u>.

Organisms Are **Named** According to the **Binomial System**

1) In the binomial system, every organism is given its own <u>two-part</u> Latin name.

2) The <u>first</u> part refers to the <u>genus</u> that the organism belongs to. This gives you information on the organism's <u>ancestry</u>. The <u>second</u> part refers to the <u>species</u>. E.g. humans are known as *Homo sapiens*. '*Homo*' is the genus and '*sapiens*' is the species.

3) The binomial system is used <u>worldwide</u> and means that scientists in <u>different countries</u> or who speak <u>different languages</u> all refer to a particular species by the <u>same name</u> — avoiding potential confusion.

Evolutionary Trees Show Evolutionary Relationships

1) Evolutionary trees show how scientists think <u>different species</u> are <u>related</u> to each other.

2) They show <u>common ancestors</u> and relationships between species. The more <u>recent</u> the common ancestor, the more <u>closely related</u> the two species — and the more <u>characteristics</u> they're likely to share.

3) Scientists analyse lots of different types of <u>data</u> to work out evolutionary relationships. For <u>living</u> organisms, they use the <u>current classification data</u> (e.g. DNA analysis and structural similarities). For <u>extinct</u> species, they use information from the <u>fossil record</u> (see page 143).

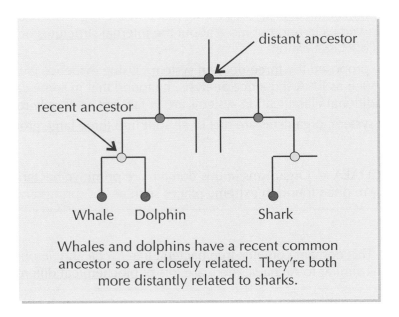

Whales and dolphins have a recent common ancestor so are closely related. They're both more distantly related to sharks.

Binomial system — uh oh, sounds like maths...

In the binomial system the <u>genus</u> comes first, then the <u>species</u>. I think about a good <u>S</u>amaritan to remember it, but you don't have to. You might prefer to think about <u>G</u>wen <u>S</u>tefani, for example. Sometimes, the <u>genus</u> in a binomial name is abbreviated to a <u>capital letter</u> with a <u>full stop</u> after it.

Warm-Up & Exam Questions

The end of the topic is in sight now — just a few more questions to check you've been paying attention.

Warm-Up Questions

1) Suggest what makes low-oxygen environments suitable for the formation of fossils.
2) Suggest a situation where antibiotics could be prescribed inappropriately.
3) Explain why it's important that people take the full course of antibiotics they are prescribed.
4) What species does the Eurasian beaver, *Castor fiber*, belong to?

Exam Questions

1 **Figure 1** shows a section of an evolutionary tree.

Figure 1

1.1 Which species is the most recent common ancestor of Species **F** and Species **G**?

[1 mark]

1.2 Would you expect Species **D** to look similar to Species **E**? Give a reason for your answer.

[1 mark]

2 *Staphylococcus aureus* (*S. aureus*) is a common bacterium that is found on the skin and mucous membranes. It can cause serious illness in people with weakened immune systems. Some strains of the bacterium have developed resistance to the antibiotic methicillin, and are known as MRSA.

2.1 **Table 1** shows the different stages that led to *S. aureus* becoming resistant to methicillin. The stages are shown in the wrong order. Write out the letters **A-D** to show the stages in the correct order.

Table 1

	Stage
A	The gene for methicillin resistance became more common in the population over time, eventually giving a large proportion of the population resistance.
B	Individual bacteria with the mutated genes were more likely to survive and reproduce in a host being treated with methicillin.
C	Random mutations in the DNA of *S. aureus* led to it being less affected by methicillin.
D	The gene for methicillin resistance was passed on to lots of offspring, which also survived and reproduced.

[2 marks]

2.2 Suggest why MRSA is a more serious problem in hospitals than in wider society.

[2 marks]

2.3 Explain why antibiotic resistance in bacteria is a concern for humans.

[1 mark]

2.4 Suggest why the National Health Service (NHS) is trying to reduce the use of antibiotics.

[3 marks]

Revision Summary for Topic 6

So you've finished <u>Topic 6</u> — hoorah. Now here's a page full of questions to test your knowledge.
- Try these questions and <u>tick off each one</u> when you <u>get it right</u>.
- When you've done <u>all the questions</u> under a heading and are <u>completely happy</u> with it, tick it off.

DNA, Reproduction, Meiosis and Sex Chromosomes (p.125-130) ☐

1) What do genes code for?
2) Name the male and female gametes of animals.
3) Which type of reproduction produces genetically identical cells?
4) State the type of cell division used to make gametes in humans.
5) What is the probability that offspring will have the XX combination of sex chromosomes?

Genetic Diagrams and Inherited Disorders (p.132-137) ☐

6) How many genes are responsible for controlling fur colour in mice?
7) What does it mean if someone is heterozygous for a gene?
8) What is the chance of a child being born with polydactyly if one parent has a single dominant allele for the gene that controls it?
9) Give two arguments for and two arguments against screening embryos for genetic disorders.

Variation, Evolution, Selective Breeding and Genetic Engineering (p.140-147) ☐

10) What is variation?
11) Explain how beneficial characteristics can become more common in a population over time.
12) What is selective breeding?
13) How might farmers use selective breeding?
14) What is genetic engineering?

Fossils, Antibiotic-Resistant Bacteria and Classification (p.149-152) ☐

15) Give two ways that fossils can be formed.
16) What leads to the formation of antibiotic-resistant strains of bacteria?
17) Name the groups that organisms are classified into in the Linnaean system.
18) Who proposed the 'three-domain system' of classification in 1990?

Competition

Ecology is all about <u>organisms</u> and the <u>environment</u> they live in, and how the two <u>interact</u>. Simple.

First **Learn** Some Words to Help You **Understand Ecology...**

This topic will make a lot more sense if you become familiar with these terms first:

1) <u>Habitat</u> — the place where an organism <u>lives</u>.
2) <u>Population</u> — <u>all</u> the organisms of <u>one species</u> living in a <u>habitat</u>.
3) <u>Community</u> — the <u>populations</u> of <u>different species</u> living in a habitat.
4) <u>Abiotic</u> factors — <u>non-living</u> factors of the environment, e.g. temperature.
5) <u>Biotic</u> factors — <u>living</u> factors of the environment, e.g. food.
6) <u>Ecosystem</u> — the <u>interaction</u> of a <u>community</u> of <u>living</u> organisms (biotic) with the non-living (<u>abiotic</u>) parts of their environment.

There's more about abiotic and biotic factors on the next two pages.

Organisms **Compete** for **Resources** to **Survive**

Organisms need things from their <u>environment</u> and from <u>other organisms</u> in order to <u>survive</u> and <u>reproduce</u>:

1) <u>Plants</u> need <u>light</u> and <u>space</u>, as well as <u>water</u> and <u>mineral ions (nutrients)</u> from the soil.
2) <u>Animals</u> need <u>space (territory)</u>, <u>food</u>, <u>water</u> and <u>mates</u>.

Organisms <u>compete with other species</u> (and members of their <u>own species</u>) for the <u>same resources</u>.

Any Change in **Any** Environment can Have **Knock-on Effects**

1) In a community, each species <u>depends</u> on other species for things such as <u>food</u>, <u>shelter</u>, <u>pollination</u> and <u>seed dispersal</u> — this is called <u>interdependence</u>.

2) The <u>interdependence</u> of all the living things in an ecosystem means that any major <u>change</u> in the ecosystem (such as one species being removed) can have <u>far-reaching effects</u>.

3) The diagram on the right shows part of a <u>food web</u> (a diagram of what eats what) from a <u>stream</u>.

4) <u>Stonefly larvae</u> are particularly sensitive to <u>pollution</u>. Suppose pollution <u>killed</u> them in this stream. The table below shows some of the <u>effects</u> this might have on some of the other organisms in the food web.

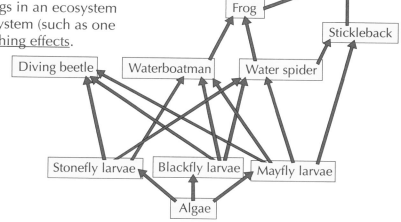

Organism	Effect of loss of stonefly larvae	Effect on population
Blackfly larvae	Less competition for algae	Increase
	More likely to be eaten by predators	Decrease
Water spider	Less food	Decrease
Stickleback	Less food (if water spider or mayfly larvae numbers decrease)	Decrease

Remember that food webs are very complex and that these effects are difficult to predict accurately.

5) In some communities, all the species and environmental factors are in <u>balance</u> so that the <u>population sizes</u> are <u>roughly constant</u> (they may go up and down in cycles — see p.159). These are called <u>stable communities</u>. Stable communities include <u>tropical rainforests</u> and <u>ancient oak woodlands</u>.

Abiotic and Biotic Factors

The environment in which organisms live <u>changes</u> all the time. The things that change are either <u>abiotic</u> (non-living) or <u>biotic</u> (living) factors. These can have a big <u>effect</u> on a community...

Abiotic Factors Can **Vary** in an **Ecosystem**...

Abiotic factors are <u>non-living</u> factors. For example:

1) <u>Moisture level</u>
2) <u>Light intensity</u>
3) <u>Temperature</u>
4) <u>Carbon dioxide level</u> (for plants)
5) <u>Wind intensity</u> and <u>direction</u>
6) <u>Oxygen level</u> (for aquatic animals)
7) <u>Soil pH</u> and <u>mineral content</u>

Light intensity can vary within an ecosystem because of shading caused by, e.g. tree cover.

Different organisms are <u>adapted</u> (see page 158) to different abiotic <u>conditions</u>.

Changes in Abiotic Factors Can **Affect Populations**

1) A <u>change</u> in the environment could be an <u>increase</u> or <u>decrease</u> in an abiotic factor, e.g. an increase in temperature. These changes can affect the <u>sizes</u> of <u>populations</u> in a <u>community</u>.

2) This means they can also affect the <u>population sizes</u> of other organisms that <u>depend</u> on them (see previous page).

3) For example, animals depend on <u>plants</u> for food, so a decrease in a <u>plant population</u> could affect the <u>animal species</u> in a community.

4) Here are <u>two examples</u> of changes in <u>abiotic factors</u> which may affect <u>plant populations</u>:

- A <u>decrease</u> in light intensity, temperature or level of carbon dioxide could <u>decrease</u> the <u>rate of photosynthesis</u> in a plant species (see p.92-93).
- This could affect <u>plant growth</u> and cause a <u>decrease</u> in the <u>population size</u>.

- A <u>decrease</u> in the <u>mineral content</u> of the soil (e.g. a lack of nitrates) could cause <u>nutrient deficiencies</u>.
- This could also affect <u>plant growth</u> and cause a <u>decrease</u> in the <u>population size</u>.

A = not, biotic = living, so abiotic means non-living

Some <u>human activities</u> can affect the <u>abiotic factors</u> of ecosystems, see pages 168, 171 and 172 for more. As you can see from this page, this can affect some organisms <u>directly</u> and other organisms <u>indirectly</u>.

Abiotic and Biotic Factors

The previous page shows how abiotic factors can affect the <u>populations</u> in an ecosystem, but changes in <u>biotic factors</u> can also have big consequences. This page has a few examples to show you how.

Biotic Factors Can Also Vary in an Ecosystem

Biotic factors are <u>living</u> factors.
Here are some examples of biotic factors that might affect organisms in an ecosystem:

1) <u>New predators</u> arriving
2) <u>Competition</u> — one species may outcompete another so that numbers are too low to breed
3) <u>New pathogens</u>
4) <u>Availability of food</u>

Changes in Biotic Factors Can have Knock-On Effects

1) A <u>change</u> in the environment could be the introduction of a <u>new</u> biotic factor, e.g. a new predator or pathogen.

2) These changes can affect the <u>sizes</u> of <u>populations</u> in a <u>community</u>, which can have <u>knock-on effects</u> because of interdependence (see page 155). Here are a few examples:

A new predator could cause a decrease in the <u>prey</u> population. There's more about predator-prey populations on p.159.

Red and grey <u>squirrels</u> live in the same habitat and eat the same food. Grey squirrels outcompete the red squirrels — so the <u>population</u> of red squirrels is <u>decreasing</u>.

1) The following graph shows the effect of a <u>new pathogen</u> on <u>Species A</u>.
2) The population size of Species A was <u>increasing</u> up until 1985, when it <u>decreased rapidly</u> until 1990 — suggesting that <u>1985</u> was the year that the new pathogen arrived.
3) The population started to <u>rise</u> again after 1990.

Changing biotic factors — it's like dominoes...

<u>Learn</u> the list of factors here, as well as on the previous page. I reckon this is a prime time for shutting the book, <u>scribbling</u> them all down and then <u>checking</u> how you did.

Adaptations

Life exists in so many different environments because the organisms that live in them have adapted to them.

Adaptations Allow Organisms to Survive

Organisms, including microorganisms, are adapted to live in different environmental conditions. The features or characteristics that allow them to do this are called adaptations. Adaptations can be:

1. Structural

These are features of an organism's body structure — such as shape or colour. For example:

Arctic animals like the Arctic fox have white fur so they're camouflaged against the snow. This helps them avoid predators and sneak up on prey.

Animals that live in cold places (like whales) have a thick layer of blubber (fat) and a low surface area to volume ratio to help them retain heat.

Animals that live in hot places (like camels) have a thin layer of fat and a large surface area to volume ratio to help them lose heat.

2. Behavioural

These are ways that organisms behave. Many species (e.g. swallows) migrate to warmer climates during the winter to avoid the problems of living in cold conditions.

3. Functional

These are things that go on inside an organism's body that can be related to processes like reproduction and metabolism (all the chemical reactions happening in the body). For example:

Desert animals conserve water by producing very little sweat and small amounts of concentrated urine.

Brown bears hibernate over winter. They lower their metabolism, which conserves energy, so they don't have to hunt when there's not much food about.

Microorganisms Have a Huge Variety of Adaptations...

...so that they can live in a wide range of environments:

- Some microorganisms (e.g. bacteria) are known as extremophiles — they're adapted to live in very extreme conditions.
- For example, some can live at high temperatures (e.g. in super hot volcanic vents), and others can live in places with a high salt concentration (e.g. very salty lakes) or at high pressure (e.g. deep sea vents).

Organisms can adapt to life in even the most extreme environments

In the exam, you might have to say how an organism is adapted to its environment. Look at its characteristics (e.g. colour) and the conditions it has to cope with (e.g. predation) and you'll be sorted.

Food Chains

You might remember <u>food webs</u> from page 155. Well, <u>food chains</u> are a similar idea — except that you only really show one part of a food web in a food chain. Read on to find out more...

Food Chains Show **What's Eaten by What** in an Ecosystem

1) <u>Food chains</u> always start with a <u>producer</u>.
   Producers <u>make</u> (produce) <u>their own food</u> using energy from the Sun.

2) Producers are usually <u>green plants</u> or <u>algae</u> — they make <u>glucose</u> by <u>photosynthesis</u> (see page 91).

3) When a green plant produces glucose, some of it is used to make <u>other biological molecules</u> in the plant.

4) These biological molecules are the plant's <u>biomass</u> — the <u>mass</u> of <u>living material</u>.

5) Biomass can be thought of as <u>energy stored</u> in a plant.

6) <u>Energy</u> is <u>transferred</u> through living organisms in an ecosystem when organisms <u>eat</u> other organisms.

7) Producers are eaten by <u>primary consumers</u>. Primary consumers are then eaten by <u>secondary consumers</u> and secondary consumers are eaten by <u>tertiary consumers</u>. Here's an example of a food chain:

Producers	Primary consumers	Secondary consumer

<u>5000</u> dandelions... feed...   <u>100</u> rabbits... which feed...   <u>1</u> fox.

Consumers are organisms that eat other organisms. 'Primary' means 'first', so primary consumers are the first consumers in a food chain. Secondary consumers are second and tertiary consumers are third.

Populations of **Prey** and **Predators** Go in **Cycles**

Consumers that <u>hunt and kill</u> other animals are called <u>predators</u>, and their <u>prey</u> are what they eat.
In a <u>stable community</u> containing <u>prey</u> and <u>predators</u> (as most of them do of course):

1) The <u>population</u> of any species is usually <u>limited</u> by the amount of <u>food</u> available.

2) If the population of the <u>prey</u> increases, then so will the population of the <u>predators</u>.

3) However as the population of predators <u>increases</u>, the number of prey will <u>decrease</u>.

For more about a stable community see page 155.

Population

Rabbits

A peak in rabbit numbers is followed by a peak in foxes

Foxes

Time

- E.g. <u>more grass</u> means <u>more rabbits</u>.
- More rabbits means <u>more foxes</u>.
- But more foxes means <u>fewer rabbits</u>.
- Eventually fewer rabbits will mean <u>fewer foxes again</u>.
- This <u>up and down pattern</u> continues...

4) Predator-prey cycles are always <u>out of phase</u> with each other. This is because it <u>takes a while</u> for one population to <u>respond</u> to changes in the other population.

E.g. when the number of rabbits goes up, the number of foxes doesn't increase immediately because it takes time for them to reproduce.

Warm-Up & Exam Questions

This ecology topic's a long one — so make sure you've really got these first few pages stuck in your head before moving on and learning the rest. These questions should help you out.

Warm-Up Questions

1) What is the correct scientific term for all the different species in a habitat?
2) What is an ecosystem?
3) Give four examples of abiotic factors that could affect a land-based plant species.
4) What is meant by a structural adaptation?
5) What is meant by a producer in a food chain?

Exam Questions

1   **Figure 1** shows a food chain for a particular area: *(Grade 4-6)*

Figure 1

$$\boxed{\text{algae} \rightarrow \text{shrimp} \rightarrow \text{sea turtle} \rightarrow \text{tiger shark}}$$

1.1   What term is used to describe the tiger shark in **Figure 1**? Tick **one** box.

    ☐ producer   ☐ primary consumer   ☐ secondary consumer   ☐ tertiary consumer

[1 mark]

1.2   Explain the importance of the algae in **Figure 1**.

[2 marks]

2   **Figure 2** shows a penguin. Penguins live in the cold, icy environment of the Antarctic. They swim in the sea to hunt for fish to eat. Some penguins also huddle together in large groups to keep warm.   *(Grade 6-7)*

Figure 2

2.1   What type of adaptation is being described when penguins 'huddle together'?

[1 mark]

2.2   Explain **one** structural adaptation a penguin has to its environment.

[2 marks]

3   Cutthroat trout are present in lakes in Yellowstone National Park. In the last few decades, lake trout have been introduced to the lakes. However, lake trout have emerged as predators of the cutthroat trout.   *(Grade 6-7)*

3.1   Explain how the introduction of the lake trout might cause the population sizes of both species of fish to fluctuate over time.

[5 marks]

3.2   Give **two** other biotic factors that could affect the size of the cutthroat trout population.

[2 marks]

Using Quadrats

This is where the <u>fun</u> starts. Studying <u>ecology</u> gives you the chance to <u>rummage around</u> in bushes, get your hands <u>dirty</u> and look at some <u>real organisms</u>, living in the <u>wild</u>.

Environmental Variation Affects the Distribution of Organisms

1) As you know from page 155, a <u>habitat</u> is the place where an organism <u>lives</u>, e.g. a playing field.

2) The <u>distribution</u> of an organism is <u>where</u> an organism is <u>found</u>, e.g. in a part of the playing field.

3) Where an organism is found is affected by <u>environmental factors</u> (see pages 156-157). An organism might be <u>more common</u> in <u>one area</u> than another due to <u>differences</u> in environmental factors between the two areas. For example, in the playing field, you might find that daisies are <u>more common</u> in the open than under trees, because there's <u>more light</u> available in the open.

4) There are a couple of ways to <u>study</u> the distribution of an organism. You can:
   - <u>measure</u> how common an organism is in <u>two sample areas</u> (e.g. using <u>quadrats</u>) and compare them.
   - study how the distribution <u>changes</u> across an area, e.g. by placing quadrats along a <u>transect</u> (p.162).

   Both of these methods give <u>quantitative</u> data (numbers) about the distribution.

Use Quadrats to Study The Distribution of Small Organisms

A <u>quadrat</u> is a <u>square</u> frame enclosing a <u>known area</u>, e.g. 1 m^2. To compare <u>how common</u> an organism is in <u>two sample areas</u> (e.g. shady and sunny spots in that playing field) just follow these simple steps:

1) Place a <u>1 m^2 quadrat</u> on the ground at a <u>random point</u> within the <u>first</u> sample area. E.g. divide the area into a grid and use a random number generator to pick coordinates.

2) <u>Count</u> all the organisms <u>within</u> the quadrat.

3) <u>Repeat</u> steps 1 and 2 as many times as you can.

4) <u>Work out</u> the <u>mean</u> number of organisms per quadrat within the first sample area.

A quadrat

 Anna counted the number of daisies in 7 quadrats within her first sample area and recorded the following results: 18, 20, 22, 23, 23, 23, 25.

Here the MEAN is: $\dfrac{\text{TOTAL number of organisms}}{\text{NUMBER of quadrats}} = \dfrac{154}{7} = 22$ daisies per quadrat

5) <u>Repeat</u> steps 1 to 4 in the <u>second</u> sample area.

6) Finally <u>compare</u> the two means. E.g. you might find 2 daisies per m^2 in the shade, and 22 daisies per m^2 (lots more) in the open field.

You Can Also Work Out the Population Size of an Organism in One Area

 Students used 0.5 m^2 quadrats to randomly sample daisies on an open field. The students found a mean of 10.5 daisies per quadrat. The field had an area of 800 m^2. Estimate the population of daisies on the field.

1) Work out the <u>mean number of organisms per m^2</u>.

2) Then multiply the <u>mean</u> by the <u>total area</u> (in m^2) of the habitat.

$1 \div 0.5 = 2$
$2 \times 10.5 = 21$ daisies per m^2
$800 \times 21 = 16\ 800$
daisies on the open field

The population size of an organism is sometimes called its abundance.

If your quadrat has an area of 1 m^2, the mean number of organisms per m^2 is just the same as the mean number per quadrat.

Using Transects

So, now you think you've learnt <u>all about</u> distribution. Well <u>hold on</u> — there's more <u>ecology fun</u> to be had.

Use **Transects** to **Study** The **Distribution** of Organisms

You can use lines called <u>transects</u> to help find out how organisms (like plants) are <u>distributed</u> across an area — e.g. if an organism becomes <u>more or less common</u> as you move from a hedge towards the middle of a field. Here's what to do:

1) <u>Mark out a line</u> in the area you want to study using a tape measure.

2) Then <u>collect data</u> along the line.

3) You can do this by just <u>counting</u> all the organisms you're interested in that <u>touch</u> the line.

tape measure

quadrat

Transects can be used in any ecosystem, not just fields. For example, along a beach.

4) Or, you can collect data by using <u>quadrats</u> (see previous page). These can be placed <u>next to</u> each other along the line or <u>at intervals</u>, for example, every 2 m.

You Can **Estimate** the **Percentage Cover** of a **Quadrat**

If it's difficult to count all the individual organisms in the quadrat (e.g. if they're grass) you can calculate the <u>percentage cover</u>. This means estimating the percentage <u>area</u> of the quadrat covered by a particular type of organism, e.g. by <u>counting</u> the number of little squares covered by the organisms.

Some students were measuring the distribution of organisms from one corner of a school playing field to another, using quadrats placed at regular intervals along a transect. Below is a picture of one of the quadrats. Calculate the percentage cover of each organism, A and B.

Measuring % cover

☐ Organism Type A

☐ Organism Type B

You count a square if it's more than half covered.

1) <u>Count</u> the <u>number of squares</u> covered by organism A.

2) Make this into a <u>percentage</u> — divide the number of squares covered by the organism by the total number of squares in the quadrat (100), then multiply the result by 100.

3) Do the same for <u>organism B</u>.

Type A = 42 squares

(42/100) × 100
= 0.42 × 100 = 42%

Type B = 47 squares

(47/100) × 100
= 0.47 × 100 = 47%

You don't need fancy kit to study the distribution of organisms

So if you want to measure the distribution of a organism <u>across</u> an area, you could use a <u>transect</u>. You can use them <u>alone</u> or along with <u>quadrats</u>. Using <u>percentage cover</u> instead of <u>number</u> of organisms is a good way of studying the distribution of plants, as there may be <u>too many</u> to count.

The Water Cycle

The <u>amount</u> of water on Earth is pretty much <u>constant</u> — but <u>where</u> it is changes.
Water moves between <u>rivers</u>, <u>lakes</u>, <u>oceans</u> and the <u>atmosphere</u> in what's known as the <u>water cycle</u>.

The **Water Cycle** Means Water is **Endlessly Recycled**

The water here on planet Earth is constantly <u>recycled</u>.
There are four key steps you should understand:

1) <u>Energy</u> from the <u>Sun</u> makes water <u>evaporate</u> from the land and sea, turning it into <u>water vapour</u>. Water also evaporates from plants — this is known as <u>transpiration</u> (see p.70).

As warm water vapour rises it cools down and forms clouds.

2) The warm water vapour is <u>carried upwards</u> (as warm air rises). When it gets higher up it <u>cools</u> and <u>condenses</u> to form <u>clouds</u>.

3) Water falls from the clouds as <u>precipitation</u> (usually rain, but sometimes snow or hail) onto <u>land</u>, where it provides <u>fresh water</u> for <u>plants</u> and <u>animals</u>.

4) It then <u>drains</u> into the <u>sea</u>, before the whole process starts again.

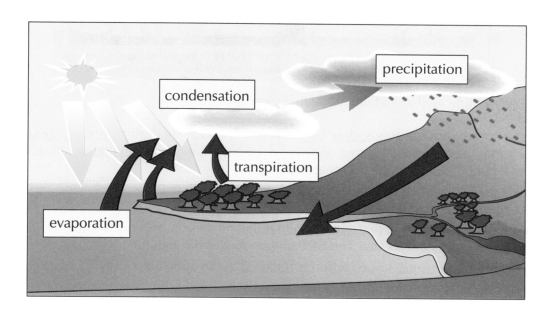

Evaporation, transpiration, condensation, precipitation

The water cycle is really easy — there are <u>four main stages</u> and they're all pretty straightforward. So there's absolutely no excuse not to learn it inside out. The most important thing to remember is that it's a <u>cycle</u> — a <u>continuous</u> process with no beginning or end. Water that falls to the ground as rain (or any other kind of precipitation for that matter) will eventually end up back in the clouds again.

The Carbon Cycle

Recycling may be a buzz word for us but it's old school for nature. All the nutrients in our environment are constantly being recycled — there's a nice balance between what goes in and what goes out again.

Elements are Cycled Back to the Start of the Food Chain by Decay

1) Living things are made of materials they take from the world around them. E.g. plants turn elements like carbon, oxygen, hydrogen and nitrogen from the soil and the air into the complex compounds (carbohydrates, proteins and fats) that make up living organisms. These get passed up the food chain.

2) These materials are returned to the environment in waste products, or when the organisms die and decay.

3) Materials decay because they're broken down (digested) by microorganisms. This happens faster in warm, moist, aerobic (oxygen rich) conditions because microorganisms are more active in these conditions.

4) Decay puts the stuff that plants need to grow (e.g. mineral ions) back into the soil.

5) In a stable community, the materials that are taken out of the soil and used by plants etc. are balanced by those that are put back in. There's a constant cycle happening.

The Constant Cycling of Carbon is called the Carbon Cycle

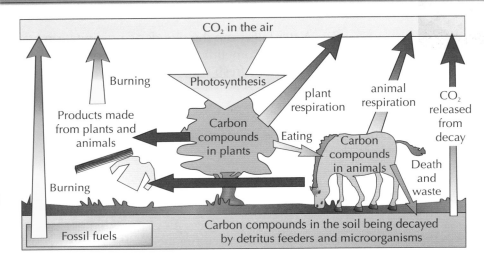

That can look a bit complicated at first, but it's actually pretty simple:

1) CO_2 is removed from the atmosphere by green plants and algae during photosynthesis. The carbon is used to make glucose, which can be turned into carbohydrates, fats and proteins that make up the bodies of the plants and algae.

2) When the plants and algae respire, some carbon is returned to the atmosphere as CO_2.

The energy that green plants and algae get from photosynthesis is transferred up the food chain.

3) When the plants and algae are eaten by animals, some carbon becomes part of the fats and proteins in their bodies. The carbon then moves through the food chain.

4) When the animals respire, some carbon is returned to the atmosphere as CO_2.

5) When plants, algae and animals die, other animals (called detritus feeders) and microorganisms feed on their remains. When these organisms respire, CO_2 is returned to the atmosphere.

6) Animals also produce waste that is broken down by detritus feeders and microorganisms.

7) The combustion (burning) of wood and fossil fuels also releases CO_2 back into the air.

8) So the carbon (and energy) is constantly being cycled — from the air, through food chains (via plants, algae and animals, and detritus feeders and microorganisms) and eventually back out into the air again.

Warm-Up & Exam Questions

You can't just stare at these pages and expect all of the information to go in. Especially the practical pages with the maths examples. Do these questions to see how well you really know the stuff.

Warm-Up Questions

1) What is a transect?
2) A student counted the number of daises in five quadrats and recorded the following results: 14, 11, 11, 12, 12. What is the mean number of daises per quadrat?
3) What is the role of microorganisms in the carbon cycle?
4) How is the carbon in fossil fuels returned to the atmosphere?

Exam Questions

1   **Figure 1** shows a simplified version of the carbon cycle.

Figure 1

carbon dioxide

A

carbon compounds in plants

B

C

carbon compounds in animals

carbon compounds in dead matter

1.1   Name the process that is occurring at stage **B**.

[1 mark]

1.2   Name the process that is occurring at stage **C**.

[1 mark]

1.3   Explain how carbon is released from dead matter in the soil (stage **A**).

[2 marks]

1.4   Name the only process in the carbon cycle that removes carbon dioxide from the air.

[1 mark]

2   The water cycle describes the constant movement of water molecules on the Earth.

2.1   In the water cycle, how does water move from plants into the air?

[1 mark]

2.2   Describe the shortest route a water molecule could take
through the water cycle to get from an ocean to a garden pond.

[4 marks]

Exam Questions

3   Some students investigated the distribution of poppies across a field next to a wood. A sketch of the area is shown in **Figure 2**.

Figure 2

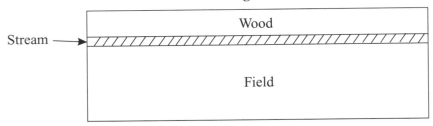

The students' results are shown in **Table 1**.

Table 1

Number of poppies per m²	5	9	14	19	26
Distance from wood (m)	2	4	6	8	10

3.1 Describe how the students could have used quadrats to obtain the results in **Table 1**.

[3 marks]

3.2 Describe the trend in the results in **Table 1**.

[1 mark]

3.3 The students suggest that a change in light intensity across the field may affect the distribution of the poppies. Give **two** additional factors which may also affect the distribution of the poppies.

[2 marks]

The students decided to investigate the distribution of two grass species in the field as well.
Figure 3 shows a sketch that the students made of the two grass species in one of their quadrats.

Figure 3

Species A

Species B

3.4 Use **Figure 3** to estimate the percentage cover of species A and species B in the quadrat.

[2 marks]

3.5 Give **one** reason why the students may have decided to estimate the percentage cover of the two grasses.

[1 mark]

4*   An area of woodland is cleared to build a house. The tree trunks are taken away to be dried and used in furniture making. The smaller tree branches are used for firewood. The green plants are piled up at the edge of the building site.

Describe how carbon stored in the vegetation that has been cleared could be returned to the atmosphere.

[6 marks]

Biodiversity and Waste Management

Unfortunately, human activity can <u>negatively affect</u> the <u>planet</u> and its <u>variety of life</u>.

Earth's **Biodiversity** is Important

> Biodiversity is the <u>variety of different species</u> of organisms on Earth, or within an ecosystem.

1) <u>High</u> biodiversity is important. It makes sure that <u>ecosystems</u> (see p.155) are <u>stable</u> because different species depend on each other for things like <u>shelter</u> and <u>food</u>. Different species can also help to maintain the right <u>physical environment</u> for each other (e.g. the acidity of the soil).

2) For the human species to <u>survive</u>, it's important that a good level of biodiversity is maintained.

3) Lots of human actions, including <u>waste production</u> (see the next page) and <u>deforestation</u> (see p.172), as well as <u>global warming</u> (see p.169) are reducing biodiversity. However, it's only <u>recently</u> that we've started <u>taking measures</u> to <u>stop</u> this from continuing.

There are Over **Seven Billion People** in the World

1) The <u>population</u> of the world is currently <u>rising</u> very quickly, and it's not slowing down — look at the graph...

2) This is mostly due to modern <u>medicine</u> and <u>farming</u> methods, which have <u>reduced</u> the number of <u>people dying</u> from <u>disease</u> and <u>hunger</u>.

3) This is great for all of us <u>humans</u>, but it means we're having a <u>bigger effect</u> on the <u>environment</u> we live in.

Biodiversity and Waste Management

We're Making **Increasing Demands** on the **Environment**

When the Earth's population was much smaller, the effects of human activity were usually small and local. Nowadays though, our actions can have a far more widespread effect.

1) Our increasing population puts pressure on the environment, as we take the resources we need to survive.

2) But people around the world are also demanding a higher standard of living (and so demand luxuries to make life more comfortable — cars, computers, etc.). So we use more raw materials (e.g. oil to make plastics), but we also use more energy for the manufacturing processes. This all means we're taking more and more resources from the environment more and more quickly.

3) Unfortunately, many raw materials are being used up quicker than they're being replaced. So if we carry on like we are, one day we're going to run out.

We're Also Producing **More Waste**

As we make more and more things we produce more and more waste, including waste chemicals. And unless this waste is properly handled, more harmful pollution will be caused. Pollution affects water, land and air and kills plants and animals, reducing biodiversity.

Water

- Sewage and toxic chemicals from industry can pollute lakes, rivers and oceans, affecting the plants and animals that rely on them for survival (including humans).
- And the chemicals used on land (e.g. fertilisers, pesticides and herbicides) can be washed into water.

Land

- We use toxic chemicals for farming (e.g. pesticides and herbicides).
- We also bury nuclear waste underground, and we dump a lot of household waste in landfill sites.

Air

Smoke and acidic gases released into the atmosphere can pollute the air, e.g. sulfur dioxide can cause acid rain.

More people, more mess, less space, fewer resources...

...you might call it a recipe for disaster. As you can see, there's a lot of work for us to do in improving our waste management and also finding ways to deal with a growing human population.

Global Warming

You might remember the <u>carbon cycle</u> from p.164. Well, carbon dioxide has an important role in keeping the Earth <u>warm enough</u> for life. It's not so good when there's <u>too much</u> of it in the atmosphere though...

Carbon Dioxide and Methane Trap Energy from the Sun

1) The <u>temperature</u> of the Earth is a <u>balance</u> between the energy it gets from the Sun and the energy it radiates back out into space.

2) Gases in the <u>atmosphere</u> naturally act like an <u>insulating layer</u>. They absorb most of the energy that would normally be radiated out into space, and re-radiate it in all directions (including back towards the Earth). This increases the <u>temperature</u> of the planet.

This is what happens in a greenhouse. The Sun shines in, and the glass helps keeps some of the energy in.

3) If this didn't happen, then at night there'd be nothing to keep any energy <u>in</u>, and we'd quickly get <u>very cold</u> indeed. But recently we've started to worry that this effect is getting a bit out of hand.

4) There are several different gases in the atmosphere which help keep the <u>energy in</u>. They're called "<u>greenhouse gases</u>", and the <u>main ones</u> whose levels we worry about are <u>carbon dioxide</u> (CO_2) and <u>methane</u> — because the levels of these two gases are rising quite sharply.

5) The Earth is gradually heating up because of the increasing levels of greenhouse gases — this is <u>global warming</u>. Global warming is a type of <u>climate change</u> and causes other types of climate change, e.g. changing rainfall patterns.

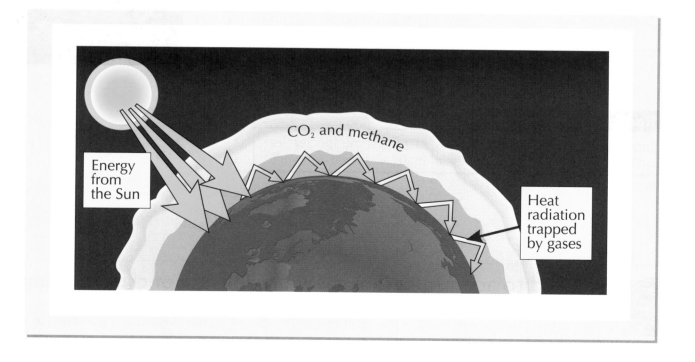

Global Warming

The Earth is getting warmer. Climate scientists are now trying to work out what the effects of global warming might be — sadly, it's not as simple as everyone having nicer summers.

The **Consequences** of **Global Warming** Could be Pretty **Serious**

There are several reasons to be worried about global warming. Here are a few:

Sea levels rising

1) Higher temperatures cause seawater to expand and ice to melt, causing the sea level to rise.
2) It has risen a little bit over the last 100 years.
3) If it keeps rising it'll be bad news for people and animals living in low-lying places.
4) It will lead to flooding, resulting in the loss of habitats (where organisms live).

Changes in species distribution

1) The distribution of many wild animal and plant species may change as temperatures increase and the amount of rainfall changes in different areas.
2) Some species may become more widely distributed, e.g. species that need warmer temperatures may spread further as the conditions they thrive in exist over a wider area.
3) Other species may become less widely distributed, e.g. species that need cooler temperatures may have smaller ranges as the conditions they thrive in exist over a smaller area.

Changes in migration patterns

There could be changes in migration patterns, e.g. some birds may migrate further north, as more northern areas are getting warmer.

Reduction in biodiversity

Biodiversity (see p.167) could be reduced if some species are unable to survive a change in the climate, so become extinct.

We need to act fast, before the worst effects of climate change

Global warming is rarely out of the news. Most scientists accept that it's happening and that human activity has caused most of the recent warming, based on the evidence that has so far been collected. However, they don't know exactly what the effects will be and scientists will have to collect more data before these questions can really be answered.

Deforestation and Land Use

Trees and peat bogs trap carbon dioxide and lock it up. The problems start when it escapes...

Humans Use **Lots of Land** for **Lots of Purposes**

1) We use land for things like building, quarrying, farming and dumping waste.
2) This means that there's less land available for other organisms.
3) Sometimes, the way we use land has a bad effect on the environment — for example, if it requires deforestation (see next page) or the destruction of habitats like peat bogs and other areas of peat (see below).

Destroying Peat Bogs Adds **More CO$_2$** to the Atmosphere

1) Bogs are areas of land that are acidic and waterlogged. Plants that live in bogs don't fully decay when they die, because there's not enough oxygen. The partly-rotted plants gradually build up to form peat.

2) So the carbon in the plants is stored in the peat instead of being released into the atmosphere.

3) However, peat bogs are often drained so that the area can be used as farmland, or the peat is cut up and dried to use as fuel. It's also sold to gardeners as compost. Peat is being used faster than it forms.

4) When peat is drained, it comes into more contact with air and some microorganisms start to decompose it.

5) When these microorganisms respire, they use oxygen and release carbon dioxide, contributing to global warming (see page 169). Carbon dioxide is also released when peat is burned as a fuel.

6) Destroying the bogs also destroys (or reduces the area of) the habitats of some of the animals, plants and microorganisms that live there, so reduces biodiversity.

We need to use land, but we also need a healthy environment

We can't really avoid using land — we've got to if we want to e.g. grow enough food or build enough houses for people. The human population is increasing so it's likely that we'll use even more land in the future — we'll have to find a way to manage land use to reduce the negative effects on the environment.

Deforestation and Land Use

Many parts of the world have <u>already</u> been radically changed by deforestation — for example, much of the <u>UK</u> used to be covered in forests. Deforestation can be <u>bad news</u> for several reasons.

Deforestation Means Chopping Down Trees

1) <u>Deforestation</u> is the <u>cutting down</u> of <u>forests</u>.
2) This causes big problems when it's done on a <u>large-scale</u>, such as cutting down rainforests in <u>tropical areas</u>.
3) It's done for various reasons, including:

- To <u>clear land</u> for farming (e.g. cattle or rice crops) to provide <u>more food</u>.
- To grow <u>crops</u> from which <u>biofuels</u> based on ethanol can be produced.

Deforestation Can Cause Many Problems

Less carbon dioxide taken in

- Cutting down <u>loads of trees</u> means that the amount of carbon dioxide <u>removed</u> from the atmosphere during <u>photosynthesis</u> is <u>reduced</u>.
- Trees '<u>lock up</u>' some of the <u>carbon</u> that they absorb during photosynthesis in their wood, which can <u>remove</u> it from the <u>atmosphere</u> for hundreds of years. Removing trees means that less is locked up.

More CO_2 in the atmosphere causes global warming (see page 169), which leads to climate change.

More carbon dioxide in the atmosphere

- Carbon dioxide is <u>released</u> when trees are <u>burnt</u> to clear land. (Carbon in wood doesn't contribute to atmospheric pollution until it's released by burning.)
- <u>Microorganisms</u> feeding on bits of <u>dead wood</u> release carbon dioxide as a waste product of <u>respiration</u>.

Less biodiversity

- Biodiversity (p.167) is the <u>variety of different species</u> — the more species, the greater the biodiversity.
- Habitats like forests can contain a <u>huge number</u> of different species of <u>plants</u> and <u>animals</u>, so when they are destroyed there is a danger of <u>many species becoming extinct</u> — biodiversity is <u>reduced</u>.

Not a very cheerful page, I know...

Make sure you can link together all the information on pages 169-172 — for example, how <u>deforestation</u> and <u>peat burning</u> can contribute to <u>global warming</u>, and how this might affect <u>biodiversity</u>. In the exam, you might get an extended response question that requires you to draw on several different areas of knowledge like this.

Maintaining Ecosystems and Biodiversity

It's really important that biodiversity is <u>maintained</u> as damage to ecosystems or populations of species can be <u>hard to undo</u>. This page is about some of the different <u>methods</u> that can be used to maintain biodiversity.

There are **Programmes** to **Protect Ecosystems** and **Biodiversity**

1) It's important that <u>biodiversity</u> is maintained at a <u>high enough level</u> to make sure that <u>ecosystems</u> are <u>stable</u> (see page 155).

2) In some areas, <u>programmes</u> have been set up by <u>concerned citizens</u> and <u>scientists</u> to <u>minimise damage</u> by <u>human activities</u> (see page 168) to <u>ecosystems</u> and <u>biodiversity</u>. Here are a few examples:

1. Breeding Programmes

1) <u>Breeding programmes</u> have been set up to help prevent <u>endangered species</u> from becoming <u>extinct</u>.

2) These are where animals are bred in <u>captivity</u> to make sure the species survives if it dies out in the wild.

3) Individuals can sometimes be <u>released</u> into the <u>wild</u> to boost or re-establish a population.

Pandas are an endangered species. Many efforts have been made to breed pandas in captivity.

2. Habitat Protection

1) Programmes to <u>protect</u> and <u>regenerate rare habitats</u> like <u>mangroves</u>, <u>heathland</u> and <u>coral reefs</u> have been started. Protecting these habitats helps to <u>protect</u> the species that live there — <u>preserving</u> the <u>ecosystem</u> and <u>biodiversity</u> in the area.

2) There are programmes to <u>reintroduce hedgerows</u> and <u>field margins</u> around fields on farms where only a <u>single type</u> of crop is grown. Field margins are areas of land around the <u>edges</u> of fields where <u>wild flowers</u> and <u>grasses</u> are left to <u>grow</u>. Hedgerows and field margins provide a <u>habitat</u> for a <u>wider variety</u> of organisms than could survive in a single crop habitat.

3. Preventing **Global Warming**

1) Some governments have introduced regulations and programmes to <u>reduce</u> the level of <u>deforestation</u> taking place and the amount of <u>carbon dioxide</u> being released into the atmosphere by businesses.

2) This could reduce the increase of <u>global warming</u> (see page 169).

4. Reducing **Waste**

1) People are encouraged to recycle to <u>reduce</u> the amount of <u>waste</u> that gets dumped in <u>landfill</u> sites.

2) This could <u>reduce</u> the amount of <u>land</u> taken over for landfill, leaving <u>ecosystems</u> in place.

Maintaining Ecosystems and Biodiversity

Conflicting Pressures Affect How Biodiversity is Maintained

Sadly for noble biodiversity warriors, maintaining biodiversity isn't as simple as you would hope. There are lots of conflicting pressures that have to be taken into account. For example:

1. The Costs of Programmes

1) Protecting biodiversity costs money.
2) For example, governments sometimes pay farmers a subsidy to reintroduce hedgerows and field margins to their land.
3) It can also cost money to keep a watch on whether the programmes and regulations designed to maintain biodiversity are being followed.
4) There can be conflict between protecting biodiversity and saving money — money may be prioritised for other things.

2. The Effect on the Local Economy

1) Protecting biodiversity may come at a cost to local people's livelihoods.
2) For example, reducing the amount of deforestation is great for biodiversity, but the people who were previously employed in the tree-felling industry could be left unemployed.
3) This could affect the local economy if people move away with their family to find work.

3. Protecting Food Security

1) There can be conflict between protecting biodiversity and protecting our food security.
2) Sometimes certain organisms are seen as pests by farmers (e.g. locusts and foxes) and are killed to protect crops and livestock so that more food can be produced.
3) As a result, however, the food chain and biodiversity can be affected.

4. The Development of Society

1) Development is important, but it can affect the environment.
2) Many people want to protect biodiversity in the face of development, but sometimes land is in such high demand that previously untouched land with high biodiversity has to be used for development.
3) For example, for housing developments on the edges of towns, or for new agricultural land in developing countries.

So we should do what we can — within some limits

Like many situations in ecology, maintaining biodiversity isn't black and white. There are lots of factors to take into account before decisions on the best way to go forward can be made.

Warm-Up & Exam Questions

I hope you've got all of that important information in your head. There's a lot to remember here, so have a flick back when you're doing these questions in case you've forgotten any little details.

Warm-Up Questions

1) What is meant by the term 'biodiversity'?
2) Give two greenhouse gases.
3) How are populations of endangered species preserved by breeding programmes?
4) Explain how biodiversity can be increased in areas that farm single crops.

Exam Questions

1   Humans are producing increasing amounts of waste.
     This has negative consequences for biodiversity and the environment.

1.1 Give **two** types of waste that pollute the air.

                                                                                    [2 marks]

1.2 Describe **one** way in which waste produced by humans pollutes water.

                                                                                    [1 mark]

1.3 Give **two** reasons why humans are producing increasingly more waste.

                                                                                    [2 marks]

2   Global warming may lead to a decline in biodiversity in the future.

2.1 Apart from a decline in biodiversity, suggest **two** possible
     biological consequences of global warming.

                                                                                    [2 marks]

2.2 Describe **two** measures being used by some governments in order to reduce global warming.

                                                                                    [2 marks]

3   Peat bogs can be drained, so that the peat can be cut up and used as a source of fuel.

3.1 Explain why draining peat bogs and using the peat as a fuel can contribute to global warming.

                                                                                    [4 marks]

3.2 Apart from contributing to global warming, explain **one** negative consequence of destroying peat bogs.

                                                                                    [2 marks]

4   Wetlands are areas of land in which the soil is saturated with water. In New Zealand,
     the area of freshwater wetlands has decreased by a huge amount, largely due to
     human activities, such as draining the wetlands for building or farming. New Zealand
     now has conservation schemes in place which protect many of the remaining wetlands.

4.1 In terms of biodiversity, suggest why it's important for humans that New Zealand and other countries
     in the world protect their wetlands.

                                                                                    [3 marks]

4.2 Suggest **two** reasons why people in New Zealand may be against schemes which protect its wetlands.

                                                                                    [2 marks]

Revision Summary for Topic 7

That's Topic 7 done with. I bet you're in the mood for a long list of revision questions now. You're in luck.
- Try these questions and tick off each one when you get it right.
- When you've done all the questions under a heading and are completely happy with it, tick it off.

Competition, Abiotic and Biotic Factors, and Adaptations (p.155-158) ☐
1) Define 'habitat'.
2) What things do animals compete for in an ecosystem?
3) Explain what is meant by a 'stable community'.
4) What are biotic and abiotic factors?
5) What are functional adaptations?

Food Chains, Quadrats and Transects (p.159-162) ☐
6) What do food chains always start with?
7) Explain what happens to the population size of a predator if its prey becomes more common in an ecosystem.
8) Explain how a quadrat can be used to investigate the distribution of clover plants in two areas.
9) Suggest why you might use a transect when investigating the distribution of organisms.

The Water and Carbon Cycles (p.163-164) ☐
10) Describe the four main stages involved in the water cycle.
11) When water vapour cools and condenses in the atmosphere, what does it change into?
12) Explain the role of photosynthesis in the carbon cycle.
13) Explain how microorganisms return carbon to the atmosphere.

Human Impacts on the Planet (p.167-174) ☐
14) Suggest why it's important to have high biodiversity in an ecosystem.
15) Give an example of how global warming could reduce biodiversity.
16) How can recycling programmes help to protect ecosystems?

Measuring Substances

Get your lab coats on, it's time to find out about the skills you'll need in <u>experiments</u>...
First things first — make sure you're using <u>appropriate equipment</u> and know <u>how to use it</u> correctly.

Use the **Right Apparatus** to Take **Readings**

1. Mass

1) To weigh a solid, start by putting the <u>container</u> you are weighing your substance into on a <u>balance</u>.
2) Set the balance to exactly <u>zero</u> and then weigh out the correct amount of your substance.

2. Temperature

1) You can use a <u>thermometer</u> to measure the temperature of a solution.
2) Make sure that the <u>bulb</u> of the thermometer is <u>completely submerged</u> in the solution and that you wait for the temperature to <u>stabilise</u> before you take your initial reading.
3) Read off the <u>scale</u> on the thermometer at <u>eye level</u> to make sure it's correct.

When you're reading off a scale, write down the value of the graduation that the amount is closest to.

3. Volume of a Liquid

There's more than one way to measure the volume of a <u>liquid</u>. Whichever method you use, always read the volume from the <u>bottom of the meniscus</u> (the curved upper surface of the liquid) when it's at <u>eye level</u>.

Read volume from here — the bottom of the meniscus.

Using a pipette

1) <u>Pipettes</u> are used to suck up and <u>transfer</u> volumes of liquid between containers.
2) <u>Dropping pipettes</u> are used to transfer <u>drops</u> of liquid.
3) <u>Graduated pipettes</u> are used to transfer <u>accurate</u> volumes.
4) A <u>pipette filler</u> is attached to the end of a graduated pipette, to <u>control</u> the amount of liquid being drawn up.

Using a measuring cylinder

1) <u>Measuring cylinders</u> come in all different <u>sizes</u>. Make sure you choose one that's the right size for the measurement you want to make.
2) It's no good using a huge 1 dm³ cylinder to measure out 2 cm³ of a liquid — the graduations will be too big, and you'll end up with <u>massive errors</u>. It'd be much better to use one that measures up to 10 cm³.

Measuring Substances

4. Volume of a Gas

1) To accurately measure the <u>volume</u> of gas, you should use a <u>gas syringe</u>:

2) Alternatively, you can use an <u>upturned measuring cylinder</u> filled with <u>water</u>. The gas will <u>displace</u> the water so you can <u>read the volume</u> off the <u>scale</u>.

3) Other methods to measure the amount of gas include:
   - <u>counting the bubbles</u> produced
   - measuring the <u>length</u> of a gas bubble drawn along a tube (see page 95).

   These methods are <u>less accurate</u>, but will give you <u>relative</u> amounts of gas to <u>compare results</u>.

4) When you're measuring a gas, you need to make sure that the equipment is set up so that none of the gas can <u>escape</u>, otherwise your results won't be <u>accurate</u>.

5. pH

The method you should use to measure pH depends on what your experiment is.

1) <u>Indicators</u> are dyes that <u>change colour</u> depending on whether they're in an <u>acid</u> or an <u>alkali</u>. You use them by adding a couple of drops of the indicator to the solution you're interested in. <u>Universal indicator</u> is a <u>mixture</u> of indicators that changes colour <u>gradually</u> as pH changes. It's useful for <u>estimating</u> the pH of a solution based on its colour.

2) <u>Indicator paper</u> is useful if you don't want to colour the entire solution that you're testing. It <u>changes colour</u> depending on the pH of the solution it touches. You can also hold a piece of <u>damp indicator paper</u> in a <u>gas sample</u> to test its pH.

Blue litmus paper turns <u>red</u> in acidic conditions and red litmus paper turns <u>blue</u> in alkaline conditions.

3) <u>pH meters</u> have a <u>digital display</u> that gives an <u>accurate value</u> for the pH of a solution.

Read off the scale carefully when taking readings

Whether you're reading off a thermometer, a pipette or a measuring cylinder, make sure you take all readings at <u>eye level</u>. And, if it's volume you're measuring, read from the <u>bottom of the meniscus</u>.

Safety and Ethics

There's <u>danger</u> all around, particularly in science experiments. But don't let this put you off. Just be aware of the <u>hazards</u> and take <u>sensible precautions</u>. Read on to find out more...

Make Sure You're **Working Safely** in the **Lab**

1) <u>Before</u> you start any experiment, make sure you know about any <u>safety precautions</u> to do with your <u>method</u> or the <u>chemicals</u> you're using. You need to <u>follow</u> any instructions that your teacher gives you <u>carefully</u>. The chemicals you're using may be <u>hazardous</u> — for example, they might be <u>flammable</u> (<u>catch fire easily</u>), or they might <u>irritate</u> or <u>burn</u> your <u>skin</u> if it comes into contact with them.

2) Make sure that you're wearing <u>sensible clothing</u> when you're in the lab (e.g. open shoes won't protect your feet from spillages). When you're doing an experiment, you should wear a <u>lab coat</u> to protect your skin and clothing. Depending on the experiment, you may need to also wear <u>safety goggles</u> and <u>gloves</u>.

3) You also need to be aware of <u>general safety</u> in the lab, e.g. keep anything <u>flammable</u> away from lit Bunsen burners, don't directly touch any <u>hot equipment</u>, handle <u>glassware</u> carefully so it doesn't <u>break</u>, etc.

You Need to Think About **Ethical Issues** In Your Experiments

1) Any <u>organisms</u> involved in your investigations need to be treated <u>safely</u> and <u>ethically</u>.
2) <u>Animals</u> need to be treated <u>humanely</u> — they should be <u>handled carefully</u> and any wild animals captured for studying (e.g. during an investigation of the distribution of an organism) should be <u>returned to their original habitat</u>.
3) Any animals kept in the lab should also be <u>cared for</u> in a humane way, e.g. they should not be kept in <u>overcrowded conditions</u>.
4) If you are carrying out an experiment involving other <u>students</u> (e.g. investigating the effect of caffeine on reaction time), they should not be forced to participate <u>against their will</u> or feel <u>pressured</u> to take part.

BEWARE — hazardous biology experiments about...
<u>Before</u> you carry out an experiment, you must <u>consider all of the hazards</u>. They can be anything from <u>chemicals</u> to <u>sharp objects</u>, <u>pathogens</u> to <u>heating equipment</u>. Whatever the hazard, make sure you know all the <u>safety precautions</u> you should follow to keep yourself, and others, safe.

Sampling

You need to be able to carry out <u>sampling</u> that'll give you <u>non-biased results</u>. First up <u>why</u>, then <u>how</u>...

Sampling Should be **Random**

1) When you're investigating a population, it's generally <u>not possible</u> to study <u>every single organism</u> in the population. This means that you need to take <u>samples</u> of the population you're interested in.

2) The sample data will be used to <u>draw conclusions</u> about the <u>whole</u> population, so it's important that it <u>accurately</u> represents the <u>whole population</u>. *If a sample doesn't represent the population as a whole, it's said to be biased.*

3) To make sure a sample represents the population, it should be <u>random</u>.

Organisms Should Be Sampled At **Random Sites** in an Area

1) If you're interested in the <u>distribution</u> of an organism in an area, or its <u>population size</u>, you can take population samples in the area you're interested in using <u>quadrats</u> or <u>transects</u> (see pages 161-162).

2) If you only take samples from <u>one part</u> of the area, your results will be <u>biased</u> — they may not give an <u>accurate representation</u> of the <u>whole area</u>.

3) To make sure that your sampling isn't biased, you need to use a method of <u>choosing sampling sites</u> in which every site has an <u>equal chance</u> of being chosen. For example:

If you're looking at plant species in a field...

1) <u>Divide</u> the field into a <u>grid</u>.

2) <u>Label the grid</u> along the bottom and up the side with numbers.

3) Use a <u>random number generator</u> (on a computer or calculator) to select coordinates, e.g. (2,6).

4) Take your <u>samples</u> at these coordinates.

Non-random sampling
Only looks at a small part of the field.

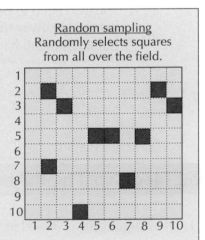

Random sampling
Randomly selects squares from all over the field.

Health Data Should be Taken from **Randomly Selected People**

1) As mentioned above, it's not practical (or even possible) to study an <u>entire human population</u>.

2) You need to use <u>random sampling</u> to choose members of the population you're interested in. For example:

A <u>health professional</u> is investigating <u>how many</u> people diagnosed with <u>Type 2 diabetes</u> in a particular country <u>also</u> have <u>heart disease</u>:

1) All the people who have been diagnosed with Type 2 diabetes in the country of interest are identified by <u>hospital records</u>. In total, there are <u>270 196</u> people.

2) These people are assigned a <u>number</u> between 1 and 270 196.

3) A <u>random number generator</u> is used to choose the sample group (e.g. it selects the individuals #72 063, #11 822, #193 123, etc.)

4) The <u>proportion</u> of people in the <u>sample</u> that have heart disease can be used to <u>estimate</u> the <u>total number</u> of people with Type 2 diabetes that also have heart disease.

Heating Substances

Some more useful lab stuff for you now — a bit about <u>heating things up</u>.

Bunsen Burners Have a **Naked Flame**

Bunsen burners are good for <u>heating things quickly</u>. But you need to make sure you're using them <u>safely</u>:

- You should always use a Bunsen burner on a <u>heat-proof mat</u>.
- If your Bunsen burner is alight but not heating anything, make sure you <u>close</u> the hole so that the flame becomes <u>yellow</u> and <u>clearly visible</u>.
- Use the <u>blue</u> flame to heat things. If you're heating a vessel <u>in</u> the flame, hold it at the <u>top</u> (e.g. with <u>tongs</u>) and point the opening <u>away from</u> yourself (and others).
- If you're heating something <u>over</u> the flame (e.g. a beaker of water), you should put a <u>tripod and gauze</u> over the Bunsen burner before you light it, and place the vessel on this.

Hole is closed

Heat-proof mat

to gas

The Temperature of **Electric Water Baths** and **Heaters** Can Be **Set**

1) A <u>water bath</u> is a container filled with water that can be heated to a <u>specific temperature</u>.

2) A <u>simple</u> water bath can be made by heating a <u>beaker of water</u> over a <u>Bunsen burner</u> and monitoring the temperature with a <u>thermometer</u>. However, it is difficult to keep the temperature of the water <u>constant</u>.

3) An <u>electric water bath</u> will monitor and adjust the temperature for you. Here's how you use one:

- <u>Set</u> the temperature on the water bath, and allow the water to <u>heat up</u>.
- To make sure it's reached the right temperature, use a <u>thermometer</u>.
- Place the vessel containing your substance in the water bath using test tube holders or tongs. The level of water outside the vessel should be <u>just above</u> the level of the substance in the vessel.
- The substance will then be warmed to the <u>same temperature</u> as the water. As the substance in the vessel is surrounded by water, the heating is very <u>even</u>.

4) <u>Electric heaters</u> are often made up of a metal plate that can be heated to a specified temperature. The vessel containing the substance you want to heat is placed on top of the hot plate. The vessel is only heated from below, so you'll usually have to <u>stir</u> the substance inside to make sure it's <u>heated evenly</u>.

Electric water baths are great for keeping the temperature constant

Make sure you're clear on how to use <u>Bunsen burners</u>, <u>electric water baths</u> and <u>heaters</u>, and more importantly, on how to use them <u>safely</u>. Obviously flames and hot things are <u>very dangerous</u>, so <u>take care</u>.

More on Microscopy and Potometers

Next up, how to use two extra bits of <u>apparatus</u> with your <u>microscope</u>, then on to <u>potometers</u>...

Stage Micrometers and Eyepiece Graticules Help You Measure

You can use a <u>stage micrometer</u> and <u>eyepiece graticule</u> to work out the <u>actual size</u> of what you're looking at down a microscope. The micrometer is used to work out the <u>value</u> of the divisions on the graticule at a <u>certain magnification</u>. When you replace it with your slide, you'll be able to measure the size of, e.g. cells. Here's an example of how...

1) <u>Line up</u> the eyepiece graticule and the stage micrometer (see below).
2) Each <u>division</u> on the stage micrometer is <u>0.1 mm</u> long.
3) At this magnification, <u>1 division</u> on the micrometer is the same as <u>4.5 divisions</u> on the graticule:

4) To work out the size of 1 division on the graticule, you need to <u>divide</u> the <u>size of the division</u> on the micrometer by the <u>number of divisions</u> on the graticule:

$0.1 \div 4.5 = 0.022...$ mm

5) So if you look at a cell under the microscope at this magnification and it's 4 eyepiece divisions long, you know it measures:

$4 \times 0.022... = 0.088...$
$= \underline{0.09 \text{ mm}}$ (1 s.f.)

Remember, if you change the objective lens you're using, you need to re-calibrate the micrometer and graticule — one division on the micrometer will then be equal to a different number of divisions on the graticule.

Potometers Should Be Set Up Under Water

You first met <u>potometers</u> on p.72. It's a special piece of apparatus used to measure the <u>water uptake</u> by a plant. Here's how to set one up:

1) <u>Cut</u> a shoot <u>underwater</u> to prevent air from entering the xylem. Cut it at a <u>slant</u> to increase the surface area available for water uptake.

2) <u>Assemble</u> the potometer <u>in water</u> and insert the shoot <u>under water</u>, so no <u>air</u> can enter.

3) Remove the apparatus from the water but keep the end of the capillary tube <u>submerged</u> in a beaker of water.

4) Check that the apparatus is <u>watertight</u> and <u>airtight</u>.

5) <u>Dry</u> the leaves, allow time for the shoot to <u>acclimatise</u> and then <u>shut</u> the tap.

6) Remove the end of the capillary tube from the beaker of water until <u>one air bubble</u> has formed, then put the end of the tube <u>back into the water</u>.

7) A potometer can be used to estimate the <u>transpiration rate</u> of a plant. There's more about this on page 72.

As the plant takes up water, the air bubble moves along the scale.

reservoir of water

Tap is shut off during experiment.

Water moves this way.

capillary tube with a scale

Bubble moves this way.

Beaker of water.

If there are air bubbles in the apparatus or the plant's xylem it will affect your results.

Comparing Results

Once you've had fun collecting all your data, a few <u>calculations</u> might be needed to work out what your data actually shows. Calculating <u>percentage change</u> is a great way to <u>compare results</u>...

Percentage Change Allows you to Compare Results

1) When investigating the <u>change</u> in a variable, you may want to <u>compare</u> results that didn't have the <u>same initial value</u>.

For example, you may want to compare the <u>change in mass</u> of potato cylinders left in different concentrations of sugar solution that had <u>different initial masses</u> (see page 31).

2) One way to do this is to calculate the <u>percentage change</u>. You work it out like this:

$$\text{percentage (\%) change} = \frac{\text{final value} - \text{original value}}{\text{original value}} \times 100$$

EXAMPLE:

A student is investigating the effect of the concentration of sugar solution on potato cells. She records the mass of potato cylinders before and after placing them in sugar solutions of different concentrations. The table below shows some of her results. Which potato cylinder had the largest percentage change?

Potato cylinder	Concentration (mol/dm³)	Mass at start (g)	Mass at end (g)
1	0.0	7.5	8.7
2	1.0	8.0	6.8

1) Stick each set of results into the <u>equation</u>:

$$\frac{\%}{\text{change}} = \frac{\text{final value} - \text{original value}}{\text{original value}} \times 100$$

1. $\frac{8.7 - 7.5}{7.5} \times 100 = 16\%$

The mass at the <u>start</u> is the <u>original value</u> and the mass at the <u>end</u> is the <u>final value</u>.

2) <u>Compare</u> the results.

2. $\frac{6.8 - 8.0}{8.0} \times 100 = -15\%$

16% is greater than 15%, so the potato cylinder in the 0.0 mol/dm³ sugar solution had the largest percentage change.

Here, the mass has <u>decreased</u> so the percentage change is <u>negative</u>.

Good practical skills are needed when you're doing an investigation...

...but you also need to know about them for your <u>exams</u>. You're <u>guaranteed</u> to be tested on your <u>practical knowledge</u>, so if you've merrily skipped through this section, you'd better <u>go back</u> and <u>read it through again</u>.

Practice Exams

Once you've been through all the questions in this book, you should feel pretty confident about the exams.
As final preparation, here is a set of **practice exams** to really get you set for the real thing. The time allowed for each paper is 1 hour 15 minutes. These papers are designed to give you the best possible preparation for your exams.

GCSE Combined Science

Biology Paper 1

Higher Tier

In addition to this paper you should have:
• A ruler.
• A calculator.

Centre name				
Centre number				
Candidate number				

Time allowed:
• 1 hour 15 minutes

Surname	
Other names	
Candidate signature	

Instructions to candidates
• Write your name and other details in the spaces provided above.
• Answer **all** questions in the spaces provided.
• Do all rough work on the paper.
• Cross out any work you do not want to be marked.

Information for candidates
• The marks available are given in brackets at the end of each question.
• There are 70 marks available for this paper.
• You are allowed to use a calculator.
• You should use good English and present your answers in a clear and organised way.
• For Questions 1.4, 2.2, 4.5 and 7 ensure that your answers have a clear and logical structure, include the right scientific terms, spelt correctly and include detailed, relevant information.

Advice to candidates
• In calculations show clearly how you worked out your answers.

For examiner's use						
Q	Attempt Nº			Q	Attempt Nº		
	1	2	3		1	2	3
1				5			
2				6			
3				7			
4				8			
Total							

1   **Figure 1** shows a single-celled organism called *Euglena*, found in pond water.

Figure 1

1.1   Name part **X**.

....

[1 mark]

1.2   *Euglena* is a eukaryote. Which of the following is **not** a eukaryote?
Tick **one** box.

☐ sperm cell   ☐ muscle cell   ☐ fruit fly   ☐ *E. coli* bacteria

[1 mark]

1.3   A scientist viewed an individual *Euglena* under a microscope with × 150 magnification.
He calculated the real length of the *Euglena* to be 0.054 mm.
Calculate the length of the image of the Euglena. Use the formula:

$$\text{magnification} = \frac{\text{image size}}{\text{real size}}$$

....

....

.... mm

[2 marks]

Question 1 continues on the next page

Turn over ▶

1.4 When *Euglena* was first discovered, scientists disagreed over whether it was a plant or an animal.
Compare the features of plant and animal cells.
Include details of their features in your answer.

....

....

....

....

....

....

....

....

....

....

....

....

[6 marks]

2   Measles, mumps and rubella are all examples of communicable diseases.

2.1   How is measles spread between people?
Tick **one** box.

☐   By droplets from an infected person's sneeze or cough.

☐   By sexual contact.

☐   By eating contaminated food.

☐   By a vector.

[1 mark]

2.2   The MMR vaccine protects against measles, mumps and rubella.
Explain how vaccination helps to protect the body against a disease.

....

....

....

....

....

....

[4 marks]

Zika virus disease is another example of a communicable disease.
Symptoms of infection include fever, skin rashes, muscle and joint pain, and
headaches. The virus that causes the disease is spread by a mosquito vector.

2.3   Suggest **two** ways that the spread of the Zika virus disease could be reduced.

....

....

....

[2 marks]

Turn over for the next question

Turn over ▶

3   Different chemical reagents can be used to test for the presence of certain molecules in samples of food.

3.1   A student prepared a food sample in order to test whether the sample contained protein. What reagent should be used for this test?
Tick **one** box.

☐   Benedict's solution

☐   iodine solution

☐   biuret solution

☐   Sudan III stain solution

[1 mark]

The student tested four different food samples for reducing sugars.
She obtained the results shown in **Table 1**.

Table 1

Sample	Colour of sample
A	blue
B	brick-red
C	yellow
D	green

3.2   Name the reagent that the student would have used to test for reducing sugars.

....
[1 mark]

3.3   Which of the samples in **Table 1** didn't contain reducing sugars?
Tick **one** box.

☐   A

☐   B

☐   C

☐   D

[1 mark]

Lactose is a reducing sugar commonly found in dairy products, such as milk and cheese. An enzyme called lactase breaks down lactose during digestion. The resulting products are the sugars glucose and galactose. These are absorbed into the blood from the small intestine.

3.4 Describe how the small intestine is adapted to absorb molecules such as glucose.

....

....

....

....

[3 marks]

3.5 Lactose intolerance is a digestive problem caused by insufficient production of lactase.

To test a person for lactose intolerance, they are given a drink of lactose solution.
A blood sample is then taken from them every 30 minutes for two hours.
The blood is tested to see how much sugar it contains.
Suggest what will happen to the blood sugar level of a person who is lactose intolerant during the test. Explain your answer.

....

....

....

....

[2 marks]

Turn over for the next question

Turn over ▶

4 **Figure 2** shows a human heart.

Figure 2

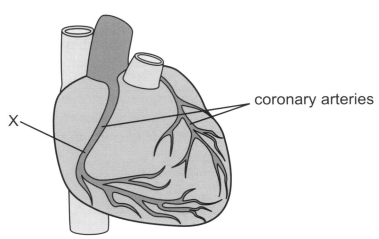

coronary arteries

X

4.1 Explain what would happen if the coronary artery was blocked at the point labelled **X**.

....

....
[2 marks]

A patient has fatty deposits in the walls of one of his coronary arteries.
The patient's doctor recommends that the patient is treated using a stent.

4.2 Explain how having a stent fitted could help the patient.

....

....
[1 mark]

Statins are a type of drug used to reduce the risk of coronary heart disease.

A new statin has been developed and was initially put through preclinical testing. Following this, the drug was given to thirty healthy volunteers in a clinical trial.

A trial was then carried out on 2000 patients who had previously had a heart attack — half were given the drug and half were given a placebo.

Figure 3 shows the results after five years of treatment.

Figure 3

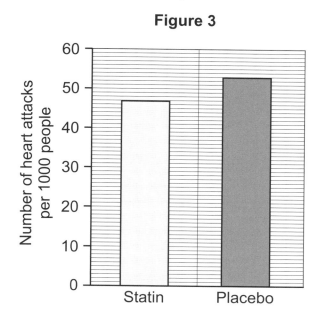

4.3   During the clinical trial, what was the main reason for giving the drug to healthy human volunteers?

....

[1 mark]

4.4   Give **one** reason why the results of the trial could be considered valid.

....

....

[1 mark]

Question 4 continues on the next page

Turn over ▶

4.5 A person with heart failure may need to have their heart replaced. The replacement heart can either be from a donor or it can be an artificial heart.

Evaluate the treatment of heart failure using a heart transplant from a donor and using an artificial heart. Include a justified conclusion in your evaluation.

....

....

....

....

....

....

....

....

....

....

....

....

[6 marks]

5   A student did an experiment to investigate the effect of temperature on the action of the enzyme amylase. The method used is shown below.

---

1. Add a set volume of starch solution to a test tube and the same volume of amylase solution to another.

2. Place the test tubes in a water bath at 10 °C.

3. Allow the starch and amylase solutions to reach the temperature of the water bath, then mix them together and return the mixture to the water bath.

4. Take a small sample of the mixture every ten seconds and test for starch.

5. Stop the experiment when starch is no longer present in the sample.

6. Repeat the experiment at different temperatures.

5.1   What happens to the starch solution during the experiment?

....
[1 mark]

5.2   Suggest how the student could have tested for the presence of starch in **Step 4**.

....

....

....

....
[3 marks]

Question 5 continues on the next page

Turn over ▶

Figure 4 shows a graph of the student's results.

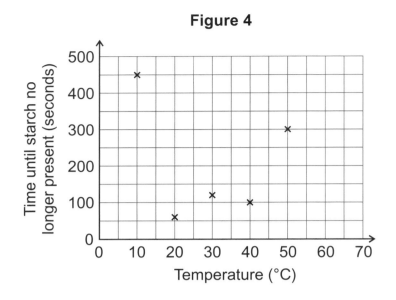

Figure 4

5.3 Calculate the rate of the reaction at 40 °C.
Use the formula:

$$\text{Rate} = \frac{1000}{\text{time}}$$

....

....

.... s^{-1}

[2 marks]

5.4 At 60 °C, the amount of starch in the mixture did not decrease.
Explain why.

....

....

....

....

[3 marks]

5.5 The student thinks that one of the results shown in **Figure 4** is likely to be anomalous. Explain which is the anomalous result and suggest what the student might have done to cause this anomalous result.

....

....

....

[3 marks]

The student plans to alter the experiment in order to investigate the effect of pH on the action of amylase.

5.6 Describe how the pH could be altered in the experiment.

....

....

[1 mark]

Turn over for the next question

Turn over ▶

6 A scientist measured the rate of transpiration in two plants over 48 hours.
The results are shown in **Figure 5**.

Figure 5

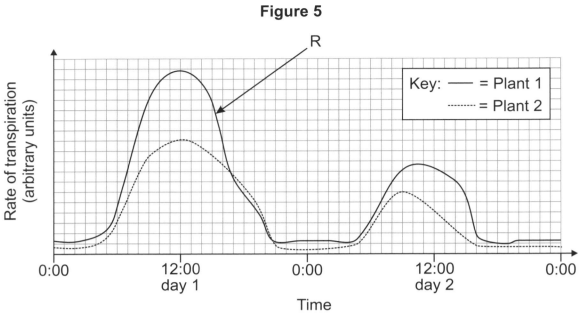

6.1 The rate of transpiration for both plants was slower on **day 2** than on **day 1**.
Suggest **one** explanation for this.

....

....

....
[2 marks]

6.2 At time **R** on the graph, **plant 1** was wilting. Suggest **one** explanation for this.

....

....
[1 mark]

6.3 Describe how a transpiration stream moves water through a plant.

....

....

....

....

....
[3 marks]

7   Herbicides are chemicals that are used to kill unwanted plants.
Some herbicides work by disrupting the cell cycle within plants.

Describe the stages of the cell cycle and suggest why disrupting the cell cycle by using herbicides can kill plants.

....

....

....

....

....

....

....

....

....

....

....

....

....

[6 marks]

Turn over for the next question

Turn over ▶

8   A student is investigating how his heart rate changes during and after exercise.
He measures his heart rate using a portable heart rate monitor.
He takes his resting heart rate before running around the school track
for two minutes. Then he rests again. His results are shown in **Table 2**.

Table 2

Time after first heart rate measurement taken (min)	First run — Heart rate (beats/min)
0	72
1	118
2	132
3	129
4	116
5	98
6	84
7	76
8	72
9	72

8.1   Complete **Figure 6** using the data from **Table 2**.
   •   Complete the *x*-axis. Include a label and use a suitable scale.
   •   Plot the heart rate.
   •   Draw a curve of best fit.

Figure 6

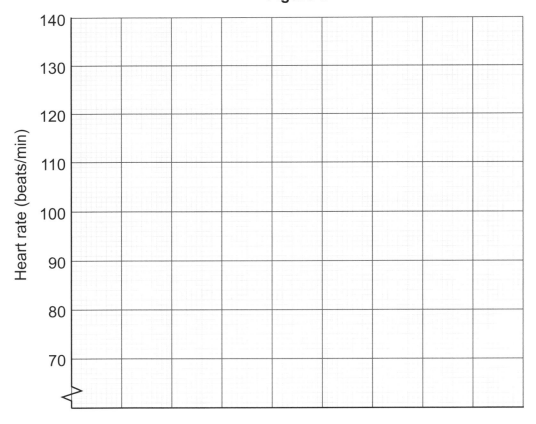

[4 marks]

8.2 Use your graph in **Figure 6** to estimate the student's heart rate after thirty seconds.

heart rate = ... (beats/min)

[1 mark]

8.3 Describe how the student's heart rate changes with exercise.
Explain why this change occurs.

....

....

....

....

....

[4 marks]

END OF QUESTIONS

GCSE Combined Science

Biology Paper 2

Higher Tier

In addition to this paper you should have:
*   A ruler.
*   A calculator.

Centre name				
Centre number				
Candidate number				

Time allowed:
*   1 hour 15 minutes

Surname
Other names
Candidate signature

Instructions to candidates
*   Write your name and other details in the spaces provided above.
*   Answer **all** questions in the spaces provided.
*   Do all rough work on the paper.
*   Cross out any work you do not want to be marked.

Information for candidates
*   The marks available are given in brackets at the end of each question.
*   There are 70 marks available for this paper.
*   You are allowed to use a calculator.
*   You should use good English and present your answers in a clear and organised way.
*   For Questions 2.5, 4.7 and 6.2 ensure that your answers have a clear and logical structure, include the right scientific terms, spelt correctly and include detailed, relevant information.

Advice to candidates
*   In calculations show clearly how you worked out your answers.

For examiner's use

Q	Attempt Nº			Q	Attempt Nº		
	1	2	3		1	2	3
1				5			
2				6			
3				7			
4				8			
Total							

1   The endocrine system is important for regulating many different processes in the body.

Figure 1 shows some of the glands in the endocrine system.

Figure 1

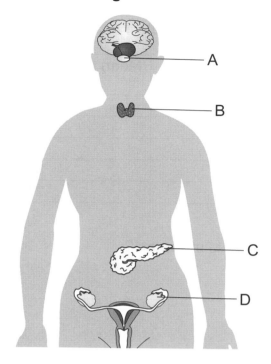

The thyroid gland releases a hormone called thyroxine. One way in which thyroxine affects the body is by increasing the strength of the heart beat.

1.1   Which label on **Figure 1** points to the thyroid gland? Tick **one** box.

☐ A   ☐ B   ☐ C   ☐ D

[1 mark]

1.2   Describe how thyroxine is able to directly affect cells in the heart.

....

....

....

[2 marks]

The pituitary gland is an important part of the endocrine system.

1.3   Explain why the pituitary gland is often referred to as the 'master gland'.

....

....

....

[2 marks]

Turn over for the next question

Turn over ▶

2   A student was investigating the distribution of buttercups
in an area around his school.
He counted the number of buttercups in 10 quadrats in five different fields.
His quadrat measured 1 m². His results are shown in **Table 1**.

Table 1

Field	Mean number of buttercups per quadrat
A	10
B	35
C	21
D	37
E	21

2.1   What is the median of the data in **Table 1**?

....

[1 mark]

2.2   A week later, the student repeated his experiment in a sixth field, Field **F**.
His results for each quadrat are shown below:

6   15   9   14   20   5   3   11   10   7

Using this data, calculate the mean number of buttercups per m² in Field **F**.

....

....

Mean = ... buttercups per m²

[2 marks]

2.3   Field **F** measures 90 m by 120 m.
Estimate the population of buttercups in Field **F**.

....

....

Estimated population = ... buttercups

[2 marks]

The student observed that the distribution of buttercups changed across Field **A**. Buttercups grow well in damp soil, so the student thinks that the change in the distribution of buttercups is due to variability in the moisture level of the soil across the field. The student wants to investigate this.

2.4 Suggest a hypothesis about the distribution of buttercups in Field **A**, based on the student's observations.

....

....

[1 mark]

2.5 Describe how the student could investigate this hypothesis.

....

....

....

....

....

....

....

[4 marks]

Turn over for the next question

Turn over ▶

3 The peppered moth is an insect that lives on the trunks of trees in Britain.
The moths are prey for birds such as thrushes.

The peppered moth exists in two varieties:
- A light-coloured variety that is better camouflaged on tree trunks in unpolluted areas.
- A dark-coloured variety that is better camouflaged on sooty tree trunks in badly polluted areas.

Figures 2 and **3** show these two varieties of moths on different tree trunks.

Figure 2   **Figure 3**

The dark variety of the moth was first recorded in the North of England in 1848.

It became increasingly common in polluted areas until the 1960s, when the number of soot covered trees declined because of the introduction of new laws.

3.1 The binomial name of the peppered moth is *Biston betularia*.
What is the moth's genus?

....

[1 mark]

3.2 Which variety of moth has a better chance of survival in a soot polluted area?

....

[1 mark]

3.3 Using the idea of natural selection, explain why the variety of moth given in **3.2** became more common in soot polluted areas.

....

....

....

....

[3 marks]

4 A scientist was investigating the reflex actions of males and females.

The scientist made the following hypothesis:

'Males have faster reaction times than females.'

The reaction times of eight participants were tested in the investigation.
Each participant was tapped just below the knee with a small rubber hammer.
When the leg was tapped it automatically kicked outwards at the knee.

The scientist recorded how long it took each participant to respond to
the stimulus of the tap on the leg. Each participant did the test 20 times,
and a mean reaction time was calculated (to 2 decimal places).

The results are shown in **Table 2**.

Table 2

Sex	Participant	Age (years)	Mean reaction time (s)
Female	1	29	0.05
	2	26	0.06
	3	24	0.06
	4	27	0.04
Male	5	19	0.05
	6	22	0.04
	7	25	0.04
	8	20	0.05

4.1 How can you tell that the participants' response was a reflex?
Give **two** reasons.

....

....

....

....

[2 marks]

4.2 What was the dependent variable in this experiment?
Tick **one** box.

☐ age   ☐ stimulus   ☐ reaction time   ☐ sex

[1 mark]

Question 4 continues on the next page

Turn over ▶

4.3   What was the independent variable in this experiment?
Tick **one** box.

☐ age   ☐ stimulus   ☐ reaction time   ☐ sex

[1 mark]

4.4   **Figure 4** shows the mean reaction times for males and females in the investigation.

Figure 4

What can be concluded from the data in **Figure 4**?
Refer back to the scientist's hypothesis in your answer.

....

....

[2 marks]

4.5   Suggest **one** variable that the scientist should have controlled in this experiment.

....

....

[1 mark]

Another example of a reflex is the response of moving your hand away from a painful stimulus. **Figure 5** shows the parts of the nervous system involved in this reflex.

Figure 5

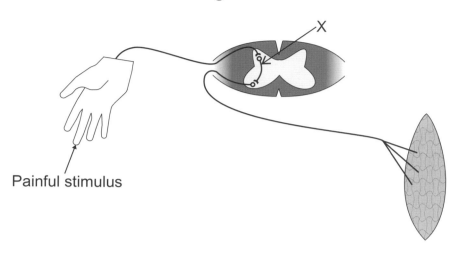

Painful stimulus

4.6 Name part **X** shown in **Figure 5**.

....

[1 mark]

4.7 The pain stimulus is detected by receptors in the skin and causes a reflex response. Describe the path taken by a nervous impulse in this reflex, beginning at the receptors.

....

....

....

....

....

....

....

....

....

....

[6 marks]

Turn over for the next question

Turn over ▶

208

5   Various research programmes aim to improve human health through research into the human genome.

5.1   What is meant by the term 'genome'?

....

[1 mark]

Cystic fibrosis is an inherited disorder caused by a recessive allele.

5.2   How could research into the human genome have the potential to help people with cystic fibrosis?

....

....

[1 mark]

A couple have a baby boy. The doctor tells them that the baby has inherited cystic fibrosis. Neither parent shows signs of the disorder.

5.3   Construct a Punnett square to show how the baby inherited cystic fibrosis. Use the diagram to work out the probability of any future child of the couple inheriting cystic fibrosis.

Use **F** to represent the dominant allele and **f** to represent the recessive allele.

Probability = ...

[4 marks]

5.4 Is the baby homozygous or heterozygous for cystic fibrosis?
Explain your answer.

....

....

[1 mark]

Turn over for the next question

6 Hepatitis B is a viral disease that can severely damage the liver. The disease can be prevented in people who have been vaccinated against it. Being vaccinated involves being deliberately exposed to antigens carried by the hepatitis B virus. Scientists have successfully genetically engineered potatoes so that they can be used as a vaccine against hepatitis B.

6.1 Production of the genetically engineered potatoes involves the introduction of the HBsAg gene into the potatoes. Suggest the role of the HBsAg gene.

....

....

[1 mark]

6.2 Describe the process involved in producing genetically engineered organisms.

....

....

....

....

....

....

....

[4 marks]

7 Reproduction can be sexual or asexual.

7.1 Give **three** differences between sexual and asexual reproduction.

....

....

....

....

....

....

[3 marks]

In humans, sexual reproduction involves the reproductive system.

7.2 The male reproductive system includes the testes.
What hormone is produced by the testes?

....

[1 mark]

7.3 The female reproductive system includes the ovaries.

The ovaries produce the hormone oestrogen.
Describe the role of oestrogen in the menstrual cycle.

....

....

....

....

[2 marks]

Question 7 continues on the next page

Turn over ▶

Figure 6 shows the fluctuations in the levels of four different hormones during one 28 day menstrual cycle.

Figure 6

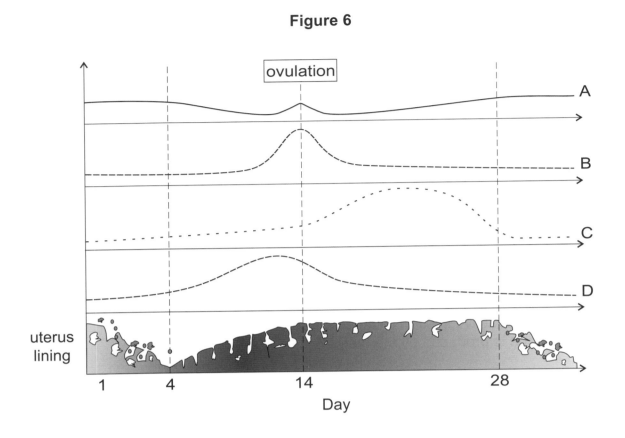

7.4   Which line in **Figure 6** represents progesterone?
Explain your answer.

Line ....

Explanation ....

....

....

[2 marks]

Some methods of contraception use reproductive hormones to control fertility. One such method is the contraceptive implant, shown in **Figure 7**.

Figure 7

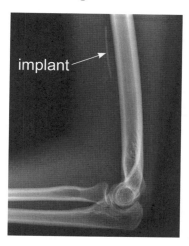

implant

The contraceptive implant:

- is a small, plastic rod that is inserted by a doctor or nurse
- releases progesterone, which reduces fertility
- is effective for three years
- is over 99% effective at preventing pregnancy
- can cause side effects such as headaches and nausea
- can be made less effective by certain medications

Figure 8 shows a condom. The condom is a barrier method of contraception.

Figure 8

The condom:

- is worn over the penis during intercourse
- prevents sperm from entering the vagina
- can only be used once
- is 98% effective at preventing pregnancy when used correctly
- protects against sexually transmitted disease (STDs)

7.5 Use the information to evaluate the implant and condom as methods of contraception. Give a conclusion of which you think is the better method of contraception. Justify your conclusion.

....

....

....

....

....

....

....

....

[4 marks]

Turn over for the next question

Turn over ▶

8   **Figure 9** shows the carbon cycle.

Figure 9

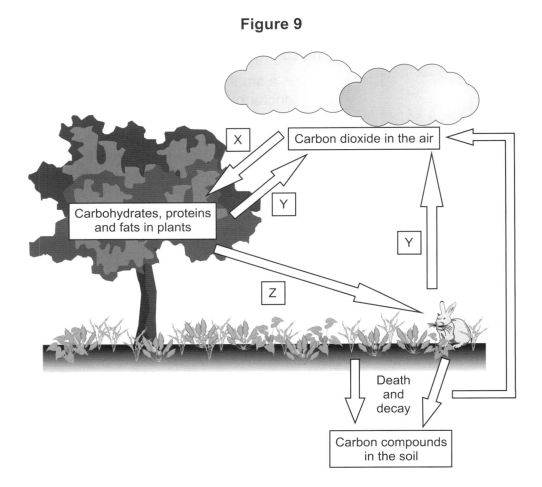

8.1   Describe what is occurring at points **X**, **Y** and **Z** in the cycle.

....

....

....

....

....

[3 marks]

8.2   How are microorganisms involved in the carbon cycle?

....

....

....

[2 marks]

A scientist was examining some data to see if there is a link between the global human population and the carbon dioxide concentration in the atmosphere.

Figure 10 shows the two graphs that the scientist examined.

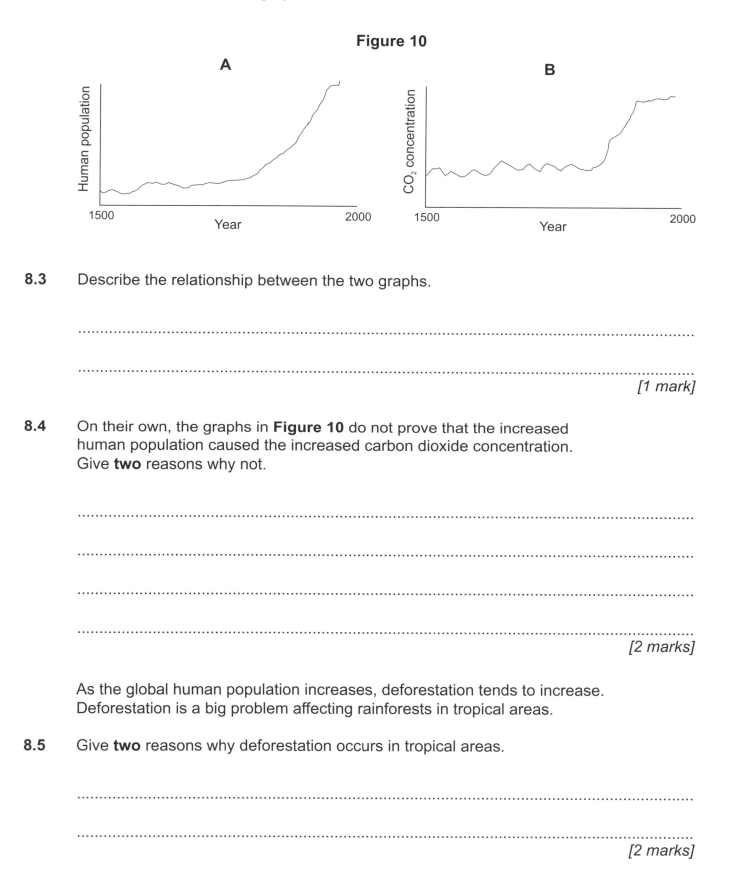

Figure 10

8.3 Describe the relationship between the two graphs.

....

....
[1 mark]

8.4 On their own, the graphs in **Figure 10** do not prove that the increased human population caused the increased carbon dioxide concentration. Give **two** reasons why not.

....

....

....

....
[2 marks]

As the global human population increases, deforestation tends to increase. Deforestation is a big problem affecting rainforests in tropical areas.

8.5 Give **two** reasons why deforestation occurs in tropical areas.

....

....
[2 marks]

Question 8 continues on the next page

Turn over ▶

8.6 Deforestation is one factor that can cause the amount of carbon dioxide in the atmosphere to increase. The rising concentration of carbon dioxide in our atmosphere has been linked to global warming.

Describe **two** possible biological consequences of global warming.

....

....

....

....

....

....

[2 marks]

END OF QUESTIONS

Topic 1 — Cell Biology

Page 21

Warm-Up Questions

1) mitochondria
2) Plant cells have a rigid cell wall, they have a permanent vacuole and they contain chloroplasts.
3) Any two from: e.g. prokaryotic cells are smaller than eukaryotic cells. / Prokaryotic cells don't have mitochondria but eukaryotic cells do. / Prokaryotic cells don't have a true nucleus but eukaryotic cells do. / Prokaryotic cells have circular DNA but eukaryotic cells don't.
4) electron microscope
5) 4.5×10^{-4} µm

Exam Questions

1 nucleus *[1 mark]*
Remember, DNA in prokaryotic cells floats freely in the cytoplasm — it's not stored in a nucleus.
2.1 C *[1 mark]*
2.2 They absorb light needed for photosynthesis to make food for the plant *[1 mark]*.
2.3 They're where proteins are made in the cell *[1 mark]*.
3.1 How to grade your answer:
Level 0: There is no relevant information. *[No marks]*
Level 1: There is a brief explanation of how to prepare a slide or how to use a light microscope. *[1 to 2 marks]*
Level 2: There is some explanation of how to prepare a slide and use a light microscope. *[3 to 4 marks]*
Level 3: There is a clear and detailed explanation of how to prepare a slide and use a light microscope. *[5 to 6 marks]*
Here are some points your answer may include:
To prepare a slide:
Add a drop of water to the middle of a clean slide.
Cut up an onion and separate it out into layers.
Use tweezers to peel off some epidermal tissue from the bottom of one of the layers.
Use tweezers to place the epidermal tissue into the water on the slide.
Add a drop of iodine solution/stain.
Place a cover slip on top by standing it upright on the slide, next to the water droplet, then carefully tilting and lowering it so it covers the onion tissue without trapping any air bubbles.
To use a light microscope:
Clip the slide onto the stage.
Select the lowest-powered objective lens.
Use the coarse adjustment knob to move the stage up to just below the objective lens (without looking down the eyepiece).
Look down the eyepiece and use the coarse adjustment knob to move the stage downwards until the image is roughly in focus.
Adjust the focus with the fine adjustment knob, until a clear image of the cells is visible.
To see the cells with greater magnification, swap to a higher-powered objective lens and refocus.
3.2 real size = image size ÷ magnification
= 7.5 mm ÷ 100
= 0.075 mm
$0.075 \times 1000 =$ **75 µm** *[3 marks for correct answer, otherwise 1 mark for correctly rearranging the equation and 1 mark for 0.075 mm.]*

Page 28

Warm-Up Questions

1) It's the process by which a cell changes to become specialised for its job.
2) The cell has a hair-like shape, which gives it a large surface area to absorb water and minerals from the soil.
3) Copies of the plant can be made by taking stem cells from the meristem and growing them into new, genetically identical plants (clones).
4) in the nucleus
5) True

Exam Questions

1.1 The amount of DNA is doubling *[1 mark]* so that there is one copy for each new cell *[1 mark]*.
1.2 The two new cells separate *[1 mark]*.
1.3 two *[1 mark]*
2.1 They could be grown into a particular type of cell, which can then be used to replace faulty cells *[1 mark]*.
2.2 Embryonic stem cells have the potential to develop into any kind of cell, whereas adult stem cells can only develop into certain types of cell *[1 mark]*.
2.3 E.g. bone marrow *[1 mark]*.

Pages 37-38

Warm-Up Questions

1) The higher the temperature, the faster the rate of diffusion because the particles have more energy and so move around faster.
2) A partially permeable membrane only allows small molecules (e.g. water) to diffuse through it.
3) Osmosis and active transport.
4) They're thin, they have a large surface area, they have lots of blood vessels and they're often ventilated.
5) E.g. alveoli (in the lung) and villi (in the small intestine).
6) Any two from: e.g. it is made up of gill filaments which give a large surface area. / Each gill filament is covered in lamellae, which further increases the surface area. / The lamellae have a thin surface layer of cells. / The lamellae have lots of capillaries. / A large concentration gradient is maintained between the water and the blood.

Exam Questions

1.1 The ink will diffuse / spread out through the water *[1 mark]*. This is because the ink particles will move from where there is a higher concentration of them (the drop of ink) to where there is a lower concentration of them (the surrounding water) *[1 mark]*.
1.2 The ink particles will diffuse/spread out faster *[1 mark]*.
2.1 The potato cylinder in tube D, because this tube contains the most concentrated sugar solution so this cylinder will have lost the most water *[1 mark]* by osmosis *[1 mark]*.
2.2 Tube A contained distilled water, so some of the water moved by osmosis into the potato cylinder *[1 mark]* from an area of high water concentration to an area of low water concentration *[1 mark]*.
3.1 By diffusion down their concentration gradients into the blood *[1 mark]*, and by active transport, against their concentration gradient *[1 mark]*.

3.2 E.g. they increase the surface area to maximise absorption *[1 mark]*. They have a thin wall/a single layer of surface cells to reduce the distance across which diffusion occurs *[1 mark]*. They have a good blood supply for the uptake of substances *[1 mark]*.

4.1 diffusion *[1 mark]*

The acid must by moving by diffusion here as it is moving from a region of higher concentration (outside the cubes) to a region of lower concentration (inside the cubes, which don't contain any acid to start with).

4.2 $(835 + 825 + 842 + 838) \div 4 = $ **835 s**
[2 marks for correct answer, otherwise 1 mark for correct working.]

4.3 Surface area: $(10 \times 10) \times 6 = 600$ mm^2
Volume: $10 \times 10 \times 10 = 1000$ mm^3
So the surface area to volume ratio is 600 : 1000, which simplifies to **3 : 5**
[3 marks for correct answer, otherwise 1 mark for correct surface area and 1 mark for correct volume.]

600 and 1000 are both divisible by 200. If you don't spot this straight away, you could simplify the ratio by first dividing both sides by 100, then by 2.

4.4 As the size of the gelatine cube increases, the time taken for the cube to become yellow increases *[1 mark]*. This is because there is a greater distance for the acid to travel in the bigger cubes / the bigger cubes have a smaller surface area to volume ratio *[1 mark]*, which decreases the rate of diffusion *[1 mark]*.

5 Surface area:
$(2 \times 2) \times 2 = 8$
$(2 \times 1) \times 4 = 8$
$8 + 8 = 16$ µm^2
Volume: $2 \times 2 \times 1 = 4$ µm^3
So the surface area to volume ratio is **16 : 4**, or **4 : 1**.
[3 marks for correct answer, otherwise 1 mark for correct surface area and 1 mark for correct volume.]

Topic 2 — Organisation

Pages 49-50

Warm-Up Questions

1) A group of organs working together to perform a particular function.
2) The pH at which the enzyme works best.
3) a) amylase
   b) protease
   c) lipase

Carbohydrases (e.g. amylase) break down carbohydrates, such as starch. Proteases break down proteins, and lipases break down lipids (fats).

4) a) (simple) sugars
   b) amino acids
   c) glycerol and fatty acids
5) stomach, pancreas, small intestine
6) E.g. break up the food using a pestle and mortar. Then transfer the ground up food to a beaker and add some distilled water. Next, stir the mixture with a glass rod, and finally filter the solution using a funnel lined with filter paper.

Exam Questions

1.1

Place where bile is produced

[1 mark]

1.2 It neutralises the hydrochloric acid from the stomach *[1 mark]*.

1.3 It emulsifies fats *[1 mark]* to give a much bigger surface area of fat for the enzyme lipase to work on *[1 mark]*.

2.1 The enzyme has a specific shape which will only fit with one type of substrate *[1 mark]*.

2.2 It would break the bonds in the enzyme and change the shape of the enzyme's active site/denature the enzyme *[1 mark]*. This would mean the substrate would no longer fit into it so the enzyme wouldn't work anymore *[1 mark]*.

A similar thing happens when the pH or the temperature is too high — the bonds are disrupted and the shape of the active site may change.

3.1 Accept answers between 38 °C and 40 °C *[1 mark]*.

3.2 Enzyme B, because it has an unusually high optimum temperature which it would need to work in the hot vent *[1 mark]*.

4 The food sample contains starch *[1 mark]* and lipids *[1 mark]*, but no proteins *[1 mark]*.

5.1 To prevent the starch coming into contact with amylase in the syringe, which would have started the reaction before he had started the stop clock *[1 mark]*.

5.2 Rate $= 1000 \div 60 = $ **17 s^{-1}** (2 s.f.) *[1 mark]*

5.3 Repeat the experiment using buffers with a range of different pH values and compare the results *[1 mark]*.

Pages 56-57

Warm-Up Questions

1) bronchi
2) They supply oxygenated blood to the heart itself.
3) A device that is implanted under the skin and has a wire going to the heart. It produces an electric current to keep the heart beating regularly.
4) They carry blood back to the heart.
5) They help the blood to clot at a wound.

Exam Questions

1.1 $495 \div 12$
= 41 breaths per minute. *[1 mark]*

You might be wondering why the answer has been rounded to 41 when the calculator said 41.25. That's because you can't get a quarter of a breath.

1.2 Resting heart rate is controlled by a group of cells in the right atrium wall that act as a pacemaker *[1 mark]*.

2.1 It is biconcave, which gives it a large surface area for absorbing oxygen *[1 mark]*.

2.2 E.g. it contains haemoglobin *[1 mark]* which binds with oxygen so it can be carried to the body tissues *[1 mark]*. / It has no nucleus *[1 mark]* so there is space to carry oxygen *[1 mark]*.

2.3 White blood cells *[1 mark]*. They defend the body against infection *[1 mark]*.

2.4 They have permeable walls *[1 mark]*, so substances can diffuse in and out *[1 mark]*. Their walls are usually only one cell thick *[1 mark]*, which increases the rate of diffusion by decreasing the distance over which it occurs *[1 mark]*.

2.5 1.155 l × 1000 = 1155 ml
= 1155 ÷ 2.5 = 462 ml/min *[2 marks for correct answer, otherwise 1 mark for correct working.]*

Make sure you read the question carefully — if you gave your answer in l/min you wouldn't have got all the marks available.

3.1 A — aorta, B — vena cava, C — left atrium *[1 mark]*

3.2 It pumps blood around the body *[1 mark]*.

3.3 To prevent the backflow of blood *[1 mark]*.

3.4 How to grade your answer:
Level 0: There is no relevant information. *[No marks]*
Level 1: There are some relevant points describing how deoxygenated blood passes through the heart to reach the lungs but the answer is missing some detail. *[1 to 2 marks]*
Level 2: There is a clear, detailed description of how deoxygenated blood passes through the heart to reach the lungs. *[3 to 4 marks]*
Here are some points your answer may include:
Deoxygenated blood enters the right atrium through the vena cava.
The right atrium contracts.
The blood passes through a valve into the right ventricle.
The right ventricle contracts, forcing the blood through the pulmonary artery and out of the heart towards the lungs.

4.1 E.g. the vein has a bigger lumen/thinner wall/valves *[1 mark]*. / The artery has a smaller lumen/thicker wall/ no valves *[1 mark]*.

To answer this question, you needed to think about how the structure of veins and arteries differ — and how you could tell them apart by just looking at them.

4.2 The vein, because it has a thinner wall/less muscle in its wall/ isn't as strong *[1 mark]*.

Page 61

Warm-Up Questions

1) the coronary arteries
2) a) a stent
   b) E.g. complications during the operation, infection from surgery and developing a blood clot/thrombosis.
3) A mechanical device that is put into a person to pump blood if their own heart fails.

Exam Questions

1.1 fatty material *[1 mark]*

1.2 The fatty material causes the coronary arteries to become narrow, so blood flow to the heart muscle is restricted *[1 mark]*. This reduces (or stops) the delivery of oxygen to the heart muscle *[1 mark]*.

2.1 It could mean that blood flows in both directions rather than just forward *[1 mark]*, so the blood wouldn't circulate as effectively as normal *[1 mark]*.

2.2 Biological valves *[1 mark]* — these are replacement valves that can be taken from humans or other mammals *[1 mark]*. Mechanical valves *[1 mark]* — these are man-made replacement valves *[1 mark]*.

2.3 E.g. it requires surgery, which could lead to bleeding/ infection. / There could be problems with blood clots *[1 mark]*.

3.1 Statins are drugs that can reduce the amount of 'bad' cholesterol present in the bloodstream *[1 mark]*. This slows down the rate of fatty deposits forming, which reduces the likelihood of coronary heart disease developing *[1 mark]*.

3.2 E.g. the patient has to remember to take them every day. / Statins can sometimes cause negative side effects. / The effect of taking statins isn't instant *[1 mark]*.

Page 67

Warm-Up Questions

1) The state of physical and mental wellbeing.
2) It can be spread from person to person or between people and animals.
3) E.g. money is needed to research/treat the diseases. / People with non-communicable diseases may be unable to work, which may reduce the country's economy.
4) The presence of certain substances in the body. / The presence of certain substances in the environment.

Exam Questions

1.1 A risk factor is something that is linked to an increase in the likelihood that a person will develop a certain disease during their lifetime *[1 mark]*.

1.2 E.g. smoking *[1 mark]*

1.3 E.g. ionising radiation *[1 mark]*

2.1 Uncontrolled cell division *[1 mark]*.

2.2 malignant *[1 mark]*

2.3 Tumour cells can break off and spread to other parts of the body by travelling in the bloodstream *[1 mark]*. The malignant cells then invade healthy tissues elsewhere in the body and form secondary tumours *[1 mark]*.

3.1 A disease that cannot spread between people or between animals and people *[1 mark]*.

3.2 Because of the problem with their immune system, their body is less likely to be able to defend itself against the pathogen that causes influenza *[1 mark]*.

Pages 73-74

Warm-Up Questions

1) Meristem tissue is found at the growing tips of roots and shoots and is able to differentiate into lots of different types of plant cell.
2) palisade mesophyll tissue
3) False
4) light intensity, temperature, air flow, humidity

Exam Questions

1 spongy mesophyll tissue *[1 mark]*

2.1 xylem vessels *[1 mark]*

2.2 They are made of dead cells joined end to end *[1 mark]* with no end walls between them and therefore a hole down the middle *[1 mark]*. They're strengthened with a material called lignin *[1 mark]*.

2.3 transpiration *[1 mark]*

3.1 phloem *[1 mark]*

3.2 They are made of columns of elongated living cells with small pores in the end walls *[1 mark]* to allow cell sap to flow through *[1 mark]*.

3.3 translocation *[1 mark]*

4.1 The water level in the vase would decrease more slowly *[1 mark]*, as the rate of transpiration would be lower *[1 mark]*. This is because water molecules have less energy at lower temperatures, meaning they don't diffuse/evaporate as quickly from the leaves *[1 mark]*.

4.2 How to grade your answer:

Level 0: There is no relevant information. *[No marks]*

Level 1: The correct diagram is identified and the answer links the shape of the guard cell to the closing of the stomata at night. *[1 to 2 marks]*

Level 2: The correct diagram is identified and the answer clearly explains how the shape of the guard cell changes at night, allowing the stomata to close to reduce water loss when gas exchange is not required. *[3 to 4 marks]*

Here are some points your answer may include:
A, because the guard cell is most flaccid.
Flaccid guard cells mean that the stomata would be closed.
The stomata close at night as they don't need to be open for gas exchange as photosynthesis doesn't happen in the dark.
The closing of the stomata at night prevents water being lost through transpiration.

5.1 $(10 + 11 + 9) \div 3 = $ **10% *[2 marks for correct answer, otherwise 1 mark for correct working]***

5.2 The movement of air from the fan sweeps away water vapour, maintaining a low concentration of water outside the leaf *[1 mark]* and increasing the rate at which water is lost through diffusion *[1 mark]*. This means that the plants next to the fan would lose more water (and therefore more mass) than the plants in a still room in the same amount of time *[1 mark]*.

5.3 The rate of transpiration would be slower *[1 mark]* since most water loss occurs through the stomata, which are on the underside of the leaves *[1 mark]*.

5.4 E.g. you could put a new group of 3 basil plants in a separate room *[1 mark]* and increase the humidity in the room by misting/spraying the air with water *[1 mark]*.

If you've thought of another sensible way to increase or decrease the humidity around the plants, you'd still get the mark in the exam.

Topic 3 — Infection and Response

Page 81

Warm-Up Questions

1) A communicable disease is a disease that is easily spread.
2) E.g. measles, HIV and tobacco mosaic virus.
3) A red skin rash.
4) It causes purple or black spots to develop on the leaves, which can then turn yellow and drop off.
5) By sexual contact.
6) Vaccinations stop people from developing the disease, so that they cannot pass it on to someone else.

Exam Questions

1.1 Initial symptoms are flu-like *[1 mark]*.

1.2 Pain when the infected person urinates *[1 mark]*. Thick yellow or green discharge from the vagina or penis *[1 mark]*.

1.3 Any two from: e.g. fever / stomach cramps / vomiting / diarrhoea *[2 marks]*.

2.1 A microorganism that can cause disease *[1 mark]*.

2.2 The tobacco mosaic virus *[1 mark]*. It can reduce the growth of the plant *[1 mark]*.

2.3 By sexual contact *[1 mark]*, or by exchanging bodily fluids such as blood *[1 mark]*.

3.1 To prevent the contamination of food by disease-causing pathogens that may be on the chefs' hands *[1 mark]*.

3.2 Malaria is spread by vectors *[1 mark]* and not through contaminated food/surfaces / skin to skin contact *[1 mark]*.

3.3 E.g. mosquitoes are the vectors of malaria, so destroying mosquitoes will prevent malaria being spread between people *[1 mark]*.

Pages 88-89

Warm-Up Questions

1) The skin acts as a barrier to pathogens and secretes antimicrobial substances that kill them.
2) To destroy pathogens that enter the body.
3) foxgloves
4) Whether the drug works and produces the effect you're looking for.
5) A placebo is a substance that's like the real drug but doesn't do anything.
6) Using a placebo allows the doctor to see the actual difference the drug makes (to a patient's illness/symptoms).

Exam Questions

1.1 They trap particles that could contain pathogens *[1 mark]*.

1.2 They waft the mucus up to the back of the throat where it can be swallowed *[1 mark]*.

1.3 (hydrochloric) acid *[1 mark]*

2.1 human volunteers *[1 mark]*

Drugs are tested on human cells, live animals and human tissue in pre-clinical trials. If a drug makes it through the pre-clinical trials, it's then tested on human volunteers in a clinical trial.

2.2 In a double blind trial neither the patient nor the doctor *[1 mark]* knows who is receiving the drug and who is receiving the placebo until all the results have been gathered *[1 mark]*.

2.3 dosage *[1 mark]*, efficacy/how well the drug works *[1 mark]*

2.4 Peer review is where other scientists check the work to make sure it is valid/has been carried out rigorously *[1 mark]*. It's done help to prevent false claims being made about the results *[1 mark]*.

3.1 Engulfing foreign cells and digesting them / phagocytosis *[1 mark]*.

3.2 A particular antibody will only lock onto a specific type of antigen from one type of pathogen *[1 mark]*.

4.1 *Penicillium* mould / *Penicillium notatum* *[1 mark]*

4.2 Overuse of antibiotics may increase the rate of development of resistant strains of bacteria *[1 mark]*. This will make bacterial infections harder to treat in the future *[1 mark]*.

4.3 Antibiotics cannot kill viruses *[1 mark]*.

5.1 E.g. a painkiller/aspirin *[1 mark]*

5.2 Rubella is a virus and viruses reproduce using your body cells *[1 mark]*, which makes it very difficult to develop drugs that destroy just the virus without killing the body's cells *[1 mark]*.

5.3 How to grade your answer:

Level 0: There is no relevant information. *[No marks]*

Level 1: There is a brief explanation of how vaccination against rubella can prevent a person catching the disease or how having a large proportion of vaccinated individuals in a population reduces the risk of rubella for people who are not vaccinated. *[1 to 2 marks]*

Level 2: There is some explanation of how vaccination against rubella can prevent a person catching the disease and how having a large proportion of vaccinated individuals in a population reduces the risk of rubella for people who are not vaccinated. *[3 to 4 marks]*

Level 3: There is a clear and detailed explanation of how vaccination against rubella can prevent a person catching the disease and how having a large proportion of vaccinated individuals in a population reduces the risk of rubella for people who are not vaccinated. *[5 to 6 marks]*

Here are some points your answer may include:

When a person is vaccinated against rubella, they are injected with dead or inactive rubella viruses.

The dead or inactive viruses carry antigens, which cause the body to produce antibodies to attack them.

If live rubella viruses infect the body after this, white blood cells can rapidly mass produce antibodies to defeat the virus.

If a large proportion of the population is vaccinated against rubella, then there are fewer people who are able to pass the disease on.

This means that even someone who hasn't been vaccinated is less likely to catch the disease.

5.4 E.g. they may be worried that they will have a bad reaction to a vaccine. / Vaccines don't always work and so the person might not be given immunity *[1 mark]*.

Topic 4 — Bioenergetics

Pages 98-99

Warm-Up Questions

1) glucose

2) A limiting factor is something that stops photosynthesis from happening any faster.

3) If the temperature's too high, the plant's enzymes will be denatured, so the rate of photosynthesis rapidly decreases.

Remember, if the temperature is too high for an enzyme, the bonds holding it together may break. This can cause the shape of the enzyme's active site to change, denaturing the enzyme.

4) E.g. oxygen production.

5) light intensity $\propto \dfrac{1}{\text{distance}^2}$

6) To increase the plants' growth so that more/bigger tomatoes are produced and a bigger profit can be made from selling them.

Exam Questions

1.1 carbon dioxide + water *[1 mark]* $\overset{\text{light}}{\to}$ glucose + oxygen *[1 mark]*

1.2 cellulose *[1 mark]*

1.3 Any two from: e.g. for respiration. / For storage as lipids/oils or fats. / For storage as insoluble starch. / For making amino acids, which are then made into proteins. *[2 marks]*

2.1 By counting the number of bubbles produced / by measuring the volume of gas produced, in a given time/at regular intervals *[1 mark]*.

2.2 Dependent variable — rate of photosynthesis/number of bubbles in a given time/volume of gas in a given time *[1 mark]*.
Independent variable — light intensity *[1 mark]*.

2.3 E.g. carbon dioxide concentration in the water/temperature/the plant being used *[1 mark]*.

3.1 At low light intensities, increasing the CO_2 concentration has no effect *[1 mark]*, but at higher light intensities, increasing the concentration of CO_2 increases the maximum rate of photosynthesis *[1 mark]*.

3.2 The rate of photosynthesis does not continue to increase because temperature or the level of carbon dioxide becomes the limiting factor *[1 mark]*.

You don't know if the temperature was kept constant or not, so either the level of carbon dioxide or temperature could have been the limiting factor here — there's no way of knowing.

4.1

[1 mark]

4.2 Plants need both chlorophyll and light to photosynthesise and produce starch — there is only chlorophyll in the green area of the plant *[1 mark]*, and light can only reach parts of the leaf not covered by black paper *[1 mark]*.

5 light intensity $= \dfrac{1}{d^2}$

$= \dfrac{1}{7.5^2}$

$= 0.018$ a.u. (2 s.f.)

[2 marks for correct answer, otherwise 1 mark for correct working.]

Page 104

Warm-Up Questions

1) Any two from: e.g. to build up larger molecules from smaller ones. / To contract muscles. / To keep body temperature steady.

2) The sum of all of the reactions that happen in a cell or the body.

3) Glucose and oxygen.

4) fermentation

5) Breathing rate increases, breath volume increases and heart rate increases.

Answers

Exam Questions

1.1 Any two from: e.g. aerobic respiration uses oxygen, anaerobic respiration does not. / Glucose is broken down fully during aerobic respiration but is only partially broken down during anaerobic respiration. / Aerobic respiration doesn't produce lactic acid, anaerobic respiration does. / Aerobic respiration releases more energy than anaerobic respiration. *[2 marks]*

1.2 glucose + oxygen *[1 mark]* → carbon dioxide + water *[1 mark]*

2.1 glucose → lactic acid *[1 mark]*

2.2 During vigorous exercise, the body can't supply enough oxygen to the muscles *[1 mark]*. It uses anaerobic respiration to provide energy without using oxygen, which keeps the muscles going for longer *[1 mark]*.

3.1 Because during exercise the muscles need more energy from respiration *[1 mark]*, and this respiration requires oxygen *[1 mark]*.

3.2 Because there is an oxygen debt / oxygen is needed to react with the lactic acid that has built up *[1 mark]*.

4 E.g. during vigorous exercise, the muscles use glucose rapidly *[1 mark]*. Blood glucagon level may rise so that some of the glycogen stored in the liver can be converted back to glucose to provide more energy for respiration *[1 mark]*.

Topic 5 — Homeostasis and Response

Page 111

Warm-Up Questions

1) The maintenance of a stable internal environment in response to changes in both internal and external conditions.
2) E.g. body temperature, blood glucose level, water content.
3) synapse
4) sensory neurone, relay neurone, motor neurone
5) E.g. age / gender / drugs / caffeine.

Exam Questions

1.1 Stimulus: appearance of red triangle *[1 mark]*
Receptors: cells in the eye / light receptor cells *[1 mark]*
Effectors: muscles (in hand controlling mouse) *[1 mark]*

1.2 $343 \times 3 = 1029$
$1029 - 328 - 346 =$ **355 ms** *[2 marks for the correct answer, otherwise 1 mark for the correct calculation]*

2.1 motor neurone *[1 mark]*

2.2 Muscle *[1 mark]*, which contracts to move the baby's finger *[1 mark]*.

2.3 When the electrical impulse reaches the end of the neurone, it stimulates the release of a chemical *[1 mark]*. The chemical diffuses across the synapse to activate an electrical impulse in the next neurone *[1 mark]*.

2.4 In a baby older than 6 months, the pathway will involve conscious parts of the brain, whereas in a newborn baby it won't. / In a baby older than 6 months, the response will not be produced as rapidly as in the newborn baby *[1 mark]*.

The response in the baby older than 6 months is not a reflex — it chooses whether it wants to grasp an object. Remember, reflexes are automatic — they don't involve conscious parts of the brain, which makes the response much faster.

Page 116

Warm-Up Questions

1) In the blood.
2) E.g. pituitary gland, thyroid gland, adrenal gland, pancreas, testes.
3) Removes glucose from the blood. / Makes the liver turn glucose into glycogen for storage.
4) A condition in which the body becomes resistant to its own insulin.

Exam Questions

1.1 Organ A is the pancreas *[1 mark]*
Organ B is the liver *[1 mark]*

1.2 Eating carbohydrates *[1 mark]*.

1.3 The pancreas/organ A produces little or no insulin *[1 mark]*. This means that the liver/organ B is unable to remove glucose from the blood for storage *[1 mark]*. So the blood glucose level is able to rise to a dangerously high level *[1 mark]*.

1.4 It makes the liver/organ B turn glycogen into glucose for release into the blood *[1 mark]*.

2 The pituitary gland releases hormones that act on other glands, directing them to release hormones *[1 mark]*. If a pituitary hormone that acts on the thyroid gland is not released *[1 mark]*, then the thyroid gland may also stop releasing hormones, resulting in the symptoms described *[1 mark]*.

3.1 in the muscles *[1 mark]*

3.2 Eating releases glucose into the bloodstream *[1 mark]*. Excess glucose cannot be converted into glycogen since there's not enough functioning glycogen synthase *[1 mark]*, so the blood glucose level increases *[1 mark]*.

Page 123

Warm-Up Questions

1) FSH/follicle-stimulating hormone
2) Any three from: e.g. progesterone-only pill / contraceptive implant / contraceptive injection / plastic IUD.
3) E.g. it doesn't always work. / It can be expensive. / Too many eggs can be stimulated, resulting in multiple pregnancies.
4) They stimulate several eggs to mature.
5) thyroid

Exam Questions

1.1 It inhibits it *[1 mark]*.
1.2 progesterone *[1 mark]*
1.3 day 14 *[1 mark]*

2.1 Keeping oestrogen levels permanently high inhibits production of FSH *[1 mark]*, so no eggs mature / so egg development and production stop *[1 mark]*.

2.2 E.g. by stimulating the production of thick cervical mucus *[1 mark]*, which prevents any sperm getting through and reaching the egg *[1 mark]*.

2.3 E.g. the contraceptive implant *[1 mark]*, as this is effective for three years once inserted and so does not have to be thought about on a daily basis *[1 mark]*. / The contraceptive injection *[1 mark]*, as this is effective for 2 to 3 months and so does not have to be thought about on a daily basis *[1 mark]*. / The contraceptive patch *[1 mark]*, as each patch lasts one week, so does not have to be thought about on a daily basis.

2.4   E.g. male/female sterilisation *[1 mark]*.

3   The cat's heart rate would increase *[1 mark]* because adrenaline is released *[1 mark]*. The increased heart rate increases the rate of delivery of glucose and oxygen *[1 mark]* to the brain and muscle cells *[1 mark]*, which prepares the cat to escape danger/the dog by fight or flight *[1 mark]*.

Topic 6 — Inheritance, Variation and Evolution

Page 131

Warm-Up Questions

1)   A small section of DNA found on a chromosome that codes for a particular sequence of amino acids that are put together to make a specific protein.

2)   Because there are two parents, the offspring contain a mixture of their parents' genes. This mixture of genetic information produces variation.

3)   two

4)   XX

Exam Questions

1.1   A polymer made up of two strands. *[1 mark]*

1.2   Its genome. *[1 mark]*

Remember, an organism's genome is its entire set of genetic material. A gene is a short section of DNA and a chromosome is a really long structure, which contains genes.

1.3   DNA contains genes *[1 mark]*. Each gene codes for a particular sequence of amino acids *[1 mark]*, which are put together to make a specific protein *[1 mark]*.

2.1   asexual *[1 mark]*

2.2   They will be genetically identical *[1 mark]*.

Remember, asexual reproduction produces clones — offspring are exactly the same as the parent.

3.1   three *[1 mark]*

When a cell undergoes meiosis, each new cell ends up with half the number of chromosomes as in the original cell.

3.2   four *[1 mark]*

Remember, when a cell undergoes meiosis, four gametes are produced — it doesn't matter whether you're talking about human cells or mosquito cells.

3.3   Meiosis produces gametes that are genetically different to each other *[1 mark]*. A male gamete and a female gamete then combine at fertilisation *[1 mark]*, so the offspring inherits a mixture of chromosomes from both parents *[1 mark]*.

Pages 138-139

Warm-Up Questions

1)   Different versions of the same gene.

2)   The combination of alleles an organism has.

3)   Because the allele which causes cystic fibrosis is recessive, so you have to have two recessive alleles to have the disorder. Heterozygous people have one dominant and one recessive allele.

4)   It's a genetic disorder where a baby is born with extra fingers or toes.

5)   Taking a cell from an embryo and analysing its genes in order to detect genetic disorders.

Exam Questions

1.1

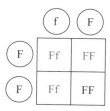

[1 mark for correct genotype of offspring, 1 mark for correct genotypes of gametes]

1.2   1 in 2 / 50% *[1 mark]*

1.3   One has cystic fibrosis *[1 mark]* and the other does not / is a carrier of cystic fibrosis *[1 mark]*.

2.1   E.g.

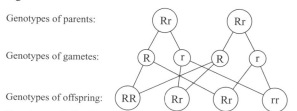

[1 mark for correct genotypes of the parents, 1 mark for correct genotypes of offspring, 1 mark for correct phenotypes of offspring]

You could have drawn a Punnett square instead here.

2.2   1 in 4 / 25% *[1 mark]*

3   Dd *[1 mark]*. Polydactyly is a dominant disorder, so if she was DD all of her children would be affected *[1 mark]*.

4.1

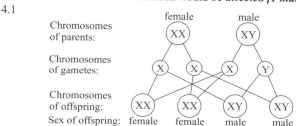

[1 mark for correct chromosomes in parents, 1 mark for correct chromosomes in offspring, 1 mark for correct sex of offspring]

4.2   Male children will not inherit the colour blindness allele because they don't inherit an X chromosome from their father *[1 mark]*.

4.3   0 / 0% *[1 mark]*

A daughter of this couple would inherit the recessive colour blindness allele from her father, but also a dominant allele from her mother, so she would not be colour blind.

5.1   AA, Aa *[1 mark]*

5.2   E.g.

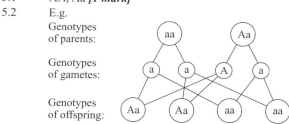

[1 mark for parent with genotype aa, 1 mark for parent with genotype Aa, 1 mark for correct genotypes of offspring]

5.3   50% *[1 mark]*

Offspring with the genotype aa will have albinism.

5.4   Fertilisation is random/the genetic diagram only shows the probability of the outcome, so the numbers of offspring produced will not always be exactly in those proportions *[1 mark]*.

224

Warm-Up Questions

1) Differences between members of the same species that have been caused by the environment/conditions something lives in.

2) Simple life forms that first started to develop over three billion years ago.

3) Any three from: e.g. the environment changes too quickly. / A new predator kills all the individuals. / A new disease kills all the individuals. / They can't compete with another species for food. / A catastrophic event (e.g. a volcanic eruption or collision with an astroid) kills all the individuals.

Exam Questions

1.1 The difference in weight must be caused by the environment *[1 mark]*, because the twins have exactly the same genes *[1 mark]*.

In this case, the environment can mean the amount of food each twin eats or the amount of exercise they each do.

1.2 No, because if they were caused by genes both twins should have the birthmark *[1 mark]*.

2.1 Variation that is caused by differences in genotype *[1 mark]*.

2.2 Mutations change an organism's DNA *[1 mark]*, which can change the protein produced by a gene *[1 mark]* and lead to new characteristics / a new phenotype, increasing variation *[1 mark]*.

2.3 E.g. if the environment changes, some mutations may give individuals a phenotype that makes them more suited to the new environment *[1 mark]*. This would make them more likely to survive (than individuals without the phenotype) *[1 mark]*.

3 How to grade your answer:

Level 0: There is no relevant information. *[No marks]*

Level 1: There are some relevant points describing how the stingray has evolved but the answer is missing some detail. *[1 to 2 marks]*

Level 2: There is a clear, detailed explanation of how the stingray has evolved through natural selection. *[3 to 4 marks]*

Here are some points your answer may include:
Ancestors of this stingray showed variation in their appearance.
The stingrays that looked more like flat rocks were better camouflaged and so less likely to be seen and eaten by predators/more likely to survive.
This means they were more likely to reproduce.
As a result, the genes that caused the stingrays to look more like flat rocks were more likely to be passed on to the next generation.
Over time, the flat rock appearance became more common in the population and the stingray evolved.

Warm-Up Questions

1) E.g. to produce plants with large or unusual flowers.
2) Selective breeding reduces the gene pool. This causes an increased chance of organisms inheriting harmful genetic defects. There is also an increased chance that a population could be wiped out by a new disease.
3) E.g. insulin.

Exam Questions

1.1 E.g. to isolate/cut the gene out of the organism's DNA *[1 mark]*.

1.2 E.g. to improve the size/quality of their fruit. / To make them make them resistant to disease/insects/herbicides *[1 mark]*.

1.3 Any two from: e.g. some people are not convinced that GM crops are safe and are concerned that we might not fully understand the effects of eating them on human health. / Some people say that growing GM crops will negatively affect the number of wild flowers and insects that live in and around the crops. / There is concern that the transplanted genes could get out into the natural environment, which could lead to the creation of 'superweeds'. *[2 marks]*

2 The tall and dwarf wheat plants could be bred together *[1 mark]*. The best of the offspring/the offspring with the highest grain yield and highest bad weather resistance could then be bred together *[1 mark]*, and this process repeated over several generations *[1 mark]*.

3.1 Yes, because the average milk yield has increased over the generations *[1 mark]*.

3.2 $\dfrac{(5750 - 5000)}{5000} \times 100$

= **15% *[2 marks for the correct answer, otherwise 1 mark for correct working.]***

Warm-Up Questions

1) The microbes that cause decay can't survive in low oxygen conditions, so the dead organisms are preserved rather than decayed.

2) Any one from: e.g. when the illness is only minor. / When the infection is being caused by a virus.

3) Taking the complete course makes sure that all the bacteria are destroyed. This means that there are none left to mutate and develop into antibiotic-resistant strains.

4) *fiber*

Exam Questions

1.1 Species C *[1 mark]*

1.2 Yes, you would expect Species D to look similar to Species E because they share a recent common ancestor, so they are closely related/have similar genes *[1 mark]*.

2.1 **C, B, D, A *[2 marks for correct answer, otherwise 1 mark for three stages in the correct order]***

2.2 E.g. people in hospital are more likely to have weakened immune systems than people in the rest of society *[1 mark]*, and so are more likely to develop serious illness as a result of MRSA infection *[1 mark]*.

2.3 E.g. it can lead to infections becoming more widespread/difficult to control *[1 mark]*.

2.4 When antibiotics are used, resistant bacteria have an advantage over non-resistant bacteria *[1 mark]*, so they will increase in number meaning the resistance spreads *[1 mark]*. Reducing the use of antibiotics will slow/reduce the spread of antibiotic resistance *[1 mark]*.

Topic 7 — Ecology

Page 160

Warm-Up Questions

1) a community
2) The interaction of a community of living organisms (biotic) with the non-living (abiotic) parts of their environment.
3) Any four from: moisture level / light intensity / temperature / carbon dioxide level / wind intensity / wind direction / soil pH / mineral content of soil.
4) Structural adaptations are features of an organism's body structure that allow an organism to live in an environment.
5) A producer is an organism that makes its own food using energy from the Sun.

Exam Questions

1.1 tertiary consumer *[1 mark]*
1.2 The algae are producers *[1 mark]*. They are the source of biomass /energy for the food chain *[1 mark]*.
2.1 A behavioural adaptation *[1 mark]*.
2.2 E.g. it has flippers *[1 mark]* so it can swim for food *[1 mark]*. / It has a thick layer of fat *[1 mark]* so it retains heat *[1 mark]*. / It has a low surface area to volume ratio *[1 mark]* so it retains heat *[1 mark]*.

Use the picture to help you here — ask yourself what specific features the penguin has and then think about how these features could help it survive in its environment.

3.1 At first the population size of the cutthroat trout would decrease *[1 mark]*, as the lake trout would eat the cutthroat trout *[1 mark]*. This would lead to a decline in the population of the lake trout (as they'd have less to eat) *[1 mark]*, allowing an increase in the population of the cutthroat trout *[1 mark]*. The population size of the lake trout would then increase (as they'd have more to eat) and the cycle would start again *[1 mark]*.
3.2 Any two from: availability of food / competition for resources / new pathogens *[1 mark for each correct answer, up to 2 marks]*.

Pages 165-166

Warm-Up Questions

1) A line used to help find out how organisms are distributed across an area.
2) (14 + 11 + 11 + 12 + 12) ÷ 5 = 12
3) To break down/decay dead matter and animal waste.
4) Through burning.

Exam Questions

1.1 eating *[1 mark]*
1.2 respiration *[1 mark]*
1.3 Detritus feeders and microorganisms break down/decay the dead matter *[1 mark]* and return carbon to the air as carbon dioxide through respiration *[1 mark]*.
1.4 photosynthesis *[1 mark]*
2.1 By the process of transpiration / water evaporates from the plants *[1 mark]*.

2.2 Energy from the Sun evaporates water from the ocean *[1 mark]*, so the water molecule enters the atmosphere as water vapour *[1 mark]*. The warm water vapour rises, then cools and condenses into clouds *[1 mark]*. The water molecule then falls from the clouds as precipitation/rain/snow/hail into a garden pond *[1 mark]*.
3.1 E.g. they could have placed quadrats at regular intervals *[1 mark]* along a transect/in a straight line from the wood to the opposite side of the field *[1 mark]*, and counted the number of poppies in each quadrat *[1 mark]*.
3.2 E.g. the number of poppies increases with increasing distance from the wood *[1 mark]*.
3.3 Any two from: e.g. moisture level / soil pH / soil mineral content / wind intensity / wind direction. *[2 marks — 1 mark for each correct answer.]*
3.4 Species A = 47 squares out of 100 = (47 ÷ 100) × 100 = 47% *[1 mark]*
Species B = 48 squares out of 100 = (48 ÷ 100) × 100 = 48% *[1 mark]*

Remember, to calculate percentage cover of an organism in a quadrat you count the number of squares which are more than half covered by the organism.

3.5 E.g. because there may have been too many blades of grass to count each one individually / it's hard to count individual blades of grass *[1 mark]*.
4 How to grade your answer:
  Level 0: There is no relevant information. *[No marks]*
  Level 1: There is a brief description of one or two ways in which carbon stored in the vegetation could be returned to the atmosphere. *[1 to 2 marks]*
  Level 2: There is some description of more than two of the ways carbon stored in the vegetation could be returned to the atmosphere. *[3 to 4 marks]*
  Level 3: There is a clear and detailed description of all the ways carbon stored in the vegetation could be returned to the atmosphere. *[5 to 6 marks]*
  Here are some points your answer may include:
  Carbon stored in the small branches will be returned to the atmosphere as carbon dioxide when the branches are burnt. The green plants could be eaten by animals, which will release some carbon as carbon dioxide during respiration. The green plants could also be broken down by microorganisms/detritivores which will release carbon as carbon dioxide during respiration. The wood that is taken away to be made into furniture will eventually return the carbon to the atmosphere through decay/burning when its lifespan as furniture is over.

Page 175

Warm-Up Questions

1) The variety of different species of organisms on Earth, or within an ecosystem.
2) E.g. carbon dioxide, methane.
3) Breeding programmes breed endangered animals in captivity to make sure the species survives if they die out in the wild. Individuals can sometimes be released into the wild to boost or re-establish a population.
4) Hedgerows and field margins can be reintroduced around single-crop fields. These provide a habitat for organisms that would otherwise be unable to live in the area.

Hedgerows and field margins mean that more species of wild plants can grow. Remember, plants are often the producers in food chains — so the more variety there is in the plants that are growing, the more organisms that will be able to survive in the area.

Exam Questions

1.1 E.g. smoke *[1 mark]*, acidic gases *[1 mark]*.

1.2 E.g. sewage/toxic chemicals from industry can pollute lakes/rivers/oceans. / Fertilisers/pesticides/herbicides/toxic chemicals used on land can be washed into water *[1 mark]*.

1.3 E.g. the human population size is increasing *[1 mark]*, people around the world are demanding a higher standard of living *[1 mark]*.

2.1 E.g. changes in species distributions *[1 mark]*, changes in migration patterns *[1 mark]*.

2.2 Governments have introduced regulations and programmes to reduce deforestation *[1 mark]*. They have also introduced regulations to limit the amount of carbon dioxide released by businesses *[1 mark]*.

3.1 When peat is drained, it comes into more contact with air and some microorganisms start to decompose it *[1 mark]*. This releases carbon dioxide *[1 mark]*. Carbon dioxide is also released when peat is burned as a fuel *[1 mark]*. Carbon dioxide is a greenhouse gas, which contributes to global warming *[1 mark]*.

3.2 E.g. destroying peat bogs reduces biodiversity *[1 mark]*, as it destroys the habitats of the organisms that live in the bog *[1 mark]*.

4.1 E.g. protecting wetlands will protect the habitats of species that live there *[1 mark]*. This will help to preserve the level of biodiversity in the ecosystem *[1 mark]*. A high level of biodiversity is important for humans to survive *[1 mark]*.

4.2 Any two from: e.g. people may disagree with the amount of money that is spent on conserving the wetlands. / People may think it would be better to use the land for farming, which would help to protect food security. / People may worry about the effect on the local economy if the wetlands are protected, because the area couldn't be used for human activities such as farming. / People may think that the land could be better used for developing society, e.g. by using it to build houses on. *[2 marks]*

Practice Paper 1

1.1 cell membrane *[1 mark]*

1.2 *E. coli* bacteria *[1 mark]*

1.3 image size = magnification × real size
= 150 × 0.054
= **8.1 mm**
[2 marks for correct answer, otherwise 1 mark for correct working]

1.4 How to grade your answer:
Level 0: No relevant information is given. *[No marks]*
Level 1: There is a brief comparison of plant and animal cells, including at least one similarity and one difference. *[1 to 2 marks]*
Level 2: There is a comparison of plant and animal cells, including at least two similarities and two differences. Some descriptions of subcellular structures are included. *[3 to 4 marks]*
Level 3: There is a detailed comparison of plant and animal cells, including at least three similarities and three differences. Detailed descriptions of subcellular structures are included. *[5 to 6 marks]*

Here are some points your answer may include:
Similarities:
Both plant and animal cells have a nucleus, which controls the cell's activities.
Both plant and animal cells contain cytoplasm, which is where most of the cell's chemical reactions take place.
Plant cells and animal cells both have a cell membrane, which controls what goes in and out of the cell.
Mitochondria are found in both plant cells and animal cells — these are where most of the reactions for aerobic respiration take place.
Both plant cells and animal cells have ribosomes, which are where proteins are made.
Differences:
Chloroplasts, the site of photosynthesis, are present in plant cells, but not in animal cells.
Plant cells have a cell wall, which supports and strengthens the cell, but animal cells do not.
Plant cells contain a permanent vacuole, containing cell sap, but animal cells do not.

2.1 By droplets from an infected person's sneeze or cough *[1 mark]*

2.2 How to grade your answer:
Level 0: There is no relevant information. *[No marks]*
Level 1: There are some relevant points explaining how vaccination helps to protect the body against disease but the answer is missing some detail. *[1 to 2 marks]*
Level 2: There is a clear, detailed explanation of how vaccination helps to protect the body against disease. *[3 to 4 marks]*

Here are some points your answer may include:
The body is injected with small amounts of dead or inactive pathogens (which are harmless).
These carry antigens, which cause the white blood cells in the body to produce antibodies.
Antibodies attack/kill the pathogens.
If live pathogens of the same type appear again, the white blood cells can rapidly mass-produce antibodies to kill the pathogens so the person doesn't get ill.

2.3 Any two from: e.g. stop the mosquitoes from breeding / protect people from mosquito bites using mosquito nets / protect people from mosquito bites by using insecticides (to kill the mosquitoes) *[2 marks]*.

3.1 biuret solution *[1 mark]*

3.2 Benedict's solution *[1 mark]*

3.3 A *[1 mark]*

3.4 It is covered in many villi that provide a large surface area for diffusion (and active transport) to occur across *[1 mark]*. The villi have a thin wall/single layer of surface cells, which decreases the distance for diffusion to occur across *[1 mark]*. They also have a good blood supply to assist quick absorption *[1 mark]*.

3.5 Their blood sugar level will not rise very much or not rise at all *[1 mark]*. This is because a person with lactose intolerance has little or no lactase to break down the lactose in the drink, so there will be little or no sugar to be absorbed from the small intestine *[1 mark]*.

4.1 The blood supply to the area below the blockage would be cut off/reduced *[1 mark]*. Not enough oxygen would reach this part of the heart muscle, resulting in cells being unable to respire/damage/death of the muscle tissue/a heart attack *[1 mark]*.

4.2 A stent will keep the coronary artery open, making sure that enough blood can reach the heart muscle *[1 mark]*.

4.3   To make sure it did not cause any harmful side effects when the body is working normally *[1 mark]*.

4.4   E.g. a control/placebo was used *[1 mark]*.

4.5   How to grade your answer:

Level 0:   No relevant information is given. *[No marks]*

Level 1:   At least one advantage or disadvantage of each treatment method is given. No logical conclusion has been made. *[1 to 2 marks]*

Level 2:   At least one advantage and disadvantage of each treatment method is clearly described. An attempt has been made to come to a logical conclusion. *[3 to 4 marks]*

Level 3:   There is a detailed description of the advantages and disadvantages of each treatment method. A clear and justified conclusion has been made. *[5 to 6 marks]*

Here are some points your answer may include:

Advantages of a donor heart:
A donor heart is likely to work better than an artificial heart.
A donor heart may be more of a permanent treatment than an artificial heart.

Disadvantages of a donor heart:
There may be a long wait for a suitable donor heart to become available.
There is a greater risk that a donor heart will be rejected by the immune system, compared to an artificial heart.
There is a risk of bleeding and infection due to the transplant surgery.

Advantages of an artificial heart:
An artificial heart can be used as a temporary fix, which may mean that the person's heart can continue to be used once it has had time to rest and heal.
An artificial heart can be available as soon as a person needs it.
An artificial heart is less likely to be rejected by the immune system compared to a donor heart.

Disadvantages of an artificial heart:
There is a risk of bleeding and infection due to the surgery needed to fit an artificial heart.
An artificial heart doesn't work as well as a healthy natural heart — for example, parts of it may wear out or the electrical motor could fail.
Blood doesn't flow as smoothly through an artificial heart as it does through a natural heart. This increases the risk of blood clots, which can lead to strokes.
Blood thinning drugs have to be taken after treatment with an artificial heart, which can cause problems with bleeding if the person is hurt in an accident.

5.1   It is broken down into sugars/maltose *[1 mark]*.

5.2   E.g. they could have added the sample to a drop of iodine solution (e.g. in a well of a spotting tile) *[1 mark]*. If starch was present the iodine solution would have changed to blue-black *[1 mark]*. If starch was no longer present, the iodine solution would have remained browny-orange *[1 mark]*.

5.3   Time of reaction at 40 °C = 100 s.
Rate = 1000 ÷ 100 = **10 s⁻¹** *[2 marks for correct answer, otherwise 1 mark for correct working.]*

5.4   The temperature was too high *[1 mark]*, causing the enzyme to denature / the shape of the enzyme's active site to change *[1 mark]*. This means the starch could no longer fit in the active site of the enzyme, so it could not be broken down *[1 mark]*.

5.5   The result for 20 °C is anomalous *[1 mark]* because the time taken until starch is no longer present is quicker than expected/quicker than at 30 or 40 °C *[1 mark]*. To cause this result, the student may not have used the correct volume of starch/amylase solution. / The student may have started timing the experiment too late. / The student may have stopped the experiment too early *[1 mark]*.

5.6   By using buffer solutions with a range of different pH values *[1 mark]*.

6.1   E.g. day 2 was less bright, so the stomata weren't fully open and so less water could move out of the leaves. / Day 2 was colder, so the water evaporated/diffused more slowly. / Day 2 was less windy, so the water vapour was carried away more slowly, meaning that diffusion couldn't happen as quickly. / Day 2 was wetter/more humid, so there was a smaller diffusion gradient between the inside and outside of the leaf so diffusion couldn't happen as quickly *[1 mark for reason, 1 mark for explanation]*.

The rate of transpiration varies throughout the day due to the changing light intensity, but it can also be affected by the temperature, the air flow and the humidity around the leaves.

6.2   The plant has lost too much water/has lost water faster than it could be replaced through the roots *[1 mark]*.

6.3   Transpiration creates a slight shortage of water in the leaf *[1 mark]*. More water is drawn up from the rest of the plant through the xylem vessels to replace it *[1 mark]*. This in turn means that more water is drawn up from the roots, and so there's a constant transpiration stream of water through the plant *[1 mark]*.

7   How to grade your answer:

Level 0:   No relevant information is given. *[No marks]*

Level 1:   There is a basic description of at least two of the stages of the cell cycle or a suggestion of why disrupting the cell cycle may kill plants is stated. *[1 to 2 marks]*

Level 2:   There is a clear description of at least two stages of the cell cycle and a suggestion of why disrupting the cell cycle may kill plants is stated. *[3 to 4 marks]*

Level 3:   There is a detailed description of each stage of the cell cycle and a suggestion of why disrupting the cell cycle may kill plants is stated. *[5 to 6 marks]*

Here are some points your answer may include:
The cell cycle involves the division of cells to form two identical cells.
Before division takes place the cell grows and increases the amount of subcellular structures it has, such as mitochondria and ribosomes.
It then duplicates its DNA so there's one copy for each new cell.
Next, mitosis takes place. The chromosomes line up at the centre of the cell and cell fibres pull them apart. The two arms of each chromosome go to opposite ends of the cell.
Membranes form around each of the sets of chromosomes to become the nuclei of the two new cells. Finally the cytoplasm and cell membrane divide so two identical daughter cells are formed.
Disrupting the cell cycle can kill plants as plants are multicellular organisms which use mitosis to grow and to replace damaged cells. If they can no longer do this, they may die.

8.1

[1 mark for label and suitable scale for the x-axis, 2 marks for all points correctly plotted (or 1 mark for 8 points plotted correctly), 1 mark for a smooth curve of best fit.]

8.2 95 beats/min *[1 mark. Allow any value correctly read from 30 seconds on your own graph.]*

8.3 The student's heart rate increases during exercise *[1 mark]*. This is because when he exercises he needs more energy, so he respires more *[1 mark]*. Increased respiration means that his cells need more oxygen *[1 mark]*, so his heart rate increases so that the blood flows more quickly to the cells to deliver oxygen *[1 mark]*.

Practice Paper 2

1.1 B *[1 mark]*

1.2 The thyroid gland releases thyroxine directly into the blood *[1 mark]*. Thyroxine then travels in the bloodstream to its target organ/the heart *[1 mark]*.

1.3 It produces hormones that act on other glands *[1 mark]*, which directs them to release hormones that bring about change *[1 mark]*.

2.1 21 *[1 mark]*

To find the median, you write out all the results from lowest to highest, e.g. 10, 21, 21, 35, 37. 21 is in the middle of the list, so it is the median.

2.2 (6 + 15 + 9 + 14 + 20 + 5 + 3 + 11 + 10 + 7) ÷ 10
= 100 ÷ 10
= **10 buttercups per m² *[2 marks for correct answer, otherwise 1 mark for correct working.]***

2.3 90 × 120 = 10 800 m² *[1 mark]*
10 × 10 800 = **108 000 buttercups *[1 mark]***
Allow incorrect value from 2.2.

2.4 E.g. more buttercups grow where there is a higher moisture level in the soil *[1 mark]*.

2.5 How to grade your answer:
Level 0: There is no relevant information. *[No marks]*
Level 1: There is a brief description of how the student could investigate whether the change in distribution of buttercups is due to variability in the moisture level of the soil. *[1 to 2 marks]*
Level 2: There is a detailed description of how the student could investigate whether the change in distribution of buttercups is due to variability in the moisture level of the soil. *[3 to 4 marks]*

Here are some points your answer may include:
He could use a transect across Field A.
To do this he should mark out a line across the field.
Then he should record the number of buttercups in quadrats placed next to each other/at intervals along the line.
He should also measure the moisture level of the soil at each sampling point (e.g. with a probe).

3.1 *Biston [1 mark]*

3.2 the dark variety *[1 mark]*

3.3 The dark variety is less likely to be eaten by predators in soot polluted areas (because they are better camouflaged) *[1 mark]* so they are more likely to survive to reproduce *[1 mark]*, meaning that the genes for the characteristics that made them successful / genes for dark colouring are more likely to be passed on to the next generation and become more common in the population *[1 mark]*.

4.1 Their reaction time was very fast *[1 mark]*.
Their response was involuntary/automatic *[1 mark]*.
If you have to think about what response to give then it's not a reflex action.

4.2 reaction time *[1 mark]*

4.3 sex *[1 mark]*

4.4 The males in this experiment had a faster mean reaction time than the females *[1 mark]*, so the data supports the scientist's hypothesis *[1 mark]*.

4.5 E.g. the age of the participants *[1 mark]*. / The strength of the tap on the knee *[1 mark]*. / Caffeine consumption of the participants prior to the investigation *[1 mark]*.

4.6 relay neurone *[1 mark]*

4.7 How to grade your answer:
Level 0: There is no relevant information. *[No marks]*
Level 1: There is a brief description of some parts of the path taken by a nervous impulse in the reflex. *[1 to 2 marks]*
Level 2: There is some description of the path taken by a nervous impulse in the reflex, but some detail is missing. *[3 to 4 marks]*
Level 3: There is a clear and detailed description of the path taken by a nervous impulse in the reflex. *[5 to 6 marks]*

Here are some points your answer may include:
The impulse travels along a sensory neurone to the central nervous system/spinal cord.
When the impulse reaches a synapse between the sensory neurone and a relay neurone, it triggers chemicals to be released.
These chemicals cause impulses to be sent along the relay neurone.
When the impulse reaches a synapse between the relay neurone and a motor neurone, chemicals are released again which cause impulses to be sent along the motor neurone.
The impulse then reaches the muscle, which contracts to move your hand away from the source of pain.

5.1 The entire set of genetic material in an organism *[1 mark]*.

5.2 Knowing more about the cystic fibrosis gene could help us to understand the disorder better / develop effective treatments for it *[1 mark]*.

5.3 E.g.

mother's alleles

	F	f
F	FF	Ff
f	Ff	ff

father's alleles

ff offspring has cystic fibrosis.

Probability = 0.25 / 25% / 1:3 / 1 in 4 / ¼

[1 mark for correctly identifying parents' genotypes, 1 mark for correctly identifying possible genotypes of the offspring, 1 mark for correctly identifying cystic fibrosis genotype, 1 mark for identifying the correct probability of a child having cystic fibrosis.]

The parents must both be carriers, since neither of them show any sign of the disorder. This means they both have one copy of the recessive allele for cystic fibrosis — so they're both Ff.

5.4 Homozygous, because he has two alleles the same / both of his alleles are recessive *[1 mark]*.

6.1 The HBsAg gene codes for the hepatitis B antigen *[1 mark]*.

6.2 How to grade your answer:

Level 0: There is no relevant information. *[No marks]*

Level 1: There are some relevant points describing the process by which organisms are genetically engineered but the answer is missing some detail. *[1 to 2 marks]*

Level 2: There is a clear, detailed description of the process by which organisms are genetically engineered. *[3 to 4 marks]*

Here are some points your answer may include:

Enzymes are used to isolate/cut the useful gene from one organism's genome.

The gene is then inserted into a vector such as a virus or a bacterial plasmid.

When the vector is introduced to a target organism, the useful gene is inserted into its cells.

7.1 Any three from: e.g. sexual reproduction involves the fusion of male and female gametes whereas asexual reproduction doesn't involve gametes. / Sexual reproduction involves two parents whereas asexual reproduction only involves one parent. / Sexual reproduction produces offspring that are genetically different to their parents whereas asexual reproduction produces offspring that are genetically identical to their parents (clones). / Sexual reproduction produces offspring that are genetically different to each other whereas asexual reproduction produces offspring that are genetically identical. *[3 marks]*

7.2 testosterone *[1 mark]*

7.3 It causes the lining of the uterus to grow *[1 mark]*. It also stimulates the release of luteinising hormone (LH) and inhibits the release of follicle stimulating hormone (FSH) *[1 mark]*.

7.4 C *[1 mark]* — e.g. because the level corresponds to the thickness of the uterus lining, which is maintained by progesterone *[1 mark]*.

There are a few different ways that you can tell that this line represents progesterone. As long as you're able to justify your answer, you'll get the marks.

7.5 Advantages of the implant: e.g. it works for three years / protection is always available / you do not have to remember to take a pill every day / it is highly effective.

Disadvantages of the implant: e.g. it has to be inserted by a doctor or nurse which may be painful/inconvenient / if certain medications are taken, a different contraceptive method would have to be used / you could suffer from side effects / it does not protect against STDs.

Advantages of the condom: e.g. it protects against STDs / there are no side effects / it is highly effective if used correctly / it is not affected by medication.

Disadvantages of the condom: e.g. it needs to be available at the time of intercourse / if it isn't used correctly it may not be effective / it can only be used once.

[3 marks for at least one advantage and one disadvantage of each method, otherwise 2 marks for at least two advantages or disadvantages of either method or 1 mark for one advantage or disadvantage of either method. 1 mark for giving a justified conclusion that refers to at least one advantage and one disadvantage of the chosen method.]

8.1 At point X, CO_2 is being removed from the atmosphere by photosynthesis *[1 mark]*. At point Y, CO_2 is being released into the atmosphere by plants and animals respiring *[1 mark]*. At point Z, carbon compounds in the plants are being transferred to animals as they eat the plants *[1 mark]*.

8.2 Microorganisms break down waste products and dead organisms *[1 mark]* and release carbon dioxide into the atmosphere as they respire *[1 mark]*.

8.3 The two sets of data show the same pattern/increase at the same time *[1 mark]*.

8.4 Any two from: e.g. the two things may follow similar patterns by chance. / Some other factor may have caused both increases. / The concentration of carbon dioxide varied even when human population was low/fairly constant. *[2 marks]*

8.5 Any two from: e.g. to increase the amount of land available for farming cattle. / To increase the amount of land available for rice crops. / To increase the amount of land available for growing crops from which biofuels are produced *[2 marks]*.

8.6 Any two from: e.g. habitats in low-lying areas will be lost due to rising sea levels *[1 mark]*. / The distribution of organisms could change due to changes in temperature and rainfall *[1 mark]*. / Biodiversity could be reduced *[1 mark]*. / There could be changes in migration patterns (e.g. some birds may migrate further north) *[1 mark]*.

Index

gene pools 145
genes 26, 126
genetically modified crops 146, 147
genetic
  diagrams 130, 133-136
  disorders 136, 137
  engineering 146, 147
  variants 141
  variation 140, 141
genomes 126
genotypes 132
genus 151, 152
gills 36
glands 112
global warming 169, 170
glucagon 114
glucose
  in the blood 114, 115
  test for 47
  uses in plants 91
glycerol 45
glycogen 114
gonorrhoea 79
gradients 10
graphs 9, 10
greenhouse gases 169
greenhouses 97
guard cells 72
gullet 46

H

habitats 155
haemoglobin 55
hazards 4, 7
heart 53
heart valves 60
heterozygous organisms 132
HIV 78
homeostasis 106
homozygous organisms 132
hormones 112, 113
hypotheses 1, 5

I

immune system 82
independent variables 5
indicators 178
'induced fit' model 42
infertility 120, 121
insulin 114, 115
intercepts (on a graph) 10
interdependence 155
intrauterine devices (IUDs) 119
inverse
  correlations 10
  proportion 96
  square law 96
in vitro fertilisation (IVF) 121
iodine test (for starch) 44
IVF 121

K

kingdom (classification) 151

L

lactic acid 102, 103
lamellae 36
large intestine 46
leaves
  gas exchange 35
  tissues in 68
light microscopes 18-20
limiting factors
    (of photosynthesis) 92-94
line graphs 9, 10
lines of best fit 9, 10
Linnaean system 151
Linnaeus, Carl 151
lipases 45
lipids (test for) 48
liver 46, 114
'lock and key' model 42
lungs 51, 52
luteinising hormone (LH) 118, 120, 121

M

magnification 18
malaria 79
malignant tumours 66
mean (average) 8
measles 78
measuring cylinders 177
mechanical heart valves 60
median 8
meiosis 128
menstrual cycle 117, 118
meristem tissue 68
metabolism 101
microorganisms 76
microscopes 18-20
migration patterns 170
  human 126
mitochondria 16
mitosis 26, 27, 128
mode 8
models (scientific) 2
motor neurones 107-109
MRSA 85, 150
mucus 82
muscle cells 23
muscle fatigue 103
mutations 141

N

natural selection 142
negative correlations 10
negative feedback systems 106
  blood glucose 114
  thyroxine 122
nerve cells 22
nervous system 107-109
neurones 107-109
non-communicable diseases 62
nucleus 16

O

oestrogen 117-119
order (classification) 151
organ systems 40, 41

organs 40, 41
osmosis 30, 31
ovaries 112, 117, 118
ovulation 117, 118
oxygen debt 103

P

pacemakers 53
painkillers 86
palisade mesophyll tissue 68
pancreas 46, 112, 114
parasites 77
partially permeable membranes 30
pathogens 76, 77
peat bogs 171
peer review 1, 87
pepsin 45, 46
percentage
  change 183
  cover 162
phagocytosis 55, 82
phenotypes 132
phenotype variation 142
phloem cells 23
phloem tubes 68, 69
pH meters 178
photosynthesis 91-97
  rate of 92-96
phylum (classification) 151
pipettes 177
pituitary gland 112, 118, 122
placebo effect 87
plant cells 17
plasma 55
plasmids 17, 146
platelets 55
pleural membranes 51
pollution 168
polydactyly 136
population (human) 167, 168
positive correlations 10
potatoes 31
potometers 72, 182
precipitation 163
precision (of results) 6, 7

Index

SCBAS41, SCBS41